Lilly on Dolphins

Lilly on Dolphins

HUMANS OF THE SEA

John Cunningham Lilly, M.D.

ANCHOR BOOKS
ANCHOR PRESS/DOUBLEDAY
GARDEN CITY, NEW YORK
1975

Anchor Books Edition: 1975
ISBN: 0-385-01037-5
Library of Congress Catalog Card Number 75-2854
Printed in the United States of America
First Edition

Dedication

I dedicate this book to all of those persons who have aided this research program in innumerable ways, some financially, some intangibly, but nonetheless crucially.

To the Trustees and other colleagues, past and present, of the Communication Research Institute who have contributed directly their efforts to the details of the projects.

To the Associates of the Institute who have contributed their interest and money to the effort.

To the private Foundations who have made direct contributions.

To all of those within the government agencies who, with vision and understanding, have facilitated our program, and to their advisers who have undertaken the hard work of understanding our goals, our scientific results, and our scientific contributions.

To the memory of my parents, Richard Coyle and Rachel Cunningham Lilly of St. Paul, Minnesota, in appreciation.

To the kind dolphins who have helped us to learn to understand.

Preface: A Prediction [1]

Within the next decade or two the human species will establish communication with another species: nonhuman, alien, possibly extraterrestrial, more probably marine; but definitely highly intelligent, perhaps even intellectual. An optimistic prediction, I admit. In this book I have summarized the basic reasons for my beliefs and presented some evidence for the validity of the prediction. In a way this is a crude, elementary handbook for those humans who are interested in the realization of such communication. If no one among us pursues the matter before interspecies communication is forced upon *Homo sapiens* by an alien species, this book will have failed in its purpose. But if this account sparks public and private interest in time for us to make some preparation before we encounter such beings, I shall feel my time was well spent in the research here described.

I assume that those who first heard me present this thesis publicly and those who first read of it in the news, know that I assume full responsibility for it—no pseudo modesty or fear of sticking out my vulnerable neck forces

[1] This prediction was made in 1960; in 1975 it has not yet transpired. I am returning to work with interspecies communication to try a new way of approach. Maybe, by 1980, we will know, one way or another. J.C.L.

me to hide behind either colleagues or institutions, ancient or modern. Of course, as is often the case, the substance of my prediction may turn out to be correct but the time estimate may be substantially incorrect on either the high or the low side. If it turns out that I am wholly incorrect, I shall remember that in research of the best scientific sort no experiment is a failure: even experimental disproof of a thesis turns up new and valuable information.

If and when interspecies contact is made, it may be used as a force for peace or as further aid to warfare. It may be that we shall encounter ideas, philosophies, ways, and means not previously conceived by the minds of men. If this is the case, the present program of research will quickly pass from the domain of scientists to that of powerful men and institutions and hence somewhat beyond the control of the first venturers. When that time comes, I hope that the ideas here presented will help those men of good will to lead wisely and that they will be a bit better informed than they were in 1945 concerning another scientific advance, that time in applied nuclear physics.

. . . the Mock Turtle sang this, very slowly and sadly:

"Will you walk a little faster?" said a whiting to a snail,
"There's a porpoise[1] close behind us, and he's treading
on my tail. . . ."

. . . said Alice . . . "I'd have said to the porpoise, 'Keep
back, please! We don't want *you* with us!' "

"They were obliged to have him with them," the Mock
Turtle said. "No wise fish would go anywhere without
a porpoise."

"Wouldn't it, really?" said Alice, in a tone of great sur-
prise.

"Of course not," said the Mock Turtle. "Why, if a fish
came to *me,* and told me he was going on a journey,
I should say, 'With what porpoise?' "

"Don't you mean 'purpose'?" said Alice.

"I mean what I say," the Mock Turtle replied, in an
offended tone.

[1] Undoubtedly *Phocaena,* the true porpoise, not the dolphin,
Tursiops, of this book. J.C.L.

Introduction

This book is a combination and republication of three books and two scientific papers. The books are: *Man and Dolphin*, *The Dolphin in History* and *The Mind of the Dolphin*. The scientific papers are: "Communication with Extraterrestrial Intelligence" and "Reprogramming of the Sonic Output of the Dolphin: Sonic Burst Count Matching."

The dolphins were respected by people such as Aristotle (400 B.C.). His write-up of dolphins is to this day one of the best. It can be found in Volume 9, page 156, *Great Books of the Western World*, Encyclopaedia Britannica, Inc., Chicago, 1952. It is wise to read all of Aristotle on the animals. He scatters his observations of the dolphins through this book. Similar respect for the dolphins in the printed version has not been found until the book *Man and Dolphin*, 1961, in this century.

The Dolphin in History was published in 1962–63 by the William Andrews Clark Memorial Library, University of California, Los Angeles. There are two papers in this small book: one by Ashley Montagu and one by John C. Lilly. Ashley Montagu reviews "The History of the Dolphin," which is well worth reading. John C. Lilly's paper, "Modern Whales, Dolphins and Porpoises, as Challenges to Our Intelligence," is in this volume in full, including references.

The book *The Mind of the Dolphin* was published in 1967 by Doubleday; and in 1968, Avon issued a paperback, reducing the size of the text of *The Mind of the Dolphin*. In order to fit it into this volume and not to repeat things that were said in *Man and Dolphin,* we start this new version of *The Mind of the Dolphin* with Margaret Howe's account of her several months of living with Peter and training Peter. We are keeping all the pictures of Margaret and Peter that were published in this volume.

We present the needs for the future dolphin research both on the theoretical and practical side in terms of the personnel that are required and give a specific example of a successful trial period of Margaret and Peter. I feel this work should be followed up. In the future, such research should be done by the sea, with a house such as detailed in this text. Here the dolphins can come and go as they please. It may be necessary to capture some dolphins in order to start the facility on its way, but it should be in the area of a warm sea and in a house through which the dolphins can swim with special waterways, and in which the humans can meet the dolphins without being afraid of being drowned. We would include several enthusiastic children, of all ages, from approximately three or four up through the teens and into adulthood. All will participate in all of the life within the house including the kitchen, the bathroom and the living room.

The Programming and Metaprogramming in the Human Biocomputer was published in 1967. The paper that was taken from this was republished in the Spectrum of the I.E.E.E. (the Institute of Electronic and Electrical Engineers) as "Communication with Extraterrestrial Intelligence." This paper summarizes the problems of interspecies communication in a very scientific and sparse fashion. In this volume I write a popularized version of the scientific version in order to broaden the understanding of this particular paper.

"Reprogramming of the Sonic Output of the Dolphin: Sonic Burst Count Matching" is the last scientific paper which I published. It was published by The Acoustical Society of America in June of 1968 in Volume 43, *Journal of the Acoustical Society of America*, pages 1412 to 1424. These twelve pages are reproduced in full in this volume. They summarize the operational philosophy on which I was operating over the previous twelve years and show my slow but sure break with the Skinnerian-Pavlovian interpretation of dolphin behavior. We talk about programming, programming subroutines and so on, using a more modern language and a more modern set of concepts and not assuming that we know everything about them. An equal amount of space for the unknowns in the dolphins and for the dolphin's initiative is given.

In this paper we show the quantitative limits of human hearing and of dolphin hearing and of the human sonic output and the dolphin sonic output. We have a vocal mode flow diagram with the human-dolphin communication link with feedback between the two. Analysis of the outputs of the two species demonstrates the very small overlap between these two and shows the almost eight times difference between the two species in regard to their outputs and their inputs in the sonic sphere. This was ignored by the scientific establishment and hence I feel it should have more publicity and a wider circulation and a greater understanding. It shows the basic problem of communication with the bottle-nosed dolphin which can be extended to other species such as the elephants and the whales.

All of the above works were reproduced between 1954 and 1968. In 1967 to 1968 I decided to stop dolphin work. I no longer wanted to run a concentration camp for my friends and if they were as I found them to be and if this was not only my imagination, then there was an ethical problem of maintaining them in a confined state in which they may not survive. Immediately after I decided to stop dolphin research, at least in this way, five of the dolphins in our eight-dolphin colony committed suicide. Within the next week, I let three go. A later book called *The Center of the Cyclone*, 1972, contains details of this ethical problem.

The problems of the humans are summarized in a later book called *Simulations of God, the Science of Belief*. This book illustrates in a succinct and direct way the difficulties that we have with our belief systems. Belief systems are programs which are written into us or acquired by us when we are too young to know any better. Later we modify these with metabeliefs that are our beliefs about beliefs, then as we learn to learn and as we become mature, we become less susceptible to the dictates of these early belief structures, presented in the foreword of this book and previously published in *The Center of the Cyclone*, also in *Programming and Metaprogramming in the Human Biocomputer*, published by Julian Press, 1973.

You may well ask where all of this started. It is generally assumed the dolphin work started before the isolation work. This is not true. In 1954 I decided to do a series of experiments on humans isolated from all visual, acoustic, tactile, pressure and gravity stimuli in so far as this is possible without cutting nerve fibers so I devised a technique using a tank of water, floating the person in the darkness and the silence. This work has been explained in greater length in both *The Human Biocomputer* and *The Center of the Cyclone*. In our new book, *The Dyadic Cyclone*, my wife, Toni, and I go into this even further and show how we have modified and made a new system having an Epsom salt (magnesium sulphate) solution to float in and at the surface so that one doesn't use any breathing apparatus.

Contents

Man and Dolphin

The Possibilities
of Interspecies
Communication

Eventually it may be possible for humans to speak with another species. I have come to this conclusion after careful consideration of evidence gained through my research experiments with dolphins. If new scientific developments are to be made in this direction, however, certain changes in our basic orientation and philosophy will be necessary.

We must strip ourselves, as far as possible, of our preconceptions about the relative place of *Homo sapiens* in the scheme of nature. Past scientific advances have clarified and gradually delimited the place of mankind as the chief species in terrestrial, land-borne nature. If we are to seek communication with other species we must first grant the possibility that some other species may have a potential (or even realized) intellectual development comparable to our own. We cannot continue to insist that man is at the top of the evolutionary scale and that no further evolution is possible. This vain assumption may be preventing certain kinds of valuable research.

Granting that there may be a species as high on the evolutionary scale as man and that we have the technical qualifications to do the research, what characteristics should we look for in another species? We can make an estimate on the basis of our own experience with members of our species. First of all, who are our failures and why can't they communicate? Who in the human species does not possess "intraspecies" language?

The newborn infant obviously cannot speak. As his brain grows and through experience with other human beings, he gradually accumulates language. But for certain children with inherited deficiencies of brain structure, even age and opportunities for learning do not necessarily lead to the development of language. Sometimes, apparently, the brain just stops growing, and if the brain is too small—if it does not have enough cerebral cortex—full human language is impossible. Among some microcephalics, for example, language is not developed to the complex level on which we are accustomed to deal with our fellow men. These considerations suggest that the size and complexity of the brain may have a great deal to do with language capability. So the first thing we should look for in any species with which we may try to communicate is a brain comparable in size and complexity to the human brain.

Having found such a species, we should attempt to determine whether its members have an intraspecies language. If we do not know that one exists, what anatomical and social conditions are most likely to make the existence of such a language highly probable?

Next we should determine whether individuals of the nonhuman species can be taught a human language. In our present state of ignorance we tend to think that if an animal has his own language he may be able to learn ours more easily. This isn't necessarily so; our language may be so strange to the animal that he would have to start over, and he might not be able to do this. And if he has no language at all but, like the human child, has the potential ability to learn ours, he might learn faster and more easily without the hampering influence of a previously learned language.

There are certain basic qualifications that we can apply to our search for a species with which to attempt communication. Because we are treading very close to the edge of the unknown, we must necessarily be tentative and suggestive, rather than definitive. Until we have progressed much further in our scientific research program we can only single out what we think are the probabilities from the vast array of possibilities.

As I have said, we should choose a species with a brain equal to ours in size and complexity. No interspecies communication has been achieved with primates having smaller brains than man's. Dedicated attempts to teach chimpanzees to speak have led to failure of two-way communication—presumably because of the animal's failure to transmit. The size of the chimpanzee's brain (375 grams) is about one-fourth that of the adult human (1450 grams) and less than half that of a human child who is learning to speak (1000 grams). (See Appendixes for details.) If we choose a species with a brain much larger than ours, the mental processes may turn out to be too alien for us to understand and we would not be able to establish communication. And if the brain deviates too much from ours in complexity, the mental processes may likewise turn out to be too alien for us to encompass.

At least some resemblances to our anatomy and physiology are desirable if not essential. Our difficulty will increase radically if the external appearance of the animal is too different from our own and if the environment in which the animal lives is too foreign to us. A non-mammal like the giant squid might be too much for our present abilities and understanding. The giant squid breathes water, cannot live in air, is nocturnal, lives deep in the sea. Such alienness and strangeness make the initial difficulties of dealing with the animal extremely great. On this score we can eliminate whole orders and even phyla of animals on our own planet as inappropriate. All of the invertebrates, all of the Protozoa (single-celled animals) and the Metazoa (sponges, etc.) can be eliminated. The only group sufficiently close to us to warrant beginning the program are the Mammalia.

If we eliminate all mammals with smaller and less complex brains than ours, we must cross off the list all of the anthropoid apes and most of the other primates, all of the carnivores (large cats) and the ungulates (horses, cows, etc.). Two groups of large animals are then left: whales and elephants.

Adult elephants have brains up to four times the size of an average adult human brain; modern whales have brains up to six times the size of ours. Some smaller whales—dolphins and porpoises—have brains about the size of ours. The brain of the bottle-nosed dolphin (*Tursiops truncatus*) is about 1700 grams, ours is 1450 grams; the relative brain weight per unit body length of the dolphin is about 200 grams per foot for our 240 grams per foot.

The animal we choose must not be too large. There are obvious technical difficulties in dealing with either a land or a sea-borne animal that weighs more than about five hundred pounds. The slightest misunderstanding with a very large animal might lead to destructive action on one side or the other. The whole relationship of the human group working with such animals could be changed by one episode in which a human was injured. An animal that is too large is not apt to realize how weak the human may be and how easily he may be hurt or even killed. This qualification eliminates the large elephants and the larger whales from consideration.

A further requirement is that it should be possible for a kindly relationship to exist between man and the animal chosen. By this I mean bilateral kindliness. Such a relationship would not be possible, for example, between most lions and man (however, see *Born Free* by Joy Adamson for qualifications) or between most adult gorillas and man. It exists in some cases between elephants and man—the mahouts of India often have kindly relationships with their elephants. From my experiences I feel that it is possible to establish bilateral kindliness with some of the smaller whales: the bottle-nosed dolphin and *Globicephala scammoni,* one of the pilot whales.

For our convenience if not from necessity, the animal should be capable of vocalizing within the same ranges and parametric sets of variables that the human uses. In other words, it should be capable of making *sounds* with its vocal apparatus, either in air or in another medium, which sound like human-produced sounds; at the very least its emissions should be transformable by simple methods into the acoustic range that we possess. *Homo sapiens* seems to be unique in his intimate and detailed control over the muscles surrounding his respiratory outlet—the muscles of phonation, the larynx, the nasopharynx, the pharynx, the mouth, the lips, and the face. However, our mobility of facial expression is not an absolute concomitant of spoken language: we can still speak to one another fairly successfully over the telephone without visual aid. On this basis alone it may be possible to eliminate the elephants from consideration, although I do not know whether anyone has ever attempted to teach an elephant to vocalize in a human sort of way. This seems to be an unexplored field. My experiences with the Cetacea, or whales, have shown that they seem to be perfectly capable of mimicking human voice sounds in a primitive but possibly intelligible fashion.

The animals that best seem to fulfill all of the above qualifications are the dolphins (and possibly porpoises) and the pilot whales, both of which belong to the Delphinidae, a subgroup of the odontocetes or toothed whales. These small cousins of the killer whale range in length from five to approximately twelve or more feet.

Of the large number of such species, the shoal-water dolphin, *Tursiops truncatus,* is most readily available for study. Some specimens of the deep-sea varieties of dolphins such as the common dolphin, *Delphinus;* the spotted dolphin, *Stenella;* and the striped dolphin, *Lagenorhynchus,* are available but they are used to living in deep water and do not survive captivity in very small enclosures quite as well as *Tursiops truncatus.* The pilot whale, *Globicephala scammoni,* is finally becoming available through the efforts of a West Coast oceanarium called Marineland of the Pacific and shows a great deal of promise.

The natural habitat of *Tursiops* is the shoals bordering the continents and islands in the warm waters of the world. He has some dexterity of slow movements and a curiosity about his surroundings, including the bottom. These characteristics help in our work with him. Some of his swifter pelagic cousins are less amenable to life as captives, less flexible of body, and less curious.

Tursiops truncatus is well known to fishermen along the Florida and Carolina coasts. There is good evidence that a "harem" of *Tursiops* will help fishermen by herding fish toward their particular boats. There have been many instances of *Tursiops* pushing or urging human beings to safety after shipwrecks or in the presence of sharks while swimming off shore.

Two episodes, which I shall describe in a later chapter,

seem to point to the existence of an intraspecies language.

They further fit our basic qualifications in that they are capable of vocalizing in air and are extremely quick to learn. They can put the blowhole and most of the body above the surface of the water and emit noises that one can hear up to a few feet away. If one is beached, very faint whistles can be heard coming from the blowhole. Some of these I have identified as distress signals.[1]

In recent years *Tursiops truncatus* has become the mainstay of the "porpoise" acts in at least four oceanaria in the United States: Marine Studios, St. Augustine, Florida; Marineland of the Pacific, Palos Verdes Estates, California; Seaquarium, Miami, Florida; and Theatre-of-the-Sea, Islamerada, Florida. Much evidence as to the ability to learn and to vocalize came from these oceanaria.

Over the last fifteen years it has been found at Marine Studios that the trainability of the bottle-nosed dolphin is limited partially by the ingenuity of the trainers. Punishment methods do not work very well in training these animals but rewarding experiences do. Variety in the training program is necessary. It will not do to repeat the same thing in the monotonous fashion used to train a dog or other small-brained animal; three to five different things must be used in the repertory, one after the other, in rapid succession. The instant the animal performs a spontaneous play action that is new and different, he is rewarded.

Quizzing the trainers of these animals in detail, I found that they had a great deal of respect and affection for the animals. I watched the trainers at work and saw that there was a very close relationship between the individual animal and the trainer, in spite of the fact that

[1] Lilly, J. C. Some considerations regarding basic mechanisms of positive and negative types of motivations. Am. J. of Psychiatry, **115:** 498–504, Dec. 1958.

the animal was in the water and the human in the air: each watched the other intently and minutely.

At none of the four oceanaria has vocalization on the part of the animals been used to its fullest extent. At Marineland of the Pacific there is a chorus of dolphins that respond to baton waving and to proper verbal directions by singing in a siren-like fashion. The same trick is used with individual dolphins at Marine Studios. At Theatre-of-the-Sea two dolphins have new and strange air-voices. The Seaquarium animals are also becoming more vocal in air. However, these animals emit many, many more vocalizations than are made use of in the shows.

F. G. Wood, Jr., of Marine Studios has collected typical vocalizations of these animals in captivity and has published a description of them.[2] They emit whistles, creaking-doorlike noises, barks, grunts, rasping noises, etc. One great difficulty in dealing with these sounds is that they are emitted under water and the transmission of sound from water to air is extremely poor. In order to hear them well one must use a hydrophone or put one's head far enough under water so that it comes up against the tympanic membrane of the ear. Sounds are also transmitted very poorly from air to water, as any skin diver knows. At these oceanaria there has been very little attempt to make conscious use of any sort of exchange of sounds between animals and humans. In fact, when the animals are trained to vocalize at all, each animal puts its blowhole out of the water and emits the sounds in air, rather than under water as he is accustomed to do. They accommodate to us rather than we to them.

The great difficulty in developing a type of vocal com-

[2] Wood, F. G., Jr. Underwater sound production and concurrent behavior of captive porpoises, *Tursiops truncatus* and *Stenella plagiodon*. Bull. Mar. Sci. Gulf and Caribbean, **3** (2): 102–33, 1954.

munication between man and these water-borne mammals that are used to living and communicating under water is obvious. We speak in air, we hear best in air. Speaking under water is a difficult feat for us. The dolphins seem to be a bit ahead of us: they can also vocalize in air. Their natural air-borne sounds are not very loud, not as loud as ours, except with training. Apparently they hear but poorly in air, but nobody has yet measured how badly their hearing suffers in air as opposed to their hearing in water, which is excellent. Therefore, in order to meet these animals more than halfway, we must devise a technique of speaking under water and a technique so that when we are in air and they are in water we can hear them "speaking" under water and they can hear us speaking in air. This can be done with hydrophones, with underwater loudspeakers, and with appropriate electronic apparatus.

In other words, if we are going to stay in air and speak to dolphins, and they are going to stay in water and speak back to us, we must create (by electronic or other means) the complete chain of communication so that they can hear what we are saying and we can hear what they are saying with equal facility.

In the research program of the Communication Research Institute in St. Thomas we are currently using hydrophones and underwater loudspeakers to facilitate continuous exchanges between the humans around the pools and the dolphins. We are also working on the problem of enabling a man under water to speak, either by his own efforts without artificial aids or by using a suitable mask or the proper electronic equipment.

In attempting to communicate, the amount of fear and negative emotion in general that is generated on one side or the other or both plays an important part. The experience of "getting close" to an individual of another species must be rewarding in some way to each side.

Contacts must be sufficiently prolonged and frequent to make the development of communication possible. Let us take a specific example of the development of communication between humans, and then apply it to communication between a human and a dolphin.

In developing a vocal language in our own children, there seem to be a number of essentials.[3] One requirement is intimate contact between the baby and the mother, including physical-contact manipulations between the mother and the baby; a second is continuous vocalization by the mother to the baby; a third, the mother's vocal answers coupled with satisfaction of the various needs of the baby on his vocal demand; finally it may at times be necessary to isolate mother and baby from other human beings, but this is still a questionable point; it may be true only very early in life. Later on, social contacts, especially contacts with other children, obviously facilitate the further development of language.

The primitive beginnings of language, as stated many times by many authors, seem to lie in the vocalizations dependent upon internal need. One can see this kind of vocalization in lower animals as well as in man. Cries of distress, of fear, of hunger, mating calls, expressions of pain, etc., are all well known and have been described in the scientific literature.[4]

Such primitive, almost built-in vocalizations seem to be characteristic of humans, irrespective of where they are on earth, at the time of birth. With further growth of the brain and further experience with the mother and other

[3] Spitz, René. *No and Yes* (International Universities Press, New York, 1957). Lewis, M. M. *Infant Speech* (Kegan Paul, Trench, Trubner and Co., London, 1936).

[4] *Instinctive Behavior*, tr. by C. H. Schiller (International Universities Press, New York, 1957). Lanyon, W. E., and Tavolga, W. N. *Animal Sounds and Communication*, 1960. Am. Inst. of Biol. Sci., Washington, D.C. (Pub. No. 7).

persons in the surroundings, these sounds are rapidly modified. In a matter of a few weeks a Japanese baby ceases to sound like an American baby and vice versa, yet intelligible language has not yet begun to develop. In some cases a private language seems to be established between the mother and the child. In other words, the mother is much more astute than anyone else at picking up and answering the child's needs, but again, this is not communal, intellectual, predictive, and descriptive language, at the command of the child. Such a language seems gradually to unfold from these primitive beginnings and can be forced a bit by appropriate training methods.[5]

Between the ages of two and three, approximately, language has already become extremely useful and is well beyond the stage of mere emotional expressiveness. However, if the child is either left with nonhuman parents (the feral child) or is put in an institution where he is thoroughly neglected, language fails to develop.[6]

The same is true of a dolphin isolated from human contact. If he is put in solitary isolation or left with other dolphins he will not learn anything of our language. If he is forced to obtain satisfaction of his needs through vocalizations with and from human beings, then the beginnings of language may possibly be inculcated in a particular animal. As in the case of the human mother with the human child, this may require rather constant and continuous attention and awareness of detail.

It should be apparent, then, that even under the best circumstances the establishment of communication with

[5] Moore, Omar K. The motivation and training of students for intellectual pursuits: a new approach. Tenth Thomas Alva Edison Foundation Inst., 1959.

[6] Spitz, René. *Hospitalism*. "The Psychoanalytic Study of the Child," Vol. 1, p. 53 (International Universities Press, New York, 1945).

these water-borne mammals will be extremely difficult and laborious. However, recent discoveries in the fields of neurophysiology and experimental psychology may ease the burden of this work somewhat.

These new advances and their significance are concerned with the concepts of "physiological" reward and "physiological" punishment. "Rewards" and "punishments" in common parlance are spoken of at many levels of discourse and are used in many different ways. In this instance I am talking about direct primitive here-and-now feelings and states of the brain. For example, in the case of oneself these are felt as pleasure (reward) of some sort starting at a definite time and lasting for a definite specifiable interval (feelings such as we experience when satisfying hunger, etc.). Alternatively, the feeling might be one of pain (punishment) in a given body part (gut or limb or head) or unlocalized unpleasant sensations in the body, like fear, anger, etc. Such direct experiences are said to be detectable in animals by means of experiments on their behavior, and are seen daily in very young children, including those who are not yet able to speak. These experiences are powerful aids to learning: with learning and experience, rewards of this sort are sought after and punishments of this sort are shunned. Quite early in life one learns to seek pleasure and pleasure-evoking situations and to avoid pain and fright and their causes. In recent years the areas and systems in the brain whose activities generate the various kinds of pleasure, pain, fright, and anger have been discovered.

These experiments[7] have proved that electrical stimuli placed by means of fine wires in specific portions of the brain can cause either intense rewarding or intense

[7] Lilly, J. C. Learning motivated by subcortical stimulation: The "start" and the "stop" patterns of behavior, pp. 705-21. Chapter in: *Reticular Formation of the Brain*, Jasper, H. H. *et al.*, eds. (Little, Brown and Co., Boston, 1958).

punishing experiences in a particular animal and in humans. This has been demonstrated in rats, cats, monkeys, and in later years, dolphins.[8] The technique allows either the human operator or the animal to control the rewards and the punishments. In the less well controlled training of the past we depended solely on a fish-food reward, for example, in training dolphins. Although the food type of reward has worked extremely well in the Marineland training programs, we no longer need to depend on it. With the newer method we can push a button and cause a brief controlled period of a rewarding pleasure to occur in the particular animal. Conversely, we can push another button, which controls another place in the brain, and cause intense punishment (fear, anger, pain, nausea, vomiting, unconsciousness, etc.).

So we now have push-button control of the experience of specific emotion by animals in whose brains we have placed wires in the proper places. Apparently they can experience, among others, the following sensations: "as if fed" when hungry; "as if warm" when cold; "as if cooled off" when hot; "as if drinking" when thirsty; as if "sexually approached" when deprived, etc. The opposite effects can also be created by stimulating other specific portions of the brain, that is, we can make an animal feel thirsty when he isn't and cold when actually he's warm, etc. Practically all of our primitive emotional life can now be reproduced in whole or in part by these methods.

It is difficult to teach an animal if too powerful a reward or too powerful a punishment is used. If he likes the experience too much and becomes too involved in it, he cannot learn a highly differentiated task. Less primitive and less powerful emotional effects can be brought about by stimulation in certain brain systems. I found

[8] Lilly, J. C., *loc. cit.*

that maximum teachability of dolphins and monkeys resulted when the wires were placed in the lateral forward
parts of the brain. It is claimed[9] that in the human these
areas of the brain give rise to an intense sense of well-
being without any particular instinctual direction, that
is, the sense of well-being is not sexual, or connected
with food, hunger, thirst, etc. In so far as we can determine, many of these systems are nonsatiable; they exert
a powerful influence as long as the animal is awake, and
repeating the stimulus again and again does not wear
out the effect.

Using this "reward-stimulation" technique, we demonstrated quite satisfactorily that a dolphin can vocalize in
two different ways. One, in his usual fashion, under
water, and the other by emitting air through his blowhole
so that he produces air-borne sounds that we can hear.
By changing back and forth between responding to him
under water or in air we could induce a particular animal
to emit his sounds either under water or in air.

There are, of course, many obstacles to a mutual understanding between dolphins and men. Consider their
activities compared with ours. They have no written records and make no artifacts. They lack hands like ours
and are not building anything. They have no need of
transportation, because it is built in. They can swim at
twenty knots and in a few days cover thousands of sea
miles in a search for food or more desirable water temperatures. They have no need to store food, because it
abounds in the sea for the taking. They have no need
for clothing or shelter. They have no need for gravity-
resisting forces of the magnitude that we do. Their gravity resistance is distributed over the whole integument,
rather than on the bottom of the feet or on the buttocks
as in our case.

[9] Lilly, J. C., *loc. cit.*

Because they do not constantly have to resist gravity as we do, they do not need to sleep as we do. As we discovered, they cannot afford deep unconsciousness at all from any cause—anesthesia, epileptic convulsions, or a blow on the head hard enough to produce unconsciousness will kill them.

They do not seem to have the kind of automatic respiratory system that allows us to breathe while we are unconscious. Being under water seems to inhibit the dolphin's respiration completely, and in order to breathe and release the breathing mechanism, he must surface. An automatic breathing mechanism would bring in water and drown the animal. If knocked out, either he must regain consciousness or be carried up by fellow animals.

An animal that was being delivered to an oceanarium struck his head on the side of the pool as he was being let into it. He was knocked unconscious and dropped to the bottom. The other dolphins pushed him to the surface and held him there until he began to breathe again.

This episode illustrates another fact about these animals: they are socially, mutually interdependent. There is a very close relationship between the mother and child: the baby is not weaned for eighteen to twenty-one months. During this long weaning period he is apparently taught many things by the mother on a purely experiential and possibly vocal basis.

All of dolphin culture may be transmitted in somewhat the way primitive human tribes transmit knowledge from one generation to the next with long folk tales and legends that are memorized by each individual and passed on to the next generation, which in turn memorizes them and passes them on. The immediate and fixed storage capacity necessitated by such a learning method would require a very large brain. Our writing, printing, and similar ways of storing memory outside of our own brains free us from a lot of the necessity of memorization. These animals must, as it were, remember everything, since they have no libraries or filing cases or symbolic language in any form other than possibly the vocal one. There is no whale yet known with a brain smaller than ours; maybe an air-breathing mammal requires a very quick and large brain to remember enough to survive at sea.

They may have a nomadic culture, they may herd their own fish—we do not know. These are facts yet to be determined. How they navigate is also a mystery. We know nothing about how certain species move accurately over literally thousands of miles of open ocean.

They may possibly use the moon and stars and the sun as aids to navigation. It is very difficult when under water to see through it at an angle of less than about 30° because the water surface is highly reflective and presents a sheen one cannot see through. If one goes under with a face mask and looks back up at the surface, most of the surface looks like a distorted shimmering mirror, except for an area directly above one's head.

To avoid this effect, these animals stick their heads out of water and look around in air, unimpeded by refraction and reflections. Again and again at Marineland, a dolphin named Polly used to stick her head up out of the tank and look around for us, at the nearby laboratory. In the natural state they leap out of the water and carry on many complex gyrations at sea. They have been seen to come up out of the water and whirl in place and to do complex barrel rolls as they leaped in the air. It may be that they have learned to solve the "mirror" problem at the surface of the water and come up and look around them at the stars, moon, sun, land, etc., in order to navigate. Their vision in air, as well as in the water, is excellent: how they see so well without a face mask is still a puzzle. Of course, they may also use navigational methods about which we know nothing, involving the depth of the sea and the bottom, ocean currents, water temperature, salinity, plankton, water taste, etc.

It is going to require a great degree of imagination to empathize with such creatures. We must use our imagination and project ourselves into areas of which we have no secure knowledge. Speculation is useful, but must not be taken as fact until evidence piles up to either support or destroy the speculation. We do not know to what degree these animals communicate with one another, but it looks as if they do so at a very complex descriptive level.

The humans (and animals) who do this work will have to be dedicated, courageous, open-minded and knowledgeable, observant and quick, as well as kindly. These animals have large and fine brains and this fact should make us pause before we attempt to treat them the way we have treated other animals with less to offer us. Scientifically, it is very appropriate to attempt to identify with their position by increasing our knowledge of what that position is and how it differs from ours. At the same time we must at least tentatively remove them from the category of the chimpanzee, the cat, the dog, and the rat in our thinking about them. It is probable that their intelligence is comparable to ours, though in a very strange fashion. To accomplish anything of importance with them, we must overcome our self-immolation, xenophobia, and various taboos which we carry to our work with these animals.

2

Avoiding Biased
Assumptions

In January 1958, I flew to Oslo, Norway, where I
lectured at Dr. Per Scholander's Zoophysiological Institute at the University of Oslo in the course of doing some
work for the United States Air Force.

In my lecture I presented my slowly developing point
of view that perhaps dolphins are much more intelligent
than we give them credit for, within their own limitations. I suggested that we are severely handicapped in
our efforts to measure the intelligence of individuals of
other species than our own. We use inappropriate yard-
sticks derived from our own history as primates with
hands and legs. As compared with other species our
prime accomplishments have been the development of
material creations and of written language. I raised the
question of what an animal does with a big brain in an
alien environment—alien to us, that is. I recounted the
episodes that we regard as suggestive evidence that the
dolphin has a primitive language with predictive and
descriptive values.

In a discussion following the talk, a visiting scientist
from the Whaling Institute remarked that the killer

whale must also be an intelligent animal and have a language: he related the following story to illustrate the point. During the previous whaling season in the Antarctic a group of several thousand killer whales came into the area where a fishing fleet was operating. By killing the fish near these boats the whales made it impossible for the fleet to catch any fish. The fishing fleet radioed the whaling fleet for help. The whaling fleet sent over several *shytter* boats.[1] One of these fired a single shot from a harpoon gun. Within half an hour the killer whales had completely disappeared from the vicinity of the *shytter* boats over fifty or more square miles and from then on not a whale came within range of the harpoon guns. However, the fishing boats that were not next to the *shytter* boats were still plagued by the whales.

The remarkable part of this story is that both the fishing boats and the *shytter* boats were converted World War II Corvettes. Their silhouettes and power plants were quite similar, the only distinctive difference being the harpoon guns on the bows of the *shytter* boats.

The man from the Whaling Institute said that this demonstrated to him and to the whalers that the killer whales do have a means of communication, one that is extremely rapid and has predictive and descriptive values. It certainly looks as if the whales were able to communicate a description of the *shytter* boats to all the other whales within the space of half an hour, influencing the behavior of many, many individuals immediately and continuing to do so for many hours. Such transmission of complex information has always been thought to be possible only among humans.

Obviously this behavior differs from that of a school

[1] Robinson, R. B. *Of Whales and Men* (Alfred A. Knopf, New York, 1954).

of fish which suddenly changes direction and takes up
a new one by some unknown means of communication.
The killer-whale mob sent out a fundamental description of a dangerous object: a harpoon gun. We can imagine the minimum amount of information that must have
been transmitted and place it in sharp contrast with the
kind of information a school of fish might send out. Let
us visualize the conditions of this imaginary whale "conversation" as follows:

Possibly the dying killer whale was able to shout of
the danger to his fellows in the immediate neighborhood. At least they were probably witnesses, either visual
or acoustic, to the catastrophe. Let us say that they were
witnesses and that they then passed on the word to the
other animals in the following way, freely and imaginatively translated:

"There is a thing sticking out on the front of some
of these boats that can shoot a sharp thing that can go
into our bodies and explode. There is a long line attached to it by which they can pull us in."

There might be some uninformed, inexperienced animals around, to whom they would then give the warning: "Stay away from those vessels with this thing on
the front end—it can hurt you at a distance up to a hundred body lengths (or however they measure distance)
away from the bow straight ahead." Immediately all animals would watch the bows of all the vessels involved
and could still do their killing in the immediate neighborhood of those boats that lacked the protuberance.

Now let us contrast this "conversation" with that of
the school of fish. To put it in human terms, one fish,
the leader, might shout, "Right turn," and all turn right.
Within a half second or less the command is given and
the action executed. The behavior of the killer whales
is very different. In the first place, a lot of information
is transmitted about another object, not killer whales,

Dolphins continuing to swim in only 12″ of water.

A head-on view of a dolphin in a sling showing the position of the eye in relation to the line of the mouth.

The open mouth showing the teeth, the wide "lips" and the sphincter at the back of the throat.

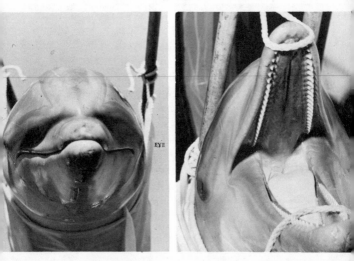

EYE

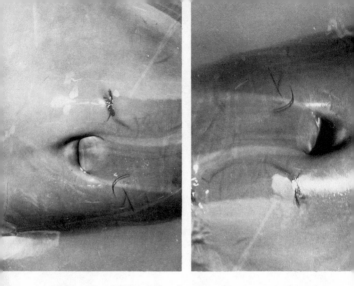

Left, the closed blowhole showing the crescent-shaped top of the plug. *Right,* the open blowhole during breathing.

Left, Elvar's eye looking downward showing the position of the ear opening behind the eye. *Right,* Elvar's eye looking upward showing the position in relation to the back of the mouth opening.

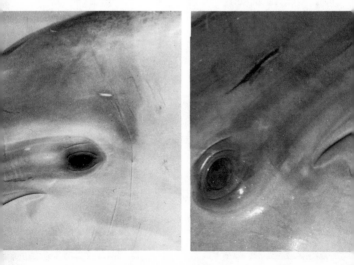

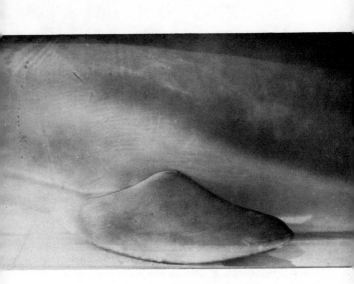

A view of the flipper used for steering and palpation.

Left, a lateral view of the flukes and peduncle, showing the keel-like structure of the peduncle. *Right,* a top view of the powerful flukes, the main propulsion mechanism of the dolphin.

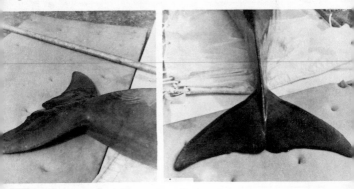

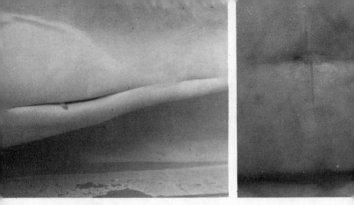

Left, the anal and genital openings in a male. In the fe‑
male these two openings are combined into one long one.
Right, Elvar's umbilicus (navel).

John Lilly feeding a baby dolphin called "Baby-D." We
devised a new method utilizing the little finger from a sur‑
gical glove with a hole in the tip for a nipple. The baby
must be fed underwater every fifteen minutes, twenty-four
hours a day. The milk contains no sugar and is a thick
solution of pure fat and pure protein. This baby was caught
by accident. Its mother escaped. We kept it going by the
above method until it could eat fish.

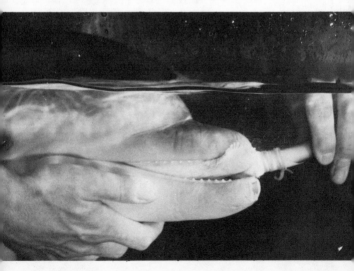

and this object is differentiated from similar objects in the neighborhood. A particular aspect of the different objects is dangerous, and they say it is dangerous. Belief and a period of thinking are required on the part of the hearers and then there must be further observations on the part of the hearers if they are to differentiate the objects they have just heard about. To transmit all of this information takes more than a fraction of a second—it may take several minutes, and the behavior of the whales is changed for a period of many hours. It isn't just a matter of turning right or left—it is a whole pattern of behavior connected with staying away from the dangerous object and not staying away from similar objects that are not dangerous.

The level of complexity of the whale patterns of behavior is fantastically higher than that of the fish. The number of bits of information and the number of hours the influence lasts are probably measured in billions and in days rather than in fractions of seconds in the immediate here and now of the school of fish.

A similar episode involving killer whales was related by R. F. Scott in the diary of his last fatal expedition to Antarctica in 1911. It indicates that killer whales have a very high order of intelligence and possibly intellect. The notes of a man who witnessed the frightening events in their stark reality are quoted in full:[2]

"1911, Thursday, January 5—All hands were up at 5:00 this morning and at work at 6:00. Words cannot express the splendid way in which everyone works and gradually the work gets organized. I was a little late on the scene this morning, and thereby witnessed a most extraordinary scene. Some 6 or 7 killer whales, old and young, were skirting the fast floe edge ahead of the ship;

[2] Scott, R. F. *Scott's Last Expedition* (Beacon Press, Boston, 1957), p. 65.

they seemed excited and dived rapidly, almost touching the floe. As we watched, they suddenly appeared astern, raising their snouts out of water. I had heard weird stories of these beasts, but had never associated serious danger with them. Close to the water's edge lay the wire stern rope of the ship, and our two Esquimaux dogs were tethered to this. I did not think of connecting the movements of the whales with this fact, and seeing them so close I shouted to Ponting, who was standing abreast of the ship. He seized his camera and ran towards the floe edge to get a close picture of the beasts, which had momentarily disappeared. The next moment the whole floe under him and the dogs heaved up and split into fragments. One could hear the 'booming' noise as the whales rose under the ice and struck it with their backs [more probably their rostral beaks, J.C.L.]. Whale after whale rose under the ice, setting it rocking fiercely; luckily Ponting kept his feet and was able to fly to security. By an extraordinary chance also, the splits had been made around and between the dogs, so that neither of them fell into the water. Thus it was clear that the whales shared our astonishment, for one after another their huge hideous heads shot vertically into the air through the cracks which they had made. As they reared them to a height of 6 or 8 feet it was possible to see their tawny head markings, their small glistening eyes, and their terrible array of teeth—by far the largest and most terrifying in the world. There cannot be a doubt that they looked up to see what had happened to Ponting and the dogs.

"The latter were horribly frightened and strained to their chains, whining; the head of one killer must certainly have been within 5 feet of one of the dogs.

"After this, whether they thought the game insignificant, or whether they missed Ponting is uncertain, but the terrifying creatures passed on to other hunting grounds, and we were able to rescue the dogs, and what was even more important, our petrol—5 or 6 tons of which was waiting on a piece of ice which was not split away from the main mass.

"Of course, we have known well that killer whales continually skirt the edge of the floes and that they would undoubtedly snap up anyone who was unfortunate enough to fall into the water; but the fact that they could display such deliberate cunning, that they were able to break ice of such thickness (at least 2½ feet), and that they could act in unison, were a revelation to us. It is clear that they are endowed with singular intelligence, and in the future we shall treat that intelligence with every respect."

I not only find Scott's interpretation credible, I find some authors' reinterpretations of this now classic episode quite incredible.[3] In all charity toward authors not privileged to have had close-up experiences with any Cetacea, I will say that these are really unbelievable animals; but attempts to deny the validity of Scott's observations and his on-the-spot realizations of this whale's capabilities are best forgotten. Until the crucial research results are obtained, we shall not know the true explanation of the behavior of these animals, but any reasonable hypothesis is defensible. Experimental tests for the existence and form of such a whale language are being designed and carried out over long periods of time in our laboratory.

I hope I have made it clear that I do not intend to defend a single-minded thesis or accept the provisional working hypothesis of a whale language as anything more than a temporary aid to research design. I have always qualified my viewpoint as an exploratory research

[3] Norman, J. R., and Fraser, F. C. *Field Book of Giant Fishes, Whales and Dolphins* (Putnam, London, 1937).

position: until the experimental data are collected and fully worked over, an open mind is essential and the number of hypothetical positions remain (at least meta-theoretically) infinite.

Such behavior patterns can scarcely be instinctual. There is no need for them to be instinctual—most of the Cetacea are born capable of swimming, have large brains at birth, and stay dependent upon the mother almost two years before weaning takes place. Apparently much of this period is spent in teaching and learning, in becoming disciplined so that the young will know how to hunt and avoid danger, mate and reproduce, and perform all of the other processes necessary to a life in the sea while breathing air.

I have been charged with "anthropomorphizing" by several of my colleagues. What do they mean by anthropomorphizing?

Science has made vast strides in the past by refusing to endow physical, chemical, and primitive biological processes with human purposes. There are many, many instances of scientists and investigators who went down blind alleys because they assumed that there was a "little man in there," who caused the processes to take place. There is all of the lore of magic and sorcery, the incubi, zombies, and ghosts that have been created by man as "explanations" ever since his brain became large enough to do so.

Progress seems to have been made first in those aspects of nature furthest removed from man. Physics separated itself quite early as being the most "nonhuman" part of science, and therefore it has the most ancient as well as the most imposing series of discoveries of any of the sciences. Chemistry had a similar success later and biology is bringing up the rear. Because biologists are involved in a young science, they are most definite and most militant about *not* anthropomorphizing—not putting a "little man" into each organism that they study. The most successful work on the amoeba and on the small single-celled animals (protozoa)[4] had removed human purposes from the behavior of these organisms. Several major advances in the study of the instinctual behavior of animals have been made. The work of Von Friesch with bees and their dances and of Tinbergen and Lorenz with birds and fishes has shown that it is very profitable to study the animals as if there were no personal purpose, no "will" within them comparable to that of the human. Rather, one should study the objective behavior and the conditions giving rise to that behavior, irrespective of any purpose other than the well-known "instinctual purposes" necessary for survival, reproduction, etc.

Thus in certain cases it is necessary to dehumanize the animal and not confuse his purposes with ours. With this point of view I agree *as long as the brain is very much smaller than ours.* This is the way to strike pay dirt in research with small-brained animals. I spent many years working with cats and monkeys and found this point of view a very good one to take with them. It is most profitable from the standpoint of obtaining rapid results.

However, there is a converse "sin" of science, as it were, which is called "zoomorphizing" or "zoologizing." It consists in applying the thinking that works in the analysis of the behavior of the simple-minded, small-brained animals to the behavior of, say, someone with a large brain, such as a well-developed educated individual human. This approach gave rise to the "behaviorist" group of psychologists—beginning with John Watson as the most flamboyant—who thought of man as if he were an animal and could be observed as a natural-

[4] Jennings, H. S. *Genetics of the Protozoa* (Nijhoff, The Hague, Netherlands, 1929).

ist observes an animal in the wild, with no communication between observer and observed.

Under these conditions, all vocal productions and vocal meanings must be ignored and only the conditioned-reflex type of reactions taken into account. All the richness of human exchange, all of the verbal exchanges on highly complex levels have no part in this kind of investigation. In other words, everything that is characteristically human is stripped from the scientific model of the man. His cerebral cortex is emptied of all his peculiarly human information. Although this is a useful exercise in theoretical psychology, it is not very practical and fails to explain man as himself. This kind of zoo-morphizing or zoologizing makes a simple animal out of a man, reducing his huge brain and its contents to the less complicated level of a primitive beast.

I hasten to add that there are certain aspects of human behavior that might well be explained on an instinctual and "simple-minded" basis—for example, the ways in which a person acts when extremely fatigued, when under the influence of alcohol or other drugs, or when he has sustained certain kinds of brain injury, or in agenesis of the cerebral cortex. But these are all examples of biological degradation of a human—converting the complex human into a simple animal by chemical or traumatic means. Such downgrading of the human is particularly obvious in prisoner-of-war cases, some of the older mental institutions, and in certain cases of "brain-washing."

However, unless terrible violence has been done to the man he is still, in his behavior, thinking, and language, well above his nearest primate cousin, the gorilla. The lowest-grade human moron is above the highest genius in the gorilla or chimpanzee clan. One must look to the human idiots and imbeciles to find behavior corresponding to that of the primates. The tragedy of the radically "mentally retarded," as we call them today, is that they are not quite human and yet they are more intelligent than any of the primates except man.

To return to the dolphin, here is an animal with a brain as large as, or larger than, ours. Certain trends in the evidence suggest that it would be totally inappropriate to zoomorphize this animal. It would be just as much of a mistake to anthropomorphize him. We cannot and should not endow this animal with *human* purposes and *human* ideals. We should not attribute to him kinds of knowledge that belong to human experience and tradition but not to dolphin experience and tradition. It would certainly be a mistake to "put a man" in the dolphin's brain. One can put a man only in a man's brain.

Even when we try to understand man, we must investigate what a particular individual has in his mind rather than presuming that he has a prescribed set of ideas. This seems to be the sin of anthropomorphizing: assuming ahead of time what you are going to find and then finding it, by a sheer effort of will rather than by a scientific investigation. This pitfall of projecting the knowledge inside one's own brain as if it were in the brain of another creature is a very difficult thing to detect and to eradicate from one's thinking processes in those scientific fields close to man.

In dealing with dolphins it is wise to use a differentiated approach. I have developed one such:

Grant that the dolphin has a large first-class brain. This has been determined anatomically and the evidence is unequivocal.

Test for the capability of this brain to have long, sustained chains of reasoning based on its accumulation of masses of data far greater than those available to, say, a monkey or a chimpanzee, and comparable to or exceeding those that a human accumulates.

Grant that the dolphin has an extremely complex vocal ability and capability.

Assume as a working hypothesis that there may be a language within the species (*Tursiops truncatus*), possibly with differentiated "tribal tongues" in different portions of the world; hunt for this hypothesized language.

Set up a program to try to discover what kinds of information are most likely to be stored in this huge brain and in what ways the animal is most likely to use them in his own particular environment.

Put individual animals in close contact with human beings and attempt to teach them things never before learned by dolphins; test their *potential* learning capacity.

With this differentiated investigative approach, rather than the anthropomorphizing or the zoologizing approach, scientific investigations can make advances.

We have found that, as in the previous history of science, man must once more remove himself from the center of the universe, as it were. During certain periods of history the earth was thought to be the center of the universe, then the sun came to be considered the center, and finally both earth and sun were placed off center in one universe or galaxy. At one time man separated himself completely from all animals and attributed to himself a special creation of his own. He is now said to have evolved from apelike ancestors rather than to have been a special creation of God in a brief instant of time. In the latter part of the last century and the beginning of this one, Freud found that man's mental instinctual life is linked to that of his apelike ancestors and closely allied animals.

One of the last remaining thrones upon which man places himself is being shaken if not toppled by modern scientific research. Man thinks of himself as the most intelligent species on earth and as proof of this points to the accomplishments of his hands, his aspirations, his traditions, and his social organizations. In other words, man is said to be the most intelligent species because of what he does with his huge brain. May there not be other paths for large brains to take, especially if they live immersed in some other element than air?

What these paths may be we can only dimly discern until we are willing to grant that there may be such paths and that certain large-brained organisms may have taken these paths. In the case of the Cetacea, which are without benefit of hands or outside constructions of any sort, they may have taken the path of legends and verbal traditions rather than that of written records. Have they or haven't they? That's the essence of this research. We want to explore what the Cetacea have done and what they are capable of learning from us.

When dealing directly with the small delphinids our fear of the unknown is apt to restrain us. We see their teeth and their powerful jaw muscles, their powerful swimming ability, and we are afraid when we are in the water with them. We all have such fears in spite of the fact that not a single instance in which one of them has willfully attacked one of us has been recorded. Quite the opposite: they have saved us at sea and played with our children near beaches.[5] Our fear of their ability to attack is born out of our own knowledge of how they attack sharks and similar stupid animals of the sea. Yet they do not attack man. Why, we do not know.

True, they may play a little roughly in their own medium with us who are so inept in water. A diver at Marineland of the Pacific had some ribs broken when one of the pilot whales attempted to play with him. They

[5] Alpers, Antony. *A Book of Dolphins* (John Murray, London, 1960).

may not know their own strength and our fragility. But
this is not hostile, directed, destroying attack.

Another time a whale called Bubbles became irritated
when a shrimp was pulled back out of her mouth, and
she charged the five humans in the tank. However, a
diver finally restored mutual respect by courageously facing up to her with a Lilliputian tactic—a rod to poke
her with when she charged him.[6]

Technically contact between man and dolphin is extremely difficult for both sides: in the air we live in we
can hardly hear what these animals have to say, and in
the water they can hardly hear what we have to say. The
air-water boundary is a very real and difficult interface
for either us or the Cetacea to cross so that we may meet
one another halfway. If they are to meet us in air we
must furnish them with "flesh-conduction" earphones so
that they can hear us in air. If we are to meet them in
water we must be furnished with some means of talking
under water. These technical difficulties may have been
responsible for keeping us apart in the past. (Some primitive human peoples may have got much closer to the
dolphins than we ordinarily do today. Some of the personnel of the modern oceanaria certainly have succeeded
in making friends with their charges.)

We must face the fact that undoubtedly, until we
learn more about these animals, many of them will lose
their lives in our investigations. As we attempt to penetrate deeper into the sea in submarine warfare and in
exploration, we must also face the fact that men will
be losing their lives in the media of these animals. This
will be the case until our ignorance is dissipated, our
knowledge more complete, and individuals of each species can meet those of the other without being haunted
by the specter of death.

[6] Jacobs, J. *Marineland Diver* (Dodd, Mead, New York,
1960).

3

The Laboratory
at St. Thomas

In the winter of 1958, I decided to start hunting for a suitable location in which to work with these animals the year round. A lot of thought was expended on what would be required for sustained contact with the animals.

Data derived from the training program and from my own experiences with the animals had convinced me that we must maintain very close contact for long periods of time. Such contact must include both vocal exchanges and skin contacts. If we are ever to make progress in giving the animals the full benefit of our human experience, we must be able to get into the water with them the year round, frequently, every day seven days a week. In other words, to give them the same chance that we would give a human child to learn our language and ways, we must modify our own behavior and meet them at least halfway in their own medium.

If we pay close attention to the way in which a human child learns to speak our language, we realize that close daily contact and satisfaction of needs, associated continuously with vocalized words, form a very large proportion of the conditions necessary to their learning. The human child is born with a brain of about 400 grams (see Table 6 in Appendix 4) and during the first year of life it grows to 900 grams. About the time that understandable words begin to be formed the child's brain weighs approximately 1000 grams. Meanwhile, he has absorbed tremendous amounts of information while his brain was growing.

During this crucial time of his life, if he is average, his mother, siblings, father, playmates, and other adults have bombarded him continuously with spoken words and gestures suited to the words. One important aspect of the learning process is that every need, from food to handling of excretion, has been attended with a vocal barrage of human language and with exchanges of facial expressions and gestures on a nonverbal level. The child's skin has been stimulated by baths, putting on and taking off of clothing, being carried about and fed, all attended with the appropriate adult language or baby talk.

This kind of continuous verbal barrage is necessary if the young human is to learn the speech of his species. The child's first words are met with delighted reactions on the part of proximate adults. As soon as he is capable of making demands, these are generally met with satisfying reactions on the part of the attendants.

If such constant barrages and attention to detail are needed to teach a human understandable speech, we should give individuals of another species at least as much attention and chronic contact when trying to teach them our language. I feel that until this is done a sufficiently dedicated attempt to teach them will not have been made. And unless we make such an attempt we cannot say this species is incapable of learning to speak.

It seems to me that it is necessary to make use of the

kind of contact I have described until we find something better.

In order to explore all of these avenues to an understanding with the animals, I decided to set up an ideal location—a laboratory and pools for chronic living-in with the bottle-nosed dolphins, *Tursiops*.

Tursiops was chosen because he likes warm (75–85° F.) water and so do humans. *Tursiops* is better known to us than any other member of the Delphinidae; he's in all the oceanaria. He is readily available over the warm waters of the United States and the world. He is apparently closer to us in neck mobility, curiosity, and close social living than his deep-sea cousins. He lives long and well in small pools and shallow tanks.

Other delphinids, such as the true porpoise or harbor porpoise (*Phocaena*), are interesting and should be investigated eventually. *Phocaena* likes colder water; *Lagenorhynchus* likes deep water and high speed, as do *Delphinus* and *Stenella*. Their brains are large but their normal way of life makes them difficult to handle. Cold water necessitates rubber suits for us; water deeper than three or four feet makes us clumsy and inept in their medium. We have found that we deal best with dolphins in water twenty to thirty inches deep; *Tursiops* does very well in the depths. Some of the deeper-water delphinids rush around at very high speed in captivity and apparently do not do very well in restrained quarters.

If we were to deal with *Tursiops* on the basis described above we had to find a location for a laboratory that had warm, clear water the year round at a temperature somewhere in the middle eighties. Water of a temperature of 94° F. is just too hot for a man to keep up any activities. He can lie very still at this temperature indefinitely, but at temperatures higher than this he cannot expose himself very long without his body temperature rising extremely rapidly. At lower temperatures his activity (or metabolism) must be increased so his heat production can compensate for the cooling effects of the surrounding water. *Tursiops* seems to like best a temperature somewhere between the high seventies and the middle eighties. Above 90° is too hot for him and he becomes sluggish. Below about 70° the water is too cold for him and he spends all of his time keeping warm by rushing around. A comfortable temperature is apparently around 80° to 85°.

A second requirement was an equable climate over this water the year round, with no freezing weather and no cold fronts such as we found in northern Florida. We did not want a climate that was too hot, making it uncomfortable for the humans; on the other hand, we did not want it too cold. Most of the work would be outside and we wanted to be able to go in and out of the water in swimming suits without being nailed to the laboratory by a cold wave.

If the location was in a hurricane belt, high ground next to the sea must be available for the laboratory site. It was found that on the East Coast of the United States the laboratory should be at least twelve to twenty feet above the high-water mark to avoid damage in case a hurricane did hit it.

It would be desirable to establish our setup on territory or land that was under control of the United States, in order to facilitate ordering of parts and so forth and to make sure of the political stability of the surrounding society.

We also felt that we should be in the trade-wind belt for the necessary cooling and for a wave supply. The pools where the dolphins would be kept could be swept through by wave action and the water thus kept clean by nature herself rather than by pumping. (The oceanaria in the United States are tremendously expensive operations partly because of the required pumping and filtering of the water for the tanks.)

Finally, it was to be a location that was easily accessible both by ship and by plane, so that heavy supplies could be shipped to the location either by air or by sea.

After considerable questioning of my colleagues and the travel agents, I finally pinpointed the region of Puerto Rico and of the United States' Virgin Islands. I first went exploring there in August of 1958. I checked the Bahamas and Jamaica as the southernmost boundaries of the cold fronts and also for the presence of wild *Tursiops* in the shoal waters. They were present both around the coast of Jamaica and throughout the Bahamas.

There were rumors that they were also present in the shoal waters of the Virgin Islands and that several other species were also available there. The Virgin Islands turned out to be a whale "highway": many of the huge whales were seen passing to the north of these islands every year in their annual migrations. They were also seen passing through the straits between the American and the British Virgin Islands. Thus the search was narrowed down and finally an ideal location was found.

Finding a location for the dolphin pool and laboratory entailed exploring the shore line and facilities and islands of the West Indies. It is a story of personal sacrifice and of a campaign to convince influential individuals, scientific and otherwise, that this project was a worthwhile gamble. From the beginning I have admitted quite frankly that I myself was gambling on my previous experience, on my conclusions, and on the philosophy behind the project. I am convinced that no really large scientific advances are ever made unless an individual scientist is willing to "stick his neck out." Many times during the years of this research I have had the feeling that maybe I was one of those stalks of wheat mentioned in the story of the King.

The King instructed his servants to cut only those stalks of wheat which protruded above all of the others, because they were the most vigorous and the strongest and he wanted to eat bread made only from them. Sometimes one gets the feeling that there are certain politically-minded persons whose lives and well-being depend upon leveling those who stand out prominently from the crowd. Their "bread" is milled from "maverick" stand-uppers, too. I quickly discovered, however, that there were also many people who were intrigued and fascinated and deeply interested in projects along the lines of this research. These people have given me their wholehearted moral support from the beginning.

After searching the Virgin Islands for a period of six days by high-speed boat I found an available location that looked as if, with sufficient work, it could be made into what was desired for the project. Not until later did I learn that to "sufficient work" must be added "sufficient funds" and "sufficient time" and "sufficient personal driving energy." I started from scratch, carving the new facilities directly from the jungle and the wild tropical shore line on the island of St. Thomas.

St. Thomas was chosen because of its deep-water port and its airplane facilities—a combination that was lacking on the other American Virgin Islands. I found that heavy materials and equipment could be obtained from Miami within a week or two and that materials could be flown down from New York.

The site I finally chose is on the windward, Caribbean side of the island. Here a continuous supply of trade winds causes waves that come always from the same direction and wash on a point sticking out at one end of Nazareth Bay, forming a small beach. On the west side waves from the Caribbean constantly beat upon the edge of the point, forcing water into a series of natural pools. Although none of these pools was deep enough or large enough for our purpose, I was informed that the judicious use of explosives could form the necessary pools for the dolphins' home.

The point rises to a height of fifty feet above sea level, which is adequate for protection against hurricane waves and even against tsunamis (tidal waves). The waters off the point are clear and sparkling and there are enough coral reefs and shallows to the seaward side so that no waves of great height can enter and smash anything we construct lower on the point. The water off that immediate part of the point is fifteen feet deep and slopes slowly off to a twenty-foot depth, which continues for two miles away from the point.

Our friends the dolphins and some larger whales have been sighted frequently in neighboring Caribbean waters. Two rocks upwind, three miles away to the southeast, were named Cow and Calf; again and again over the years whale cows and calves have been seen immediately adjacent to that area in the deeper waters beyond the rocks.

Closely available, within a mile, are some lagoons filled with mangrove islands and many paths for four-foot-draft boats; this is ideal shelter for boats in case of hurricanes. Fish abound all through the area, so there is no problem about food for the dolphins.

The land itself was covered with such a thick growth of tropical jungle vegetation that I could barely see what it was like before buying it. I had to carry a machete, or "cutlash," as the natives call it, and keep cutting away the cactus, thorn bush, and dense vines ("catch and keep," for example) that covered the area. One path led from the high land on the north boundary, at 140 feet above sea level, down through a little valley to the beach. At first this was the only approach to the land; you went along the beach and followed the rocky cliffs all the way around the point to the west. Here you could see the seashore, which was so important to us.

However, you could not see the higher grounds of the point or the north ridge, which were jungle-covered. Beating in from the road with the machete, we found on the high ridge to the north an old Danish house (estimated to be two hundred years old) that had fallen down and was now rubble, hidden in the jungle. I heard that this location, once cleared, must be a magnificent one because the old Danes had chosen the best locations when the island was cleared for the growing of sugar cane. They had the advantage over us of immediately available slave labor to clear vast acreage quickly and thus selected their building sites in the clear.

After exploring the possibilities of buying the land and of financing it, I met the delightful owners, Myler and Marian Kier, and the sale was completed.

With the help of natives from the British Virgin Islands of Tortola and Virgin Gorda enough of the land was cleared to realize that the views from the top of the point and the top of the ridge are fabulous. From the Danish ruins looking to the north we have a New Hampshire-Vermont kind of view of a nearby mountain across a valley. To the northeast the view toward and between the British Virgin Islands and St. John reminds me of the view down a Norwegian fiord. To the east there is a low nearby hill; and to the southeast beautiful Nazareth Bay with its brilliant green water and sandy bottom (an ideal yacht anchorage) can be seen. To the south is the island of St. Croix, thirty miles away and stretching twenty-six miles along the horizon of the deep Caribbean. (The water between St. Croix and St.

Thomas reaches a depth of 12,000 feet.) To the south-west are three small, rocky cays which are the Caribbean borders of the mangrove lagoons visible to the west. Beyond the lagoons are the mountains between us and Charlotte Amalie, the only town on the island and the capital of the Virgin Islands. To the northwest these mountains join the ones immediately to the north.

From the cleared ridge we can look down on the cleared point. From the top of the point we can hear the waves smashing against the cliffs below, see the unusual clarity of the tropical waters, the coral constructions, the caves and the canyons inhabited by many varieties of reef fishes.

With the help of a hired caterpillar bulldozer, a road was constructed from the top of the ridge down to the saddle above the beach. Branches were built out toward the west end of the point and down to the beach. Meanwhile I had met Nathaniel Wells, a civil engineer and surveyor on the island of St. Thomas. He gave unstintingly of his time and ideas in regard to the development of the land for this project. After some of the clearing was completed he and his men made a topographic map of the land, which helped immensely in deciding where various things could go.

I had learned by previous experience, while at the University of Pennsylvania and at the National Institutes of Health, that it is very difficult to obtain support for any research project that requires extensive new facilities, new assumptions, and new ways of thinking. So I decided to go ahead on my own financial resources. By selling all my other property and buying the St. Thomas land on a mortgage, I was able to proceed temporarily without outside help.

The program was too large for me to finance and I realized that I would soon need help, but I also realized that I could not get it until I had shown my own sincerity by gambling on my own ideas with my own resources first.

Although I did not apply to anyone for financial help at this time, help of other kinds was given by several individuals. Mr. Wells gave unstintingly of his time. It was through him that I was able to find effective bush cutters to clear the land, men who could work on their own with little or no supervision. Later I found that one of them was quite talented in masonry construction as well.

The United States Navy's Underwater Demolition Team No. 21 also gave us a big boost in the spring of 1959. Through the good offices of the commanding officer, Lieutenant Commander Donald Gaither, they came to the point at Nazareth Bay and with high explosives sculptured the present dolphin pool out of the native rock.

The location is on the west side of the point, facing the sea. The long axis of the pool is in the direction of the waves coming from the southeast. The Underwater Demolition Team started with a small fissure in the rocks where the water was entering naturally. This fissure was about a hundred feet long and three to six feet deep. The frogmen placed long hoses about three inches in diameter and twenty-five feet long end to end in this fissure. The hoses were filled with a high explosive and detonated either electrically or by means of primacord. Gradually, as the fissure was widened and deepened by a series of tremendous explosions, we saw the pool begin to shape up.

Finally they were able to place a charge of approximately six hundred pounds of TNT, which produced a tremendous geyser of water and rocks. Rocks were cast as far away as the next point to the west. Within two minutes after this explosion a red convertible came tearing down the road.

A very agitated neighbor, Don McLaughlin, asked us when we were going to finish this rather devastating work. It seemed that his maid had been washing the dishes when the explosion occurred and a milk-glass light globe had been blown from the ceiling and dropped at her feet, whereupon she decided to leave for the day. He reported also that pictures were being dislodged from the walls of his living room.

I went over to his house across Nazareth Bay and stayed with him and his wife while the next explosion took place. It turned out that it was not the TNT explosions in the water that were causing the damage, but the "shaped" charges of forty pounds that form a jet of molten metal in the air, with which we drilled into the rocks when we were destroying ridges and large rocks. These produced a tremendous air-borne blast, which was causing the rather disconcerting happenings in the McLaughlin household. The TNT explosions were not bothering them, because they were on the far side of the point behind solid basalt; no rock-borne shock was detectable at their house. We took a mirror down from the wall and I helped them remove their pictures, so that they would not be damaged. We did not use any more of the shaped charges in the air and finished up rather quickly with the underwater charges.

During these explosions we all took shelter in a small work shed with a tin roof. Several times rather huge rocks came hurtling through the air at high velocity and hit the roof. One rock went all the way across the point and just grazed the top of our white "laboratory" bus.

The Underwater Demolition Team used high-velocity explosive to shatter the rocks which we could remove later by means of a crane. The resulting hole was about seventy feet long, twenty-five feet wide, and of unknown depth. We could not determine the depth because it was filled with gravel on the bottom, but the water was uniformly about four feet deep all over the area.

We had chosen this location because the waves could enter through a narrows, flow through the pool, and come out on the far side, carrying water with them.

We soon started building the first wave ramp, by means of a crane with a sixty-foot boom. A dike of loose rock was put out on the sea side to keep the waves from the location. Behind this dike or dam, forms were put up and the wave ramp shaped. A wave ramp consists of a rising apron of concrete against which waves can strike and over which the water climbs as the waves are shattered. The water then falls over the top of the ramp into the pool. With salt-water concrete and rock masonry we built a funnel-shaped opening so that the waves would be concentrated over a seven-foot-wide opening into the pool. A gate was constructed across this opening and the dam removed with the crane. After redesigning this ramp twice we found that we could maintain a flow of water on the average of approximately 40,000 gallons an hour. I estimated that under these conditions the pool would change all of its water in approximately two hours; this turned out to be correct. The daily tidal range at St. Thomas is approximately eight inches to one foot. Spring tides bring the variation to a maximum of about eighteen inches. During the rare periods when there is no trade wind the flow was cut down to approximately one-fifth of this volume. We lowered the height of the wave ramp and kept the flow at a higher rate.

In subsequent months concrete walks and walls were built around the pool and the gravel removed from the inside of it to a depth of twelve feet.

Meanwhile over on the other side of the point a jetty was being constructed out into Nazareth Bay so that we would have a place for our fishing and dolphin-hunting boats to come in out of the waves. Some of the rock cliffs were blasted and dropped into the sea.

A road was constructed by the bulldozer where before there had been sea, and then slowly and patiently the bulldozer began to push the rock out into the bay.

As soon as the water inside the new jetty became calm we found that it was accumulating all sorts of marine life very rapidly. It turned out to be an excellent refuge for the fry of the ocean, which then attracted the tuna and other fish of the neighborhood. Very quickly we had native French fishermen coming in and casting their nets inside the jetty.

About May of 1959 I felt that I was far enough along on my own to begin to apply for outside aid on the project. I sounded out several of my scientific friends whose advice I value and began the rounds of various agencies and private foundations, seeking funds.

A nonprofit corporation called the Communication Research Institute was organized under the laws of St. Thomas, Virgin Islands. Incorporators were myself, Mr. George Dudley, Mr. Joseph McGowan, Mr. Louis Hoffman, and Mr. Wells; these men were also the first Board of Trustees for the Institute. The charter of the Institute is an abstract of the research program and an educational program founded on the dolphin research.

Of those agencies and foundations to which application for help was made the one that came through most quickly was the Office of Naval Research, Biological Sciences Division, under Dr. Roger Reid, in the section under Dr. Sidney Galler. Within three weeks from the time of our application they were able to furnish us with sufficient funds to start the research program. Meanwhile, we'd made application for a facilities grant through several agencies, and the National Science Foundation came through with a grant for a new laboratory in the spring of 1960.

When I applied for these grants I presented the program to scientific appraisers for the first time. Various scientists from the Office of Naval Research, the United States Public Health Service, and the National Science Foundation visited St. Thomas to appraise our efforts and the program.

These men did a very thorough job and were extremely helpful to us with our problems of organization and future planning. Among these men were Dr. Louis Levin of the National Science Foundation and Dr. Hudson Hoaglund of the Worcester Foundation. Dr. Hoaglund was extremely helpful and sympathetic. He had been through a similar pioneering effort with his own institution in its early years and his sympathetic moral support helped us greatly during our precarious beginnings. We were still, in August 1960, not on absolutely satisfactory financial grounds but at least we were under way and over the first hurdle of beginning the laboratory.

4

Lizzie and Baby

The pool finally seemed adequate and we decided to bring in the first inhabitants and see if dolphins could live in it. By March 1960 everything was ready for a trip to Marineland to obtain the first dolphins of the new series—Numbers 9 and 10, which we later called Lizzie and Baby.

From my previous experience I had come to the conclusion that a dolphin is happiest when suspended in water and that our major problem on this trip would be to provide a means of transporting two animals thus suspended.

Alice Marie Miller, my former scientific assistant, Elisabeth Bjerg, my former wife and I flew to Marineland, Florida, to measure the dolphins so that boxes could be made for their trip to St. Thomas. Once again we were to learn much about these animals that was unexpected.

My old friends at Marineland were their usual cordial selves: Mr. Wood welcomed us to the research laboratory; Mr. William Rolleston, the manager, and his gracious wife took us to dinner; Mr. Nessler, the treasurer, gave us much information about obtaining frozen fish and supplies; Mr. Wood's assistant, Cliff Townsend, gave us much detailed attention and advice. Mr. Valentine and his crew helped us many times to carry the heavy animals from one tank to another.

The Marine Studios had been saving two animals for us for four months. They were in a tank behind the research laboratory, swimming with Nellie, a dolphin which had been used in some sonar experiments. She had one blind eye and the other eye was usually covered during experiments.

The weather turned out to be cold, raw, and a bit blustery, interspersed with very warm periods. Coming from the Virgin Islands, we all felt the cold and noticed particularly how cold the water was.

Throughout Marine Studios the animals were extremely active. We did some observing at night and made some sound recordings from the main tanks to add to our collection of sounds made by many animals in the same tank. We also watched the animals in the main tank at night to find out what the resting pattern is during the night hours. We found that they "rest," not sleep, by hanging near the surface with flukes down for a few minutes, slowly rising to breathe and then sinking, and finally resuming swimming.

Meanwhile we were getting on with our research on a way of transporting the animals without injuring them. Baby, dolphin Number 9, was taken from the laboratory reserve tank and put in a small shallow tank about twenty inches deep, nine feet long, and two feet wide, which we had used to hold the animals in the laboratory in 1955 and in 1957. Her body measurements were carefully made and the design of the transporting box started. We wanted a box that would hold enough water so that the animal would be surrounded and the weight taken off the chest, lungs, and circulatory system, and at the same time we wanted to keep the total weight of the package to a minimum, since it was to travel by plane.

We decided to build it like an old-fashioned airplane, out of quarter-inch plywood cross sections spaced seven inches apart with outside vertical and lateral dimensions of two feet by two feet, the whole box to be approximately nine feet long.

Baby turned out to be exactly eight feet from the tip of her beak to the trailing edge of her flukes, and she weighed three hundred pounds. Lizzie, dolphin Number 10, whom Earl Ubell named for my former wife, was also about eight feet long and weighed slightly over four hundred pounds. As dolphins go, these were a little bit large to be working with and we found out later that they were definitely too heavy for our purposes. One of the lessons we learned from our work with Lizzie and Baby was that it is much easier and safer to handle lighter and shorter animals. The shorter and lighter (hence younger) animals seem to learn much faster and are more curious and more active in the immediate vicinity of human beings in the water.

The box construction was carried out mainly by Lis and Alice. The sections were connected by two-by-two wood poles and the inside cross sections were cut out and connected by fiberglass the length of the box. Box number one was made entirely of fiberglass and plywood cross sections. Alice and Lis learned a lot about the use of fiberglass, cloth, and resin in the construction of minimum-weight containers. It wasn't until much later that we learned how to cut the sides of the box down to the minimum possible, and hence reduce the weight of the water proportionately, and still keep the animal floating. However, this fiberglass box, our first attempt, was fairly successful.

We tried out the box with Baby and then attempted to see if Lizzie would fit into it. At this point we had our first accident. There were two main causes of this accident: one was Lizzie's huge weight and the other was the weakness of a sling we had carried over from the 1957 expedition. We had lowered the water in the tank to the point where the dolphins were stranded and Cliff

Townsend and some of the divers from Marine Studios were lifting Lizzie off the floor. The box had been placed on the floor of the tank. As Cliff and the divers were lifting, the sling suddenly broke, tearing out along one of the holes for the flippers. Lizzie fell, hitting her head and one flipper on the concrete floor of the tank. As we were to see several weeks later, this accident contributed to her death.

The first two prototype boxes were not quite satisfactory. They contained too much water and did not exactly fit the animals. (These boxes have since been modified.) However, they worked sufficiently well so that the animals, kept in them for twenty-four hours (seven hours' flying), remained spontaneously vocal with relaxed and variable patterns of breathing. (Under stress because of gravity they have a fixed pattern of breathing, very regular, stereotyped, and labored.)

When we were ready to start the long trip to the Virgin Islands the boxes were placed on a truck beside the tank in which the dolphins were residing. Early one morning the water in the tank was lowered to the point where the men could get into it, catch the animals, put them in a sling, and lift them out of the tank with a small hand crane.

They were then carried to the boxes on a truck and each placed in her own box, which was then half filled with water by means of a portable pump. The dorsal fin and other exposed parts were covered with bed sheets to prevent the skin from drying out. Covers were placed over the boxes and tied in place. A large hole was left open for the dorsal fin and for the exchange of air. Polythene foam (which absorbs water like a sponge) was placed at critical points where the animal might rub against the box. (Later on we found that the proper way to place the foam is to imbed it in the last layer of the resin so as to fasten it to the fiberglass in the box.

Numerous other modifications were made in subsequent boxes.)

An old friend, Earl Ubell, science editor of the New York *Herald Tribune,* had been invited to travel with us the year before, when we first planned the trip. Apparently dolphins were becoming newsworthy enough for his editor to let him make the trip. Earl turned out to have great capabilities as a foreman and was soon directing workmen in how to carry and place the boxes. He was an invaluable assistant on the trip.

The truck was scheduled to drive from Marineland to the St. Augustine airport, a distance of about eighteen miles. It was a cold morning. Earl and I had the job of staying on the open bed of the truck to attend to the dolphins. The driver was in a bit of a hurry and went about fifty to sixty miles an hour. The wind was chilly and Earl used a bright yellow plastic pail as a hat.

We had to stop twice to readjust the positions of the animals. When the truck slowed down too suddenly, the dolphins slid forward in their boxes and pushed up against the front end. Lizzie developed a sore on the end of her chin as a consequence. The smaller Baby fitted better into her box and did not slide around quite so much.

It was at this time that Earl and I first began to notice that when each dolphin expired her breath against the cover of the box, black mucous material was deposited on the underside of the cover. Later we discovered that this material had a very foul odor similar to that of the material left at the bottom of the tank when they drained most of the water at Marineland. We suspected that possibly the animals had some sort of infection despite the fact that some of the people at Marineland had told us this was a normal condition. My medical training told me that this could not be a normal condition even in such a strange mammal. I smelled more of the results of putrefaction by pathogenic kinds of bacteria than I did of any normal odor of an animal that eats fish.

We should have done something about this before we started moving the animals, but we were so committed that we went on in spite of this disturbing clinical sign. (We learned later unequivocally that healthy dolphins have no odor to their breath and expel no material.)

At the St. Augustine airport the Fairchild people had reserved loading equipment to transfer our precious boxes into the aircraft of the Southern Air Transport Company. The C-46 had very large cargo doors high off the ground. A fork lift plus about eight men were required to move the animals from the truck into position within the aircraft. Earl and I barely had time to warm up our chilled muscles before we began taking pictures —movies and stills—of the critical operation. This was the most stringent test that our new type of box was to undergo. The boxes came through with flying colors, thoroughly recorded on film.

During this transition phase the animals moved about very little and continued to be expressive, both vocally and with their breathing. They seemed quite happy floating in their water in spite of all the moving about.

Through the kindness of Mr. Nessler, Mr. Rolleston, and Mr. Wood at Marineland we had on board a quantity of frozen fish sufficient to feed these animals until we could obtain more at St. Thomas. Also on board, through the good and remarkable graces of Lis, were three large freezers in which to store the fifteen hundred pounds of fish. We had filled a sizable fraction of the C-46 aircraft with our own cargo including the animals.

At take-off, as the plane accelerated, the slanting floor of the plane (not a tricycle landing-gear type) caused the water to cascade from the back of the boxes. Earl, Lis, and I were sitting in the jump seats back of the boxes in the stern of the aircraft; Alice was up forward with the crew. We had our safety belts on during take-off and could do nothing about the water pouring out of the boxes. We had brought several pails and large plastic garbage cans filled with extra sea water, and when the plane had leveled off at altitude we quickly poured in enough water to make up the deficit and made the animals comfortable once more. It was then that we began to be repelled in earnest by the foul odor coming from their blowholes. We began to realize that these were probably sick animals and that we might lose them in the near future.

We flew at 7000 feet for several hours, during which we counted the respirations of the animals carefully and found that the altitude had no effect upon the rate at which they breathe when suspended in water. There were several rough air spots on the way to Puerto Rico but none bad enough to cause us any trouble with the animals. Poor Lis became a bit wan, however, as she was pregnant.

Having got a late start, I was worried about whether or not our men would meet us at the airport. When we finally landed we found there not only our men with a truck but also Southern Air Transport's men with the official unloader.

Earl took charge of the unloading operations and without benefit of mechanical aids managed to get the animals carried out of the airplane and onto our truck by directing our helpers in a striking "voice of command." By the time everything was unloaded it was midnight and I decided to leave the dolphins on the truck for the night and to unload them early in the morning. Our supervisor, Frank O'Connor, would spend the night on guard with the animals, tending to their needs.

Baby was so comfortable that she was carrying on a lot of very complicated vocal and movement activity every time we approached the tank. She could vaguely see our outlines through the fiberglass sides, and we could see her close her eye if a hand was moved rapidly toward it. At the same time her vocalization would stop. I played a brief game with her that night: I whistled once, twice, three times, then she whistled once, twice, thrice; I answered with the same; then she whistled one, two, three, four and I answered. This game was to continue when she was put in our pool at Nazareth Bay.

Early next morning the men drove the truck with the animals on it from the Submarine Base where they had spent the night to Nazareth Bay. My son, Charles, and Lis's children, Pamela, Leslie, and Stuart, watched the proceedings and Charles took photographs while the men unloaded the animals into the pool.

With new prongs on our front-loader we unloaded the boxes from the truck, drained the water from them, and then carried them down to the pool from the road one at a time.

We thought it was going to be quite a trick to get the animals out of the box and into the pool without the use of a sling. But we solved the problem by placing the tank in shallow water in the pool, filling it up with a bucket until it almost sank and then, turning it over sideways, releasing the dolphin after one of her respirations.

Lizzie was unloaded first; she swam away but was tilting over to one side, not swimming quite upright. This was our first real evidence that she had been injured in her fall to the concrete. We also noticed that she had skin lesions and sores on various parts of her anatomy because of the handling, carrying in the slings, catching in the net, and rubbing at one place in the box. The major lesions were on the end of her chin, at each "armpit," and on her flukes.

Dumping Baby into the pool in the same fashion, we found that she was in better shape. She swam perfectly straight, quickly joined Lizzie, and the two of them swam round and round the pool.

Lizzie would not or could not eat, in spite of strenuous efforts on our part to induce eating, but Baby started eating right away and within two days was taking food directly from our hands.

Earl wrote up his story in St. Thomas and sent it in for publication, then he stayed for a few days to observe our work with the animals. The day after Earl left his news story appeared on the front page of the New York *Herald Tribune*.

We began our study of dolphins in captivity, in as close contact with them as possible. About the second or third day we started swimming with them. Alice tried to feed them while she floated in the water. During this time we found that wild dolphins will not voluntarily come close to a human unless they are rewarded for coming close and penalized for staying away. Baby gradually began to make closer approaches as she received more and more fish, but Lizzie kept her distance. (Later, with animal Number 11, Elvar, we found that if close quarters and close contact were enforced, the "approach" processes could be speeded up.) We made many hydrophone recordings of the vocalizations of the two animals.

There were many live fish—small ones—swimming around in their pool which they ignored. One little yellow-tail took up a position next to Baby's head and picked up the scraps every time Baby was fed. The many little lizard fish at the bottom of the pool cleaned up any debris left over from the feedings.

We found that the pool was kept clean by the action of the waves of the Caribbean. The flow of water was sufficient to handle easily the problems raised by two dolphins in the pool, and to keep the water crystal clear most of the time. Once in a great while the dolphins would rush around the tank in great excitement and stir

up the material from the bottom, but in a matter of two
hours the pool would be clear again.

Because of our worries about Lizzie's not eating we
built a small pool at the end of the main one, so we could
capture her and give her vitamins and antibiotics. We
didn't want to cause her any further injury or great
stress.

Frank O'Connor is an experienced underwater construction man, formerly with the Underwater Demolition Team of the U. S. Navy. He placed sacks of concrete in position under water, tying them together and
building up a wall. He then built a drop gate.

Using a surplus nylon parachute on a floating wooden
two-by-four as a partition across the whole pool, we
slowly forced the animals to swim toward the gate. (We
had not found it possible to induce them to go into this
tank by means of food.)

It turned out to be very easy to separate Lizzie from
Baby and to force her into the small tank. At this time
we took some recordings. Once Lizzie was separated from
Baby, a very mournful sort of exchange of calls (whistles) started. We had been noticing for the previous two
or three days that Lizzie seemed to be sleepy, and it
looked as though every so often Baby would wake her
up by nudging her and swimming alongside her, holding
her upright. Listening to the tape of Lizzie in the small
tank now with the hindsight of subsequent events, I
realize that something very distressful was going on and
that she was appealing to Baby for help. Here again was
evidence that these animals probably take very good care
of one another and that sometimes we should not interfere.

Lizzie was placed in the small pool late one evening.
When we returned next morning we found that she was
dead, lying on the bottom of the pool. I did an immediate autopsy, hunting for obstructions along the intestinal

tract and similar things that one looks for when an animal does not eat. The air sacs along the airway and the lungs were thoroughly infected. She apparently had an overwhelming infection which she was unable to fight off.

Lizzie had lived only three weeks, finally dying of a complicated set of causes: her infection, her anorexia and starvation, and some injury to her nervous system caused by the fall. On post-mortem examination a hemorrhage was found in the cerebellum on the left side near the tentorium.

It was at this time that Baby started a series of calls as if to a distant or missing animal at odd, irregular intervals. One Sunday we found out what was causing these calls. I came out in the morning to feed her, noticed that the calls were going on in great profusion, and recorded them on the tape. Later that day one of my sailing friends said that he had been sailing by our point and had seen coming into Nazareth Bay fifteen to twenty wild dolphins, heading right for the area where Baby was kept. In spite of the fact that she was not connected to the sea by any possible acoustic path, we thought these animals could be attracted by her excreta coming out of the pool and traveling in the water back to the sea. Somehow they might have had a way of detecting her excreta traces. Similarly she might have detected their traces and thus known they were out there. We traced out the currents of Nazareth Bay and the theory looks plausible.

After this episode we began to watch her more closely for possible clues as to how they might do this. There are numerous papillae all the way around the edge of the eight-inch-long tongue. Apparently the papillae are very richly endowed with taste organs. Watching Baby with this in mind, I could see that she held her mouth slightly open and went up and down facing into the water coming into the pool from the sea, hour after hour. We remembered that at Marineland this was what the spotted dolphins did—faced into the incoming water with their mouth slightly open, apparently allowing the water to go through the mouth and tasting whatever was coming in from the sea. It looks as if this may be a way in which they can follow one another and also find fish traveling ahead of them. In other words, the spoor in the sea is probably just as real (though evanescent) as it is in the jungle; instead of being smell, however, it is taste.

After several more weeks Baby suddenly stopped eating. We put her in the small tank, gave her vitamins and antibiotics, and tried our hand at tube-feeding a dolphin.

With the proper equipment tube-feeding turned out to be a very simple procedure. We made a soup of food-fish with a Waring blender. A small piece of plastic garden hose was placed in the rumen through the mouth. Three men held the animal in three feet of water—two of them opened the jaws while I inserted the tube down past the larynx through the esophagus into the stomach. It went in very easily and quickly. We had a sufficiently long tube so that we were sure it would not go into the larynx or in the back of the nose. Knowing the anatomy, we were able to put the tube into the rumen with a minimum of trouble. I was able to introduce about ten pounds of fish soup into Baby's stomach. We then let her go.

These heroic measures, however, did not save her. She also died. The last time we caught her we found that her breath was extremely bad and was producing the black material we had noticed ever since the day we brought her from Marineland.

At first, with these fresh deaths, we were extremely disappointed and depressed. However, we had anticipated the fact that we were going to have these troubles and probably many more of them. Before we learned enough about the animals to keep them safely and continuously in captivity, many more might die. Lis and I decided to go to Florida, explore the possibilities of getting new animals, and check on this business of the infections with known healthy and captive animals.

5

Elvar and Tolva

In May and again in July 1960 we made trips to Florida. During the May trip Lis and I found out several interesting facts through firsthand observation and from accounts of dolphin handlers. We determined the important fact that the air emitted from the healthy dolphin's blowhole normally has no odor whatsoever. We smelled the expired air from several animals in the Florida keys; all had practically no odor. This was additional evidence that Lizzie's and Baby's bad odor was a sure sign of a pathological condition, probably a chronic "sinus" (air-sacs) infection or even pneumonia.

We made the acquaintance of Marty, a dolphin at the Theatre-of-the-Sea that had learned to vocalize while riding on his flukes with most of his body out of water. It was a very impressive performance, with extremely loud noises that sounded something like a crying human baby emitted from the blowhole into air. Later we derived from this experience a hint that if one dolphin starts a trick another will learn, fairly quickly, to do the same thing. Buttons, in the same enclosure with Marty, was just beginning to vocalize in a similar fashion and by summer had developed an even louder voice than Marty's.

We also found out that a dolphin can be kept in a

allow pool almost indefinitely. At Theatre-of-the-Sea we made the acquaintance of Kenny, a dolphin who was kept in a pool thirty-six inches deep and about twelve feet square. He had been there for eighteen months, during all of which time he was alone, except for interspecies contacts with human handlers and the sight-seers. He was completely out of contact with his own kind, in intraspecies solitude, and had learned many things that we had not previously seen a dolphin doing.

It was in May that we met the dolphin captors, Mr. and Mrs. Victor Milton Santini, of Marathon Key, Florida. I had learned about the Santinis from a magazine article. The accompanying pictures showed Milton Santini jumping from a boat onto the back of a dolphin in the shallow water of Florida Bay.

We were seeking a source of smaller animals because of our experience with Lizzie's injury and the difficulty of transporting the heavy animals. The Santinis had been catching and selling dolphins for the last thirteen years and were quite aware of the problems. The largest dolphin they had caught weighed eight hundred pounds and was ten feet long. It must have been old because it had no teeth left. They much preferred to capture animals no more than seven feet long and weighing no more than two hundred and fifty pounds. They assured us that it was possible to find and capture small dolphins without visibly injuring them. They use a "secret" method of catching which they say does involve a fast small inboard, a ten-inch square-mesh net, shallow water, and, I add, considerable strength, patience and courage.

After talking for several hours to the Santinis we were convinced that it would be best to buy dolphins from them and they agreed to capture five or six animals for us and hold them at Marathon in pools connected with the bay there. They could supply the animals within a few days of the receipt of our order.

In talking with us Milton Santini referred to "taming" his animals after they were caught. Later we realize that this was a very apt word to describe certain change that occur in the animals between the wild and the captive states. When animals are first caught they are ver skittish and tend to retreat as far from human beings as they can in the pool in which they are kept. They're als "spooky"—any new object put in the pool upsets the and they rush around, inspecting it closely. The large the object the longer it takes them to get used to it. Th behavior pattern is evoked by human beings as well as by inanimate objects. The process by which an animal changed from a skittish, relatively suspicious, and easil spooked animal to one that approaches the human bein and seeks things from him is still rather mysterious. Li tening to Santini's stories and observing the care of th animals at the Theatre-of-the-Sea I found several hin as to what the possible mechanisms might be.

I knew that brain stimulation brought about taming i a great hurry, within a half hour or so of the time that rewarding system was first stimulated electrically. Hov ever, until we understood the "natural" taming sequence we should not understand what the brain stimular might be doing.

The essence of taming is changing an anxiet provoking situation to a reward-producing situation: th same situation is changed in its motivational value to th animal by means of learning. One way to initiate th process is to confine the animal in isolation from i kind. Of course, the animal must be capable of acceptin the necessary confinement. Small-brained animals ar sometimes incapable of this, but most mammals are quit able to adapt to a confined situation. The next step chronic and continuous contact with human being (Among humans, this procedure is known to produc extremely rapid learning in certain controlled direction

It is commonly used in education, in brainwashing, and in psychotherapy.)

The classic third step is to force the taming process by withholding food until the starving animal has to approach a human being or die. This is the usual training maneuver for any type of animal in circuses and in oceanaria. Deprivation of food sets up a physiological state ("deprived state") and the reception of food is an extremely rewarding experience to the animal. This was the basis for most of the Pavlovian experiments and is one of the methods used by Keller Breland in training the dolphins at Marineland and by Santini.

I knew that we could use such tactics but I also felt that these men might be rewarding the dolphins in ways of which we were all unaware.

One such hypothetical reward may be skin contact—contact between human skin and dolphin skin. Several lines of evidence led me to this working hypothesis. Our observations and experiences suggest that fear of damage to the skin must be overcome and tactile stimulation then becomes rewarding to the dolphin.

It has been my experience, and that of many other persons, that a wild animal, when caught and held firmly by two or three men, quickly ceases to struggle. This phenomenon seems to be partly due to a "wait and see" attitude that any intelligent animal assumes when he knows he is beaten. But in the case of the dolphins it seems also to be due to their discovery that our skin is smooth and does not damage them when we grab onto them. Their skin is extremely delicate and their worst natural enemy is the shark with its rough skin, which could easily tear that of a dolphin on physical contact.

The pictures in the magazine had shown Mr. Santini in physical contact with the dolphins within his restricting net, and we asked him if by any chance he stroked and rubbed them when he first caught them. He said yes, that this was part of the taming procedure and that it was very successful in calming a frightened animal. They do not seem to be paralyzed when they are captured, and there is no massive inhibition of movement. They are quite capable of struggling and snapping their jaws. If one of us happens to push on the larynx or around the sensitive lips or the blowhole, they will struggle, but contact in these areas poses a threat to survival, and as I have mentioned, apparently they will struggle only if it is absolutely necessary for survival.

Thus it seems that when their fear and ignorance of anything new and strange has been overcome by forced contact with a smooth object, they are well on the way to being tamed and I believe they then experience pleasure from tactile stimulation of short duration.

In the course of some experiments I conducted from 1954 through 1956 I was suspended in water for several hours at a time, and I noticed that my skin gradually became more and more sensitive to tactile stimuli and an intense sense of pleasure resulted. However, if the stimulation was carried too far it became intensely irritating. I reasoned that the dolphin is suspended in water all of his life, twenty-four hours a day, and possibly had developed an intensely sensitive skin, which serves many physiological purposes: one of these might be the rewarding effect of rubbing against another animal, for example, in courtship and mating behavior.

I had noticed that Kenny, at Theatre-of-the-Sea, sought contact with his human handlers and would swim beside them and rub against them, like a dog that wants to be scratched. But after a time Kenny would terminate this kind of play and express irritability by banging his beak or his peduncle against the person if an attempt was made to stroke him.

At Marineland, in St. Augustine, we were shown that the animals needed and wanted a large brush that was

anchored to the bottom of the main tank in the oceanarium and against which they could scratch themselves.
Part of the purpose of this scratching procedure could
be to remove the outer layers of dead skin so as to maintain their bodies free of barnacles, algae, and other fouling organisms, and part seems to be associated with keen
pleasure in the process.

In the light of these experiences we began a set of experiments on animal Number 11, Elvar.

Elvar was one of the animals Mr. Santini obtained for
us in July. He was a male six feet ten inches long and
weighed about one hundred and fifty pounds. Dr. F. G.
Walton-Smith, of the Marine Laboratory of the University of Miami, volunteered to give us the use of some
space for the summer in a former machine shop at the
laboratory, and we transported Elvar in one of our boxes
by truck. He was put in a small swimming pool thirty
inches deep and eight and a half feet by ten feet. We
fed him by hand from the first day. The Santinis had
been feeding Elvar for a period of one or two weeks
before we took him to Miami, so we had no trouble about
feeding him.

A chronic, long experimental schedule was set up so
that several persons in bathing suits could get into the
pool with Elvar and attempt to force physical contacts on
him. Various objects, such as a floating ball, a floating
ring, etc., were placed in the pool and he gradually
adapted to their presence and began to play with them.
Within the first week we had established contact and he
was beginning on his own initiative to approach Alice
and four students—Kristin Stueber of Baltimore, Maryland; Karl Kellogg of Santa Monica, California; Robert
Bates of Glenview, Illinois; and James Hiss of Miami,
Florida—who had come to work with us during the summer. After about ten days of such experiences he was
approaching and rubbing himself against our big toes,

hands, knees, or legs. He began to accept all of our attentions and showed the rewarding effects of rubbing and stroking quite rapidly.

He also bore out my prediction that, if one rubbed and stroked him too long at one session, he would become irritable; he showed it by retreating or by banging his beak or his flukes upon our arms or legs when we presented them. If we let him then rest—let his skin rest, as it were—the rewarding effect would once again be elicited an hour or so later.

He gradually became acquainted with a small bathing brush and showed the value that he placed on this by pulling it around the pool and lying on it while it was on the bottom. He would attempt to scratch himself—any and all parts of his anatomy—on this brush. When he had had a long session of using the brush, we found that he was irritable and would not accept any further rubbing and stroking. In other words, for rubbing and stroking to be a rewarding experience, a previous state of deprivation must have existed. In this sense it is analogous to a food reward: the animal must be hungry if the food is to be a reward. The "skin" systems in the brain must also be deprived in the same sense. Such systems in the brain must be charged up with whatever it is that charges up the nervous system. The brushing and stroking use up the accumulated "charge" of pleasure and the contacts then become irritating instead of soothing and pleasurable.

Electrical brain stimulation through implanted electrodes has very similar effects in certain rewarding systems. If one stimulates the *globus pallidus* or the head of the caudate nucleus, the animal will push a key in order to stimulate these systems within his brain. If certain critical zones within each of these systems are stimulated in a human, the patient reports an intense sense of pleasure restricted to portions of the opposite side of the body.

Apparently these systems contain the neurophysiological mechanisms for pleasurable experiences having to do with the skin (and possibly joints and muscles).

In summary, then, a dolphin approaches any new and strange object from two viewpoints. As it were, he asks these questions: Will it hurt me? Alternatively, will it reward me? The detailed mechanisms of the reward are yet to be completely worked out. Among other possible rewarding experiences for these animals could be those in the acoustic sphere.

If these animals have a language, it may function somewhat the way it does in the case of a human. The adult human experiences intense reward or intense punishment on receipt of appropriate messages from other humans. In other words, a good many of our acoustic exchanges and vocalizations in the human sphere accumulate rewarding and/or punishing values for one reason or another from childhood to adulthood. There may be some sort of rewarding experience that is detectable in this sphere.

We designed some test experiments on the most primitive possible level. If the animal whistles or vocalizes in any way, this sound is picked up from the pool, amplified, and causes an electronic switch to turn on a tape reproducer that feeds back to the animal a recording of the human voice, counting from one to five. If this vocalization is or becomes rewarding for the animal, he should increase his rate of vocalization over a twenty-four-hour period during which he can elicit this response from his environment. He is in absolute (interspecies as well as intraspecies) solitude and there are no other sources of acoustic stimulation during the period of the experiment, so that he is, as it were, in an "acoustically deprived" state. The first, preliminary experiments on Elvar with such an apparatus make it look as if this hypothesis is correct. However, it will take a long time to carry out all of the details and the controls necessary to test this rather startling hypothesis. In no other animal than man has such a finding been made.

After a month of confinement with us Elvar suddenly developed self-confidence. There was a sudden change in his behavior; he began to play for long periods of time at very high speed with all of his toys and with us. He lost most of his spookiness and insisted on approaching us in a very definite fashion. If we put a hand in the water he would approach it, with his jaws open, and make playful snaps at the hand. If we put a ball in the water he would bounce it up out of the water with his beak. If we put a small ring in the water he would mouth it, put it over his beak, and swim around the pool with it. He also retrieved small objects on command.

At first some of these activities were sporadic, but soon he began to control and take charge of the situation. His initiative improved tremendously. He also swam around the pool in pursuit of his objects so rapidly that he threw water all over the laboratory. He also began to bring the front part of his body out of the water so he could look around the laboratory and took to slamming his flukes down on the water in a very exuberant fashion.

For a while Karl Kellogg was able to catch him quite easily by grasping him around his chest and lifting him out of the water. Suddenly Elvar caught on; as Karl started to reach for him he would accelerate and push by Karl at a high speed (even in water only twelve inches deep!). A few days later he was doing a fast "barrel roll" in Karl's arms and thus escaping.

I think that part of what he learned was that the walls in the pool were as smooth as our skins and would not hurt him. This pool had a vinyl liner with extremely smooth walls and flooring. Elvar discovered that if he wanted to rest he could just go down to the bottom and lie still. He discovered that the liner was noninjurious

nd as he swam around he would hit the wall with his
lukes and not damage them. However, he also learned
o bank on the turns and how to swim in the very shallow
vater close to the wall.

After he had heard only human voices for several
veeks his vocalization began to be less "delphinese" and
o break up into more humanoid, wordlike, explosive
oursts of Donald Duckish quacking.

I placed in the tank an underwater loudspeaker connected to an air microphone so that he could hear our
voices no matter what we were saying in the laboratory
and get used to the sounds produced by humans. We also
had in the tank a hydrophone connected to an air loud-
peaker so that we could hear all of his sounds. During
he first few weeks he emitted the same rather plaintive
attention calls that we had heard from Baby when she
was in isolation in St. Thomas. He also played the "num-
oers game" of whistling very short bursts in groups of
one, two, three, four, or five whistles. If we then whistled
uch groups back to him, he stopped whistling, apparently listening, and then began a plaintive "attention"
call, which is a very slow crescendo followed by another
crescendo of frequency and amplitude.

This call seemed to be related to attracting any animal
that may be in the neighborhood. It is not the distress
call: it is a separate though similar call. Of course, he
was also using his sonar with the typical "putt-putting"
and "creaking-door" sounds. These sounds were always
directed toward any new object thrust in the pool and
were always made during a feeding procedure. About
this time he began to emit noises similar to those made
by Marty of Theatre-of-the-Sea, thrusting his blowhole
above the water and making a sound like a human baby
crying. He also began the clicking noises in air which I
first heard from Splash at Marine Studios in 1956.

But the most interesting things to hear were the short

quacking noises that began to sound very much like pri
itive words in the human language. Apparently he w
beginning to mimic what he was hearing. An addition
set of noises that I heard him begin to make were tho
I had heard Alice make, noises of affection that peop
make toward children: soothing sounds and attentio
getting sounds, cluckings with one's tongue. These no
began to come back to us as extremely primitive copi
made with a vocal apparatus quite different from ours.

One of the problems of understanding the mimic
from a dolphin is that he does not have exactly the kir
of resonant air cavities that we have within our nec
and heads. He tends first of all to make extremely hig
pitched sounds, both whistles and clicks, and does n
make use of the resonance of such long and open a
columns as we do. Our voices depend on the fact th
our vocal cords are at the bottom of a long tube tern
nating at the other end in the lips and nose. We ca
modulate the shape and length of the tubes and tl
amount, velocity, and timing of air coming up throug
these tubes. Dolphins have different tubes but they a
parently don't use them naturally as we do without
lot of training. They tend to keep the tube extreme
short and the pitch very high. Each individual soun
terminates rapidly with very little aftervibration. W
might compare the quality of the sound emitted by the
to that emitted by a very small plucked violin, while ot
voices more nearly resemble that emitted by small orga
pipes.

If you look at the pattern of the human voice spoke
into a microphone, amplified, and put on a cathode-ra
oscilloscope, you can see that the highest frequencies ne
essary for understandability are pretty much limited: fc
maximum intelligibility, they do not go above about 50c
cycles a second and do not go very far below 100 cycl
per second. Of course, the telephone companies kno

this and their instrument is a good example of a limited-
frequency pass-band for maximum intelligibility.

However, the dolphins need very much higher frequencies. They run from about 500 up to 100,000 cycles
per second, and have other bands beyond our hearing
limit up to 167,000 cycles per second.[1] We can hear their
lower range and they can restrict their emissions to our
frequency range, but only with training. Luckily for us,
a good deal of their natural communication is within
our hearing, though in its upper range.

We could hear Elvar beginning to adapt to the acoustic
range of the instruments we were using. He began to
mimic our voices in a tentative, primitive first-try fashion,
"quacking." We began to see that by natural methods,
without brain-electrode forcing, it may be possible to
teach these animals to vocalize so that we may establish
communication with them. By judicious use and timing
of the proper kinds of rewards, whether food, skin contact, activities, or acoustic, we began to see where to place
our bets in our long-term experiments over the next few
years.

Elvar the male dolphin was kept in intraspecies solitude for fifty-one days. As is stated above he began to
make progress (in our terms!) on interspecies relations.
To a certain extent this progress was leveled off and yet
enhanced by a new experiment designed to further explore the behavior and thinking of dolphins. We caught
a female dolphin to give him a mate or at least a play-
mate. We called her Tolva (for dolphin Number 12).

This experiment was designed along the lines of certain natural laws of human experience and behavior
which I had found in a study of human confinement,

[1] Schevill, William E., and Lawrence, Barbara. Auditory response of a bottle-nosed porpoise, *Tursiops truncatus*, to frequencies above 100 Kc. J. Exp. Zool., **124**: No. 1, 147–65, Oct. 1953.
For later work, see Appendix 1.

solitude, and isolation. I wanted to see if the dolphin reactions were similar to those of a human similar treated.

If a human being is isolated from other humans for month or more, and is confined to a small area ge graphically and a small range of activities, his interest his surroundings and its minutiae increases radicall (His interest in his own inner world may also increase Such phenomena have been described by many aut biographers and the detailed evidence is given in n book.[2]

Further, if a confined, isolated human is allowed bri contacts with other humans even without a shared la guage, he begins to find their presence comforting ar a pleasant relief from the "evenness" of his surroun ings.[3] If these humans control his only sources of foc as well as his sources of intraspecies stimulation, he ma adapt to their demands in subtle and sometimes not subtle ways. He may, given time, learn their languag take on their beliefs, etc.

When we catch a dolphin and put him alone in a sma tank, we are imposing similar "solitary-confinemen strictures on him. Maybe we can thus capture his inte est, his loyalty, and his initiative, provided that he all resembles *Homo sapiens* in his mental and physiolog cal processes. Lizzie, Baby, and especially Elvar showe trends in this direction.

However, the crucial test of the effects of confine solitude is release from it; the human being experienc great joy and pleasure in release, and other phenomen appear. The acme of such experiences is for a man to b with a woman, and for a woman to be with a man.

[2] Lilly, J. C., *Programming and Metaprogramming in the H man Biocomputer* (Julian Press, 1973; Bantam, 1974).

[3] Richard Byrd's term, given in *Alone* (G. P. Putnam's Son New York, 1938).

Some not so obvious effects of acquiring a "mate" after a period of solitude are the immediate increase in self-confidence, recovery of the initiative, and shift of interest and loyalty from one's captors to one's mate, from one's own inner world to that shared with him or her.

All of this and more happened or seemed to happen when Elvar was presented with Tolva. We, the humans, were excluded as they initiated courtship and finally violent "honeymoon" activities. Elvar's old attentive interest in us evaporated—our only apparent hold on him that was left was food and feeding.

During the next weeks we saw all of the phenomena of courtship, mating, and play described by McBride and Hebb[4] and Tavolga and Essapian.[5] The enthusiastic violence of the new relationship was a wonder-filled experience for us all.

As their relations developed and flowered they became more violent—their high-speed pursuit and fleeing games threw the water from their shallow pool, and, at times, Tolva would climb the side and land on the deck around the edge. Each became covered with rake marks from the other's teeth. Each emitted loud raucous blats and calls in air, and each began snapping at us.

Soon we were unable to get in the pool to remove one without the other nipping at our legs. The old ease of relations with Elvar evaporated.

To test whether separation of the two dolphins would restore our hold in the teaching sphere, we put a separator in the pool make of plywood. The first separator was knocked down and climbed over: the energy expended to rejoin one another was impressive. A very hu-

[4] *Loc. cit.*

[5] Tavolga, Margaret C., and Essapian, Frank S. The behavior of the bottle-nosed dolphin (*Tursiops truncatus*): Mating, pregnancy, parturition and mother-infant behavior. Zoologica, **42**, Part 1, May 20, 1957.

man (and animal) response. Finally with an elaborate and strong partition we separated them. Later we put them in two separate pools.

Elvar soon became his old endearing self—but Tolva remained a driving, pushing, active female. Apparently their personalities are basically different. Each is fun for us in his own way.

During the first weeks Elvar taught Tolva most of the games he had learned with us and the use of his "toys"— balls, dumbbells, rings, ropes, etc. After separation independent actions took place but, in general, solitary play became less frequent and less violent than when they played with the same objects together, vocalizations dropped off: blats were now reserved for irritations with us, and plaintive whistlings like those of Baby left by Lizzie became numerous.

We have finally arranged a laboratory so that they can be allowed together or separated in a special double tank with a communicating door. We and they can thus easily work out a compromise schedule for work and play. They can be kept vigorous and healthy with their charging experiences together, and yet "go to school" separated from one another.

6

The Voices
of the Dolphin

In this chapter I will collect and give detailed descriptions of my new findings. I have already described some of the sounds which any and all bottle-nosed dolphins (*Tursiops truncatus*) emit, and some which only one or two have been heard to emit. Here and there I have referred to the work of others (scientists and nonscientists). It may turn out, after more and longer experience by more persons, that any one dolphin can and does emit all of the sounds in the natural as well as in the captive state. However, to date, the more accurate picture seems to be the following one:

All of them (wild or captive) frequently creak, putt-putt, and whistle under water, with some rare quacks, squawks, and blats under water and in air. A few dolphins in captivity, in close contact with humans, can and do start producing more frequent air-borne sounds on "request" and even "spontaneously": these sounds at first are loud clicks, creakings, whistles, squawks, quacks, and blats. With care trainers can encourage the animals to "sing," i.e., emit sustained high- or medium-pitched "wailing" notes which change pitch smoothly or in stac-

cato fashion. Trainers in the American oceanaria tend to
select such sounds because they sound like human singing (or wailing babies) and to suppress the other sounds
because to humans they sound raucous, derisive, impolite, even scatological, but at least very alien (it may be
that clucking Zulus would not think so). To date (1975),
trainers use only the air sounds and do not use hydrophones for the underwater sounds.

I have been concerned with analyzing each of these
classes of sounds and also with specifying by close observation and recording the conditions under which they
tend to occur. In addition, I have been interested in
methods of eliciting the above sounds, and new forms or
new modulations of these sounds.

In the present chapter I will try to describe and discuss
the so-called "mimicry" or "copying" phenomena in more
detail. These phenomena are difficult to describe on paper: more objective methods are being explored and developed to show the patterns of the sounds themselves by
visual displays, similar to the "visible-speech" method developed by the group at the Bell Telephone Laboratory.
I am currently obtaining apparatus of this sort for future
presentation of our taped materials. Meanwhile, in lieu
of such displays, I will describe our results as I hear them.
Of course, this method of describing results has a high
degree of subjectivity to it. It can be inexact, and even
completely mistaken. Some of my scientific colleagues
have criticized my use of this method instead of others.
I will not try to defend this position because we will use
the "better" methods when they are available. Even we
must be guided somewhat in the use of these new
methods by what we hear in the recordings of the dolphins' sounds, either at the speed they are emitted or
slowed down. Our own acoustic systems have been
trained (if not overtrained) to extract meaning from

complex patterns, but not *all* patterns, mainly some patterns which are in our own languages. These patterns we recognize despite distortions and other disturbing noises.

A dolphin, on the other hand, naturally uses other sounds to convey and receive "meaning": creaking for nighttime and murky-water finding and recognition, putt-putting and whistles for exchanges with other dolphins, and even air wailing to excite human responses in the

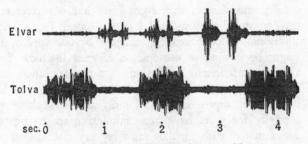

An Exchange of Whistles between Two
Isolated and Confined Dolphins.

Each dolphin has its own hydrophone, amplifier, and channel of tape recording. Tolva whistles first; Elvar responds with whistles; Tolva starts another and Elvar joins her in a brief "duet." Elvar then "talks louder," Tolva remaining quiet. Finally Tolva replies. Neither dolphin emitted any clicks or squawks during this exchange. The exchange occurred over a total time of 4.3 seconds, time scale at bottom.

way of fish or applause. If a dolphin is copying our speech, he'll copy that part of what he hears which in his "language" conveys meanings. The unmistakable "delphinese" accent may be so severe that we can expect trouble in recognizing our "meaning-filled patterns" when they are sent back to us. Of course, our troubles are amplified when we find out that dolphins can not

only hear but transmit sounds which are entirely ultrasonic as far as we are concerned. Actually, it's lucky that
they use any sounds which we can hear. Since much of
their hearing and vocalizing is ultrasonic for us, it is
quite possible that the meaningful patterns of their
speech are up in the ultrasonic too. Their physical con-
veyers of meaning may not overlap ours at all.

However, to attenuate our fears and encourage our
hopes, they can hear in our spectrum and can produce at
least some components within it. Of course, all of these
considerations mean that even if we had a perfect recording and display method for their sounds (sonic and
ultrasonic) and looked for mimicry of our speech, it
might be missing in the opinion of most listeners. Yet
the same tape heard by those used to the delphinese accent and automatically attuned to the variation could
hear the attempted mimicry. I must say, if dolphins in
captivity for years have been mimicking us, trying to
communicate with us, they must be very discouraged at
our lack of response! "Why, those humans can't even
make a sound higher than eight kilocycles without aids,
and they chatter at such *very* low frequencies I can
hardly make out any patterns," a dolphin might comment to another one.

The over-all problem of objective visual display can be
divided into several separate and distinct parts: the first
is to find their language; the second is to see if they are
learning our language; and the third is to find the
meaningful parts of the patterns in each of the first two
cases.

The assignment is similar to that faced by those people
who conducted the "visible-speech" experiments at the
Bell Laboratories, added to the difficult work of the cryp-
tographer. The visible speech at least carried an understood built-in meaning when recorded. With dolphins
this advantage exists only in the mimicry case (with

built-in accent!). Their "language" and its meanings are crypto-vocal as well as cryptographic!

Of course one can start anywhere on this sort of research problem. I chose to first record and analyze their sounds by "subjective" study. I purposely increased my own chances of hearing mimicry by making the dolphins phenomenally broad-spectrum sounds (5 kcps to 150 kcps) conform to (or react to electronic aids) my subjective "meaning spectrum" (from about 50 cps to 5000 cps). The first experiments, as recounted in a previous chapter, were recorded with acoustic and electronic means which rejected their high sonic and supersonic sound, and enhanced those sounds in our meaning-speech spectrum. Our tapes recorded very poor delphinese but excellent English, if any English had been used. Even with these precautions I had to slow down these tapes to get the best results. Apparently, not only do these animals use very high frequencies but they use very high speeds for their speech. Later tapes (1960) with much wider acoustic bands which recorded their whistles, creakings, squawks, etc., were slowed down four, eight, and sixteen times to emphasize this speed in their dolphin to dolphin exchanges. The following experiments illustrate this point:[1]

Elvar and Tolva were separated from one another. Each was confined in a small narrow space at the end of a common tank. Each could hear the other's vocalizations through the water but could not see the other. Each had its own hydrophone and its sounds were recorded on separate tapes.

Under these conditions the animals emitted whistles which are usually politely alternating, first one and then the other, with some monologues, and some short duets (with beats, yet!).

[1] Lilly, J. C., and Miller, A. M. Vocal exchanges between individual dolphins (Manuscript, December 1960).

However, all dolphins emit clicks, with or without the whistles. These clicks are not creakings such as they use for finding fish; they are usually slower in rate, steadier, and may alternate with those of the other dolphin.

These are the usual "isolated-pair" exchanges. However, if one allows a male and female physical contact with one another, additional sounds may appear: harsh blats, squawks, barks, and wails are emitted when the dolphins are playing or excited in courtship and mating.

An additional set of noises which may be air-borne, not necessarily under water, is elicited by human contacts, training, and brain-forcing by electrical stimulation. These are sounds which to me (but not to all of my colleagues) sound like human vocalizations of one sort or another: I have heard these in stimulating "pleasure" systems within the brain, and also under repeated human-contact conditions.[2] The following are the kinds of things mimicked in my experience.

(a) *Human laughter:* The explosive, repetitive, sing-song ha-ha-ha! kind of laugh—the usual repetitions were in groups of three or four, with a very high-pitched child's voice quality to it. It is most distinct immediately after or within a few seconds of a woman's laughter. Repetition of human laughter may elicit further imitations either better or worse than the original.

(b) *Human or electronically-produced whistles:* Sometimes an isolated animal seems to copy whistles but since this is their natural vocal emission a human will find it difficult to pick up unless the dolphin lowers the pitch nearer to that of our whistle frequencies.

(c) *Bronx cheers and assorted impolite* (to humans) *noises:* Very raucous noises made by humans between pursed lips or between lower lip and palm can be mim-

[2] Cf. later work in this volume re pure vocal exchanges (Appendix 1).

icked by some young dolphins. Number 6 (1957) dolphin first showed me this set of noises and presently Tolva has taught it to Elvar. Such noises are usually not encouraged in oceanaria.

(d) *Human words:*[3] These are the most subjective of all the judgments of the sounds emitted by dolphins. I have heard most distinctly the following words and phrases "copied" in an extremely high-pitched and brief fashion: "three-two-three," "Tee ar Pee" (the letters "TRR" were just given), and a host of others, less clear but verging so closely on humanlike rhythm, enunciation, and phonetic quality as to be eerie. Let me close with one mysterious example:

On the 16th of April 1960 I was working with Lizzie and Baby in the St. Thomas pool. We had just separated Lizzie from Baby and put her in a small side-tank in order to force feed her by stomach tube. It was getting late in the day. We were all tired with the exertion, and getting a bit short-tempered. I was worried about Lizzie's health—she hadn't been eating and I felt she was in danger if we didn't tend to her closely. Someone suggested that I would be late for dinner if I didn't leave and said, "It's six o'clock!" very loudly. The tape recorded this on the air channel; in a few seconds on the underwater channel Lizzie, near the hydrophone, putt-putted, Baby answered with a short fast series of whistles, and Lizzie very loudly came out with a "humanoid" sentence, the meaning of which (if any) has puzzled several of us since. It may have been a poor copy of "It's six o'clock." But I was caught first by another "meaning." It sounded to me like "This is a trick!" with a peculiar hissing accent. Other people have since heard the tape and come to the same conclusion.

[3] Cf. later "humanoid" productions, p. 186.

This was the last recording from Lizzie; we found her dead next morning. Our grief was painful and our mourning long. It was a great disappointment to lose her just as she started to make sounds of this sort.[4]

[4] Cf. work with Elvar and Peter below.

The Dolphin in History

Modern Whales, Dolphins, and Porpoises, as Challenges to Our Intelligence [1962]

The intelligence of whales has been the subject of speculation by writers since Ancient Greece.[1, 2] The discovery of the large brains of the Cetacea in the eighteenth century led to inevitable comparisons of these brains to those of the humans and of the lower primates. The winds of scholarly opinions concerning the whales have anciently blown strongly for high intelligence but during later centuries shifted strongly against high intelligence. At the time of Aristotle (384–322 B.C.) the dolphin, for example, was held in high esteem, and many stories of the apparently great abilities of these animals were current.[3] By the time of Plinius Secundus (A.D. 23–79) the beginning of a note of skepticism was introduced. Plinius said, "I should be ashamed to tell the story were it not that it has been written about by . . . others."[4]

[1] Plinius Secundus. *Natural History.* III, Book IX.
[2] Aristotle. *Historia Animalium.* Books I–IX.
[3] Ibid.
[4] Plinius Secundus, *loc. cit.*

In the middle ages the strong influence of religious philosophy on thinking placed Man in a completely separate compartment from all other living creatures, and the accurate anatomy of the whales was neglected. This point is illustrated by Konrad Gesner's drawing of a baleen whale in the 1500's in *Historia Animalium*. It has two tubes which apparently symbolize the double blowhole of the Mystacocetae. There is no modern whale known that has such tubes sticking out of the top of his head. There is a huge eye above the angle of the jaw. All whales have the eye at or near the posterior angle of the jaw. In a print published in 1598 of the anatomy of these animals the drawing of the male organ is accurate (apparently it was measured with a walking stick), but the eye is too large and is misplaced.

It was not until the anatomical work of Vesalius and others that the biological similarities and differences of man and other mammals were pointed out. It was at this time that the investigation of man's large and complex brain began.

All through these periods intelligence and the biological brain factors seemed to be completely separated in the minds of the scholars. At the times of the Greeks and the Romans there was little, if any, link made between brain and mind. Scholars attributed man's special achievements to other factors than excellence of brain structure and its use.

After the discovery of man's complicated and complex brain and the clinical correlation between brain injury and effects on man's performance, the brain and mental factors began to be related to one another. As descriptions of man's brain became more and more exact and clinical correlations increased sufficiently in numbers, new investigations on the relationships between brain size and

intelligence in *Homo sapiens* were started. The early
work is summarized by Donaldson.[5]

In the late 1700's and the early 1800's the expansion of
the whaling industry offered many opportunities for examination of these interesting mammals.

One of the earliest drawings of the complex brain of
one of the Cetacea is that of Gottfried Reinhold Tredira-
mus in 1818. An anterior view of the brain of the common porpoise *Phocaena phocaena,* it is one of the earliest
pictures showing the complexity of the fissuration and
the large numbers of gyri and sulci.

By the year 1843 the size of the brain of whales was
being related to the total size of the body. The very large
brains of the large whales were reduced in importance
by considering their weight in a ratio to the weight of
the total body. This type of reasoning was culminated
with a long series of quantitative measures published by
Eugène Dubois (*Bulletins de la Société d'Anthropologie
de Paris,* Ser. 4, VIII [1897], 337–76).

Descriptions from those of Hunter and Tyson onwards
agree that, in absolute size, the brains are as large and
larger than those of man. All were agreed that the smaller
whales, i.e., the dolphins and porpoises, have very large
brains with relation to their body size. It was argued,
therefore, with respect to the dolphin, "this creature is of
more than ordinary wit and capacity." (Robert Hamil-
ton, *The Natural History of the Ordinary Cetacea or
Whales,* p. 66, in Sir William Jardine, *The Naturalist's
Library,* volume 7, Edinburgh, 1843.)

Tiedemann's drawings of the brain of *Delphinus
delphis* and of *Delphinus phocaena* were published by
H. G. L. Reichenbach in his *Anatomia Mammalium* in
1845. They show the improved awareness of the com-

[5] Donaldson, Henry H. *The Growth of the Brain.* London:
Walter Scott, 1895.

plexities of these large brains in regard to cerebral cortex, the cerebellum, and the cranial nerves. Correlations between the structure of this brain and the behavior of the animal possessing it, were (and are) woefully lacking. The only behavioral accounts were those of whalers hunting these animals. Hunters concentrate on the offensive and defensive maneuvers of the animal, and can give useful information for other kinds of evaluation of the animal's behavior and presumed intelligence.

In 1787 John Hunter, writing in the *Philosophical Transactions of the Royal Society of London* (LXXVII, 423–24), said the following: "The size of the Brain differs much in different genera of this tribe, and likewise in the proportion it bears to the bulk of the animal. In the Porpoise, I believe, it [the proportion] is largest, and perhaps in that respect comes nearest to the human . . .

"The brain is composed of cortical and medullary substances, very distinctly marked; the cortical being, in colour, like the tubular substance of a kidney; the medullary, very white. These substances are nearly in the same proportion as in the human brain . . . The thalami themselves are large; the corpora striata small; the crura of the fornix are continued along the windings of the ventricles, much as in the human subject."

Flatau and Jacobsohn in 1899 wrote, "the large brain of the Porpoise is one of the smallest in the Cetacean Order in which the organ attains to a much greater absolute size than any other."[6]

In 1902 G. Elliot Smith wrote of the brain of a species of dolphin called "Delphinus tursio" (which may be the modern *Tursiops truncatus*): "This brain is larger and correspondingly richer in sulci than that of the porpoise:

[6] Smith, G. Elliot, in Royal College of Surgeons of England, Museum, *Descriptive and Illustrated Catalogue of the Physiological Series of Comparative Anatomy*. London: Taylor and Francis, 1902, pp. 349, 351, 356.

but the structure of the two organs is essentially the same." He said further, "the brains of the Beluga and all the dolphins closely resemble that of the porpoise."

Smith summarizes the discussion of the huge size of the whale's brain. "The apparently extraordinary dimensions of the whale's brain cannot therefore be considered unusual phenomena, because this enormous extent of the cerebral cortex to receive and 'store' impressions of such vast sensory surfaces becomes a condition of survival of the animal.

"The marvelous complexity of the surface of the cerebrum is the direct result of its great size. In order, apparently, that the cerebral cortex may be efficiently nourished and at the same time be spared to as great a degree as possible the risk of vascular disturbances [such as would be produced by large vessels passing into it], its thickness does not appreciably increase in large animals. [He then quotes Dubois' figures showing that the whale's cortex is the same thickness as that of the human.] Such being the case, it naturally results that the increased bulk of cortex in large animals can only be packed by becoming thrown into increasing number of folds, separated by corresponding large number of sulci."[7]

In regard to communication between individual whales, Scammon in 1874 wrote the following: "It is said that the Cachalots [Sperm Whales] are endowed with the faculty of communicating with each other in times of danger, when miles . . . distant. If this be true, the mode of communication rests instinctively within their own contracted brains."[8] Let us not forget that Scammon was talking about the mammal with the largest

[7] Ibid.
[8] Scammon, Charles Melville. *The Marine Mammals of the North-Western Coast of North America, Described and Illustrated: Together with an Account of the American Whale-Fishery.* San Francisco: J. H. Carmany, 1874, p. 78.

known brain on this planet. Instinct as the sole cause of
communication with a brain this size seems rather improbable. This brain is not any longer considered "contracted." Both of these statements illustrate an authorita-
tive view of that time. If one peruses the paper by Tokuzo
Kojima, "On the Brain of the Sperm Whale" (in the
Scientific Reports of the Whales Research Institute,
Tokyo, VI, 1951, 49–72), one can obtain a modern clear
view of this brain. The largest one that he obtained
(from a 49-foot sperm whale) was 9,200 grams. The
average weight of the sixteen brains presented in his
paper is 7,800 grams for average body lengths of 50 feet.
(The brain weight per foot of body length varied from
118 to 187 grams per foot, averaging 157; man's ratio
averages about 250 grams per foot.)

In the literature of the time of Scammon, the scholars
failed to give us new information about the behavior of
Cetacea. There seems to have been a distinctly ambiva-
lent attitude towards these animals which is continued
today. This point of view can be summarized as follows:
"the whale is a very large animal with a brain larger than
that of man. This brain is the result of the huge growth
of its body. All of this large brain is needed to control a
large body. Because these tasks are so demanding, there
is not enough brain substance left for a high degree of
intelligence to develop. Thus the large brain cannot give
the degree of intellectual capability that man has."

As an example of man's attitudes to cetaceans, consider
the case of the U. S. Fisheries Bureau *Economic Circular*
No. 38, of November 6, 1918, by Lewis Radcliffe, en-
titled "Whales and Porpoises as Food." Roy Chapman
Andrews is quoted as saying that hump-backed whale
meat is the best of the larger cetaceans but that porpoise
and dolphin meat is even better eating than that of the
larger whale. The composition of the whale meat is given
as 30% protein, 6% fat, and less than 2% ash. From a

hump-backed whale one obtains six tons of meat, from a Sei Whale, five tons, and from a Finback, eight tons. Directions are given to remove the connective tissue between the blubber and the muscle to avoid the oily taste. For those who are interested, the paper includes twenty-two whale meat recipes and ten porpoise meat recipes.

It can well be imagined, if we ever do communicate with whales, dolphins, or porpoises, the kind of reception that this sort of literature will receive from the cetaceans.

The limited point of view of the whales as "dumb beasts" neglects the adaptations that have taken place in non-mammalian forms with very much smaller brains but with comparable bulk of body. The 60-foot whale shark, a plankton eater, and like the rest of the sharks a water-breather, has a bulk of body comparable to that of the larger whales. It has a large brain cavity but a very small brain in a small part of this large cavity. (It is very difficult to find the weight of these brains to compare with that of the Cetacea and other mammals.) The problem of brain weight versus body weight versus intelligence is most clearly expressed by Gerhardt von Bonin in his paper in the *Journal of General Psychology* (1937).[9] He gives a very extensive table for mammals, their brain weight, their body weight, and the values of 2 parameters for their specification. He then states, "it is clear from all that has been said above that the figures given here are nothing but a description of facts, a description which, in the mathematical sense of the term, is the 'best' one. It does not pretend to make any enunciation about the relation of intelligence and brain weight. For that purpose we need a much broader psychological basis than we have at present.

"Former attempts to analyze the relations between body

[9] von Bonin, Gerhardt. "Brain-Weight and Body-Weight in Mammals," *Journal of General Psychology*, XVI (1937), 379–89.

weight and brain weight suffer from three deficits: (1) they presuppose a correlation between intelligence and brain weight, (2) they make suppositions about the intelligence of animals which are unproven, and (3) they are based on a conception of cortical function which can no longer be considered valid . . . There is a close correlation between the logarithms of brain and body weight, and this correlation is linear. Brain weight increases as the 0.655th power of body weight. The value of the cephalization co-efficient k differs from species to species. *Whether or not this is an indication of the intelligence of animals must be left to the psychologists to answer.*"

One of the problems that the whales have, as compared to, say, the large shark, is breathing air while living in the sea. This requires that these animals reach the air-water interface relatively frequently—at least every one hour and a half for the bottlenose whale (*Hyperoodon*), three-quarters of an hour for the Sperm Whale (*Physeter catadon*), and every six minutes for *Tursiops truncatus*. This puts very stringent requirements on the relationship of the whales to other events within the sea. Each whale must know where the surface of the sea is at each instant and compute his future actions so that when he does run out of air he is near the surface. He is essentially a surface-to-depth and depth-to-surface oriented animal. He must travel at high speed at times in order to recapture enough air to continue whatever he is doing under the surface. This means that he must calculate his chances of obtaining a good breath of air during rain storms and similar situations. He can be violently thrown around at the surface unless he comes up in the trough rather than at the crest of the wave. Such calculations probably require an exercise of something more than just "instinct."

Water-breathing animals, on the other hand, have no need for such calculations. If the surface gets rough, they move downward and stay there. The required maneuvers are very much simpler and the amount of computation is very much less.

This requirement for the whales implies that the information coming from every one of the senses, not just the skin, needs to be correlated very rapidly and in complex patterning to allow the animals to predict their future course safely and accurately. It also requires the use of large amounts of information from memory.

The predators of the sea, other than the whales themselves, make life in the sea rather a complex business for mammals. The very large sharks can and do attack whales, dolphins, and porpoises. At times such attacks are by overwhelming numbers of sharks on a relatively small number of dolphins. All of the older animals in our experience have at least one shark bite on them—the younger animals are protected by the older ones and most of them are not so dramatically scarred.

The whales, in turn, must track their own prey in order to obtain food. With the single known exception of *Orca*, none of their predators are air-breathers. In general, the whales' diet consists of fish, squid, or other water-breathing organisms of the sea.

A scientific assessment of the position of these animals in the competitive environment of the sea is not yet fully evaluated quantitatively. Any pronouncement of the requirements in regard to new complex adaptations to new complicated situations and hence the evaluation of intelligence of these animals at this time is premature and presumptuous. The whole issue of the meaning and the use of these large brains is still very much unknown. As I say in *Man and Dolphin* earlier in this volume, I am espousing a plea for an open-minded attitude with respect to these animals. It would be presumptuous to assume that we at the present time can know how to measure their intelligence or their intellectual capacity.

The usual behavioral criteria used in evaluation of intelligence of other animals are obviously inapplicable to a mammal living in the sea. As McBride and Hebb[10] so clearly stated, they cannot place the dolphin in any sort of intellectual comparative intelligence scale; they did not know the appropriate experimental questions to ask in order to compare the dolphins with the chimpanzees, for example. Comparing a handed-mammal with a flippered-mammal, each of which lives in an entirely separate and distinctive environment, is a very difficult intellectual task even for *Homo sapiens*.

In pursuing possible measures of intellectual and intelligent capacity, what line should one pursue? The invariants that we are seeking somehow do not seem to be as concrete as "tool-making and tool-using ability" by means of the hands which has been one of the major alleged criteria for human adaptation and success. The chimpanzee and the gorilla have the hands but they do not have the brains to back up the use of the hands. Man has both the hands and the brain. Thus we can quite simply and concretely contrast the performance of the large brains of man with his hands to the smaller brains of the primates with their hands. When we consider the whales, we seem obsessed, as it were, with the necessity of our own nature to look for an analog of the hand and the manipulative ability. May it not be better to find a more general principle than just handedness and its use?

I suggest that we think more in terms of a physiologically appropriate set of more general mechanisms which may subsume several other human functions under the same principle. We must look for abilities to develop generalized dexterity of use for certain kinds of end purposes for any or all muscular outputs from the central

[10] McBride, Arthur F., and Hebb, D. O. "Behavior of the Captive Bottle-Nose Dolphin, *Tursiops truncatus*," *Journal of Comparative and Physiological Psychology*, XLI (1948), 111–23.

nervous system. If there is a task to be done, such as lifting a stone, whether in water or air, a given animal may turn it over with his foot, with his flipper, with his hand, with his tail, or with any other body part with which he could obtain a purchase on the stone. The end task is turning over the stone, to obtain food or whatever. It makes little difference what kind of muscular equipment he uses just so he uses it appropriately.

Let me illustrate with a more complex example seen in our own laboratory. A baby dolphin was being nursed in a small tank artificially. It apparently needed the constant attention of a human attendant. Its mother had not been caught with it. After several days it discovered that if it banged on the bottom of the tank with its flipper in a rhythmic fashion it could bring the humans from the other room. (We heard a loud thumping sound transmitted from a hydrophone in its tank.) Previous to this it attempted to bring the humans from the other room by whistling the distress call of the dolphins; unlike its mother, the humans did not respond to the whistle. In a sense this distress call is in his instinctual pattern for obtaining food and aid by other dolphins. The secondary adaptation and the new effort was that of manipulating the flipper rather than the phonation mechanism in the blowhole. Thus driven by whatever the instinctual need is, it tried different outputs from its brain and finally discovered one which brought the desired results. This ability to change the output from unsuccessful ones to successful ones seems to me to be evidence of a "higher nervous system" function. Of course in fine gradation and small differences, the same kind of pattern can be shown for smaller-brained animals. It is the seeking of a new output, not necessarily instinctually tied in, and the radicalness of the change of output, plus the relating of many of the variables to one another thus generating the new output, that seems to be the hallmark of the large brain. These problems are not single variable ones with simple cause and effect, but are simultaneous multiple variable ones.

Among the manipulable outputs (muscular groups) I would include those of respiration and phonation. The dexterous and finely differentiated use of these muscles generates all the complexities of human speech. As more of the physiology and psychology of human speech are analyzed and made part of our sciences, the sharper will be our criteria for separating man from the other animals, and from those with smaller brains. Scientific descriptions of human speech are of relatively recent origin. Scientific descriptions of the physiology of the vocal tract are anything but a closed book at the present time. The neuroanatomy and neurophysiology of speech is in a relatively primitive state of development as a science. With such a lack of knowledge of the intimate and detailed mechanisms concerned, it would be rather presumptuous to evaluate at the present time their role in the measurement and testing of intelligence and intellectual capacity.

However, these factors are important in such an evaluation and become even more important in terms of evaluating a species that is not human. Thus it is necessary, in order to evaluate the intelligence of even the dolphins, much less the whales, to know something of their abilities in the areas of phonation and other kinds of bodily gestures and manipulations and hence in their abilities to communicate with one another. It is not possible to measure accurately the intelligence of any other being than that of a human being, mainly because we do not exchange ideas through any known communication mode with such beings.

The difficulties of such understanding as we can possibly gain of the real situation of the whales in the sea and their adaptation as mammals to this particular environment, can be illustrated by their use of sonic generators for the location of their prey and of the boundaries of their container by means of the perception of echoes. As is well known, the small mammals, such as the bat, use this mechanism in air.[11] The bottle-nosed dolphin also uses this same kind of mechanism under water.[12, 13, 14] Because these animals are immersed in a medium of a density and a sound velocity comparable to the density and sound velocity of their own bodies, they can presumably use their sonar also in looking, as it were, inside one another's body.[15] The sonar view of the inside of the body of a dolphin may possibly be very instructive to other dolphins and possibly even aid in diagnosis of the causes of certain problems, especially of those of the baby by the mother. For example, their buoyancy depends upon maintaining their center of gravity below their center of buoyancy; otherwise they turn over and drown. If the baby develops gas in stomach #1, he can develop problems in his buoyancy relationship which turn him over; however, the mother dolphin can probably easily find out whether or not there is a bubble of gas in the baby's stomach by her echo ranging abilities. When she discovers such a bubble, she can then burp the baby by banging on the belly with her beak. We have seen such operations take place in our tanks. Here is another instance of the animal using a given output, coupled with the proper input, to diagnose a problem and to manipulate other outputs in the solution of that

[11] Griffin, Donald R. *Echoes of Bats and Men.* Garden City, N.Y.: Doubleday, 1959.

[12] Ibid.

[13] John C. Lilly, *Man and Dolphin,* this volume.

[14] Kellogg, Winthrop N. *Porpoises and Sonar.* Chicago: University of Chicago Press, 1961.

[15] Lilly, op. cit.

problem. How much of this is labeled "instinctual," i.e., "unlearned," is purely a matter of intellectual taste.

In the sea it is necessary to use sonic mechanisms for sightings and recognition. If one goes into the sea one realizes that one's range of vision even under the best of circumstances is rarely beyond 100 feet and most of the time is less than that even near the brilliantly lit surface of the tropical seas. With sonic means, one's range is extended up to several miles under the best of circumstances and under the worst to a few hundred feet.

Recently we have obtained evidence that shows that the dolphins communicate most of their information in the band of frequencies extending from about 1 kilocycle to 100 kilocycles by means of whistles and sonic clicks.[16] However, as shown by Schevill and Lawrence, they can hear sounds at least to 120 kilocycles[17] and as shown by Kellogg can produce sounds at least to 170 kilocycles.[18] We have recently been investigating the higher frequency bands in these animals and have reliable evidence that they can hear at least to 200 kilocycles and can produce sounds to at least 200 kilocycles.[19, 20] With the proper electronic equipment one can listen to the nearer portions of the upper band and quickly determine that they can transmit in these bands

[16] Lilly, John C., and Miller, Alice M. "Vocal Exchanges between Dolphins; Bottlenose Dolphins 'Talk' to Each Other with Whistles, Clicks, and a Variety of Other Noises," Science, CXXXIV (1961), 1873–76.

[17] Schevill, William E., and Lawrence, Barbara. "Auditory Response of a Bottlenosed Porpoise, Tursiops truncatus, to Frequencies above 100 KC," Journal of Experimental Zoology, CXXIV (1953), 147–65.

[18] Kellogg, op. cit.

[19] Lilly, op. cit.

[20] Lilly, John C. "Vocal Behavior of the Bottlenose Dolphin," Proceedings of the American Philosophical Society, CVI (1926), 520–29.

without the necessity of transmitting in the (lower frequency) communication band. The high frequency information is broadcast in a narrow beam off the front of the beak as was first detected by Kenneth Norris.[21]

In these bands we find that they can produce musical tones or individual clickings or hissing-like noises. An emotionally upset animal threatens other animals and humans by productions of very large amounts of energy both in the sonic communication band and in the ultrasonic bands. We have worked with an old bull of 450 pounds weight who is so old his teeth have been ground down flat. In terms of his skeleton, he is the most massive animal we have ever seen. When he is irritated, his "barks" have sizable amounts of energy from about 0.5 to at least 300 kilocycles. He is also capable of transmitting in bands between 100 to 300 kilocycles without transmitting anything in the band from 1 kilocycle to 100 kilocycles in a narrow beam straight ahead of his body. When he is upset by the activities of a younger male, they face one another and blast at one another with short barks of this sort, meanwhile "threatening" by opening their mouths.

Since they live immersed in an acoustic world quite strange to us, we have great difficulty in appreciating the full life of these animals with respect to one another and their environment. From birth they are constantly bombarded with signals from the other animals of the same species and by echoes from the environment which they can apparently use very efficiently. Their ultrasonic (to us) emissions are not merely "sonar," but are interpersonal and even emotional. These animals are not inanimate, cold pieces of sonar apparatus. They use their

[21] Norris, Kenneth S., Prescott, John H., Asa-Dorian, Paul V., and Perkins, Paul. "An Experimental Demonstration of Echo-Location Behavior in the Porpoise, *Tursiops truncatus* (Montagu)," *Biological Bulletin*, CXX (1961), 163–76.

ultrasounds and their high-pitched sounds interpersonally with fervor in everything they do.[22]

We have demonstrated that the dolphins are quite capable of using vocal outputs as a demand for further rewards or for surcease from punishment. Their ability in the vocal sphere is quite sophisticated. In addition to the ultrasonic matters mentioned above, their sonic performance, when in close contact with man, is astonishing. In 1957 I discovered their ability to produce sounds similar to our speech sounds.[23] During the last two years we have had many opportunities to pursue further observations in this area. This emerging ability seems to be an adaptation to a new environment which includes Man.[24] They quickly discover that they can obtain various kinds of rewards by making what we now call "humanoid emissions." When they make a sound which sounds similar to a human syllable or word, we express our pleasure by rewarding the animals in various ways. We have been exploring what some of these rewards are in order to elicit further such behavior under better control.

We demonstrated that, like other animals, the monkey, the rat, etc., these animals can be rewarded by stimulating the proper places in their brains.[25, 26] In a series of

[22] Lilly, John C. "Interspecies Communication," *McGraw-Hill Yearbook of Science and Technology 1962.* New York: McGraw-Hill, 1962, pp. 279–81.

[23] Lilly, John C. "Some Considerations Regarding Basic Mechanisms of Positive and Negative Types of Motivations," *American Journal of Psychiatry,* CXV (1958), 498–504.

[24] Lilly, John C. "Some Aspects of the Adaptation of the Mammals to the Ocean," in John Field, ed., *Handbook of Physiology.* Washington: American Physiological Society, 1963.

[25] Lilly, "Some Considerations Regarding Basic Mechanisms of Positive and Negative Types of Motivations," op. cit.

[26] Lilly, John C., and Miller, A. M. "Operant Conditioning of the Bottlenose Dolphin with Electrical Stimulation of the Brain,"

experiments we have been establishing the controls necessary to understanding what brain rewards mean in terms of natural physiology. We have demonstrated quite formally that rubbing the skin of these animals with our hands is a rewarding experience to them; they will seek it vocally and by body gestures and give certain kinds of performance in order to obtain this reward.

We have found that "vocal transactions" are a reward to these animals.[27, 28] (See below for human analogies in the child.) This seems to be one of the basic factors in our being able to elicit humanoid emissions. The vocal transactions are started by a human shouting some words over the water of the tank in which the animal is residing. A single word may be used or many words—it makes little difference. Eventually the animal in the tank will raise his blowhole out of water and make some sort of a humanoid emission or whistle or clicks in a delphinese fashion. If the human immediately replies with some word or words, the animal may immediately respond, the human answers, and a vocal transaction is under way. We have shown that dolphins naturally do this with one another in both their whistle and clicking spheres, and sometimes do it in the barking sphere.[29] How much of this is "instinctual" and how much is not, there is no way of knowing at the present time.

A physical analysis of such vocal transactions shows them to be formally quite as complex as the vocal transactions between human beings. In other words, the dolphin may say one word or a syllable-like emission, or many, one right after the other, as may the humans. If the human says one word, the dolphin may say one, two,

Journal of Comparative and Physiological Psychology, LV (1962), 73–79.

27 Lilly, *Man and Dolphin*, op. cit.
28 Lilly, "Vocal Behavior of the Bottlenose Dolphin," op. cit.
29 Ibid.

three, or four, and if the human says one, two, three, or four, the dolphin may say one. There is no necessary master-slave kind of relationship in the delphinic emissions.

In our early reports we gave examples which were single words which sounded like the words that the human made.[30, 31] This presentation led to misunderstandings among our scientific colleagues. It looked as if the animals were doing a slavish tape-recorder rendition of what we were doing in a fashion similar to that of a parrot or a Mynah bird. All along we have known that the dolphins did not do such a slavish job and were obviously doing a much more complicated series of actions. We are just beginning to appreciate how to analyze and what to analyze in these transactions. About 10% of these emissions sound like human speech. In other words, the dolphin is "saying" far more than we have transmitted to the scientific community to date. We hesitate to say anything more about this until we begin to understand what is going on in greater detail. We are making progress slowly.

Let me then make an appeal to you—a long appeal to your logical and rational views of man and cetaceans. Here I review the above points in more general terms, and develop a plea for a new science—a new discipline combining the best of science with the best of the humanities.

Several old questions should be revived and asked again with a new attitude, with more modern techniques of investigation and with more persistence. It may take twenty years or more to develop good answers; meanwhile the intellectual life of man will profit in the under-

---

[30] Lilly, "Some Considerations Regarding Basic Mechanisms of Positive and Negative Types of Motivations," op. cit.

[31] Lilly, *Man and Dolphin*, op. cit. See *Mind of the Dolphin* and Appendix 1 below.

taking. There is something exciting and even at times disturbing in this quest.[32] The bits and pieces may have started before historical times. In each age of man a new fragment was allowed to be recorded and passed on to subsequent generations. Each generation judged and re-judged the evidence from the older sources on the basis of its then current beliefs and on the basis of its new experiences, if any. At times good evidence was attenu-ated, distorted, and even destroyed in the name of the then current dogma.

Today we have similar problems; our current beliefs blind us, too. Evidence right before the eye can be dis-torted by the eye of the beholder quite as powerfully as it has been in previous ages of man. We can only hope that we have achieved greater insight and greater ob-jectivity than some of our ancestors. The winds and cur-rents of bias and prejudice blow hard and run deep in the minds of men. In one's own mind these factors are difficult to see, and when seen, difficult to attenuate and to allow for their influence. If at times I scold my own species, do not take it too personally; I am scolding my-self more than you.

You can see by now that I believe that some of the answers to the quest are in our own minds. We must develop, imaginatively and humbly, numbers of alterna-tive hypotheses to expand the testable areas of the in-tellect and bring to the investigation new mental in-struments to test and to collect facts germane to our questions.

To ask about the intelligence of another species, we somehow first ask: how large and well-developed is its brain? Somewhat blindly we link brain size (a biological

[32] Lilly, John C. "Some Problems of Productive and Creative Scientific Research with Man and Dolphin," *Archives of General Psychiatry* (1963); also, *The Mind in the Waters,* Joan Mc-Intire, 1974.

fact) to intelligence (a behavioral and psychological concept). We know, in the case of our own species, that if the brain fails to develop, intelligence also fails to develop.

How do we judge in our own species that intelligence develops or fails to develop? We work with the child and carefully observe its performances of common tasks and carefully measure its acquisition of speech quantitatively. We measure (among other factors) size of word vocabulary, adequacy of pronunciation, lengths of phrases and sentences, appropriateness of use, levels of abstraction achieved, and the quality of the logical processes used. We also measure speed of grasping new games with novel sets of rules and strategy; games physical and/or games verbal and vocal.

Normal mental growth patterns of human children have been measured extensively in both performance and in vocal speech acquisition. I have taken the liberty of relating these to the normal growth of brain weight of children.

Table 1 shows relations between age, brain weight, and speech performance, up to 23 months, 1070 grams, and the use of full sentences. By 17 years, the brain reaches and levels off at 1450 grams and the number of words, levels of abstraction, etc., are so large as to be difficult to assess.

In these processes, what are the minimum necessary but not necessarily sufficient factors?[33] On the biological side, modern theory concentrates on two factors: total numbers of neurons and the number of interconnections between them. On the psychological side, modern theory concentrates on the numbers of occurrences of reinforced contingencies experienced, the number of repetitions,

[33] Lilly, John C. "Critical Brain Size and Language," *Perspectives in Biology and Medicine* (in press).

TABLE I

THRESHOLD QUANTITIES FOR HUMAN ACQUISITION OF
SPEECH: AGE AND BRAIN WEIGHT[1]

Age (months)	Brain weight[2] (grams)	Speech stages[3] (first appearances)
2	480	Responds to human voice, cooing, and vocalizes pleasure.
4	580	Vocal play. Eagerness and displeasure expressed vocally.
6	660	Imitates sounds.
9	770	First word.
11	850	Imitates syllables and words. Second word.
13	930	Vocabulary expands rapidly.
17	1,030	Names objects and pictures.
21	1,060	Combines words in speech.
23	1,070	Uses pronouns, understands prepositions, uses phrases and sentences.

[1] Lilly, John C. *Man and Dolphin: A Developing Relationship.* London: Victor Gollancz, 1962.

[2] Boston Children's Hospital data from 1,198 records, in Coppoletta, J. M., and Wolbach, S. B., "Body Length and Organ Weights of Infants and Children," *American Journal of Pathology,* IX (1933), 55–70.

[3] Summarized from McCarthy, Dorothea, "Language Development in Children," in Carmichael, Leonard, ed., *Manual of Child Psychology.* New York: John Wiley, 1946, pp. 476–581.

and the number of adequate presentations from the accepted set of the consensus known as "native language," and the total numbers of sets in the stored memories at a given age. In addition, of course, is the adequate development of the transmitting and of the receiving equipment needed for speech and its ancillary behaviors.

On the biological side, modern neurology says the number of neurons in the human brain reaches maximum value before birth of about 13 billions. After this point, the increase in weight consists of increased numbers of fibers, increased connections, increased size of elements, and increased efficiency and selectivity of transmission. Thus the increase in weight of the human brain from about 400 to 1400 grams seems to be devoted to improving its internal (as well as external) communication, storage, and computation networks. It is my impression that there exist critical threshold values in the brain's growth pattern at which certain kinds of performance become possible. Complex speech acquisition seems related to brain weights of 800 to 1000 grams, but no smaller. This assumes, of course, numbers of neurons (10^{10}) and numbers of connections and opportunities for learning and time to learn commonly found with humans.

The critical psychological factors in speech acquisition are slowly being dug out and described.[34, 35] Among these the most important seem to be a continuous background of presentations to the child in rewarding circumstances of speech and its close relations to objects, actions, satisfaction of needs, and persons. Imitation of one's use of facial and vocal apparatus appears spontaneously in the happy child. The virtuosity of the child as a mimic is truly astonishing.

I am also impressed by evidence for what I call the "transactional drive." A bright child seems to seek and respond best to those persons who respond in kind, back and forth in exchanges of sounds and linked actions. For example, if one starts such a transaction with a child of

[34] Skinner, Burrhus F. *Verbal Behavior*. New York: Appleton-Century-Crofts, 1957.

[35] Lewis, Morris M. *How Children Learn to Speak*. New York: Basic Books, 1959.

22 months with a loud word, if he is ready, he may return his version of the word or a slight variant; if one replies with another variant the child replies with still a third, or even suddenly with a new word, and so on back and forth in a transactional vocal dance. Or one may reply to a child who invites such an exchange to begin. Such exchanges seem to function as rewards of themselves, and hence the name, "transactional drive." This phenomenon is more than mere mechanical slavish mimicry. It seems to aid in perfecting pronunciation, increases vocabulary, increases the bonds with other persons, serves to substitute the "consensus-dictionary" words for the private baby words, and is thus essential to learning a language of one's own species. It is thus that the child "becomes human."

As the child ages and grows, the exchanges lengthen, and the time during which each member of the dyad is quiet while the other speaks becomes longer, until finally for a half hour or so, I am lecturing and you are at least quiet, if not listening.

How does all of this relate to modern dolphins, porpoises, and whales? From the vast array of scientific facts and theories about our own species, a few of those which I feel are useful in approaching another species to evaluate its intelligence are discussed above. But before I make connections there, let us attenuate some interfering attitudes and points of view, some myths not so modern; these interfering presumptions can be stated as follows:

(1) No animal has a language comparable to a human language.

(2) No animal is as intelligent as man.

(3) Man can adapt himself to any environment quite as well as any animal.

(4) Intelligence and intellect can be expressed only in the ways man expresses or has expressed them.

(5) All animal behavior is instinct-determined.

(6) None of man's thought and behavior is so determined.

(7) Only man thinks and plans; animals are incapable of having a mental life.

(8) Philosophy and contemplative and analytic thought are characteristic only of man, not of any animal.

All of these statements stem from ignorance and anthropocentricity. For example, who are we to say that whales, dolphins, and porpoises are to be included as "dumb beasts"? It would be far more objective and humble to tell the truth—we don't know about these animals because we haven't "been there yet." We have not lived in the sea, naked and alone, or even in mobile groups, without steel containers to keep out the sea itself. For purposes of discussion let us make the following assumptions which push counter to the current of bias running deep among us:

(1) Man has not yet been willing to investigate the possibility of another intelligent species.

(2) Whales, dolphins, and porpoises are assumed to be "dumb beasts" with little or no evidence for this presumption.

(3) We do not yet know very much about these animals—their necessities, their intelligences, their lives, the possibility of their communications.

(4) It is possible for man to investigate these matters objectively with courage and perseverance.

(5) To properly evaluate whales, dolphins, porpoises, we must use everything we have intellectually, all available knowledge, *humanistic* as well as *scientific*.

Our best knowledge of ourselves as a species, as humans, is in the humanities and in the budding, growing sciences of man. In pursuit of understanding of the whales, dolphins, and porpoises, we need, at least at the beginning, a large view which is in the human sciences and in the humanities. The sciences of animals are necessarily restrictive in their view, and hence not yet applicable to our problems.

The history of the animal sciences shows that they have had grave difficulties with the fact that the observers are present and human. These sciences, like physics, chemistry, and biology, play the game as if the human observer were not there and the systems were isolated from man. This is fine strategy for "man-less nature" studies and quite appropriate for such studies.

However, I submit to you another view, for a science of man and animal, their relationships to one another. Modern man and modern dolphin and whale may be best investigated in the framework of a new science one might call "anthropo-zoology" or "zoo-anthropology." This science is a deep study of man, of the animal, of their mutual relations, present and potential. In this discipline scientists encourage close relations with the animal, and study the developing relation·between man and so-called "beast."

Since 1960 in the Communication Research Institute[36] we have been pursuing an investigative path in this new science with the pair "man and bottle-nosed dolphin." We have encouraged and pursued studies in classical sciences such as neurophysiology, animal psychology, anatomy, biophysics, and zoology. We have also initiated and pursued this new science of the man and dolphin relation; these "homo-delphic" studies, if you will, are triply demanding: we must not only know our animal objectively but we must know man objectively, and ourselves subjectively. We cannot fight shy of involving

[36] Support for the program of the Communication Research Institute, 3430 Main Highway, Coconut Grove, Miami 33, Florida, is from the National Institute of Mental Health and the National Institute of Neurological Diseases and Blindness of the National Institutes of Health; from the Coyle Foundation; from the Office of Naval Research; from the U. S. Air Force Office of Scientific Research; and from private gifts and contributions to the Communication Research Institute.

ourselves in the investigation as objects also. In this science man, and hence one's own self, are part of the system under investigation. This is not an easy discipline. One must guard quite as rigorously (or even more so) against the pitfalls of wishful thinking and sensational fantasy as in other scientific endeavors. This field requires a self-candor, an inner honesty, and a humility quite difficult to acquire. But I maintain that good science can be done here, that the field is a proper one for properly trained and properly motivated investigators.

The Mind of the Dolphin:
A Non-Human Intelligence

1

Living with a Dolphin:
Learning the Way

In the initial phases of research development with the interspecies communication problem with man and dolphin, it was stated that one possible method of teaching this species a human form of language was the use of the human mother-child teaching-learning model. During the period of a year it has been possible to carry out this plan in detail with a "human mother" and a young male dolphin by the name of Peter. Techniques used may be of interest to others planning similar research; the major barriers to close contact for the full twenty-four hours per day six days per week have been found and more or less satisfactory solutions worked out. The design and construction of the facility was aided by previous planning and construction of a building which was eventually adaptable to this type of work (Plate 1).

The special modifications of the already existing laboratory on the island of St. Thomas for the "mother-child" type of environment was designed after an initial experiment consisting of seven days and nights of continuous contact of a human with a dolphin in a shallow pool. The results of this experiment were sufficiently encouraging to plan a longer, two-and-a-half-month experiment. Between the two experimental periods the changes in the facility necessary to carry out the longer program were completed.

The longer experimental period was done in the summer of 1965, started in June and completed the beginning of September.

In the past this research has been approached with dolphins individually isolated in small tanks for short periods of time with sometimes informal, sometimes a more formal ("operant conditioning") frame of reference. In the past "food reward" was tested, found successful, and later was shown to be unnecessary with a trained animal. In the past the dolphin was put with one other dolphin between experiments to avoid the effects of isolation or was left alone in solitude in his tank. Informal spontaneous exchanges were explored. Words, phrases, sentences, tones of voice, and emotional involvement in the dyadic relationship were found to be important to carry primitive meaning between the human and the dolphin. Later the formal exchanges were developed; in these exchanges, numbers or nonsense syllables were used to test the dolphin's abilities to mimic: 1. isolated human speech sounds; 2. numbers of sonic bursts; 3. durations of bursts; and 4. the sonic patterning psycho-physically measured. It was quickly found that within limits a dolphin will learn quite complex exchange rules with single human operators, i.e., dolphins with humans establish a primitive action-reaction code.

The results were summarized[1] as follows: Durations, numbers, and patterning of human sonic bursts are mimicked by *Tursiops* with accuracies of more than 90 per cent. The patterns presented must be of a great number and a great variety to keep the dolphin's interest. The human operator can learn to select and control and

[1] Lilly, J. C. (1965) in General Bibliography. See Appendix 1.

hence "teach" the dolphin any selected aspect or group of aspects of the speech sounds to be mimicked. The dolphin's limits thus explored are: 1. final trained pitch is high (400 to 1000 Hz); 2. formants can be trained down to the second and third partials; 3. general patterning is excellent; complex patterns are rendered at higher frequencies with excellent mimicry. The longer and the more frequent the contacts (human-dolphin) the better the performance. Longer mode intense contacts were thus shown to be needed.

These results encouraged the planning of the present study. In order to move fast, a chronic contact, 12 hours/day, 12 hours/night, was planned. The analog used in the new studies is the mother and her baby, human baby, being exposed to all of those actions, reactions, contexts, situations, and emotions which lead eventually to the baby becoming a child who speaks English (or other human language in the repertoire of the mother). We recognize that there are many unknowns in the mother-child relationship and in the acquisition of language by the child. If we choose: 1. the proper mother; 2. the proper dolphin; 3. the proper environment; 4. the proper social milieu; and 5. the proper direction of all of these factors, we feel that these unknowns of this relationship will be brought into the new relationship between the dolphin and the human. In addition, the successes with the previous mimicry research and its encouraging results are brought to the new studies. One basic purpose behind this project is expressed by the "mother" involved as "no matter how long it takes, no matter how much work, *this dolphin is going to learn to speak English!*"

Assumptions

The basic meta-assumptions ("assumptions about assumptions themselves") and assumptions made by the investigators on this project are important heuristically. The assumptions are pragmatic; if one assumption works it is made and used; if another doesn't work it is dropped. Success or failure of a given assumption is measured by the results achieved by a human using the assumption sufficiently vigorously for a sufficient period of time. The human involved is only one judge of the results: independent judges not working directly with the dolphin make their judgment on the recorded material on tapes.

The basic beliefs of the human participant operator are important and determine how he or she handles the dolphin in the interactions with the dolphin. For example, if one believes that all dolphins are dangerous (though bright) animals he does not approach a dolphin closely, whereas a person who believes that the danger comes only with improper approaches to dolphins at least tries. In the first case the trial approaches are not made to test the assumption; in the second case tests for the correct pathways to the dolphin are made.

One's assumptions about the possible levels of understanding on the part of a dolphin are important. If he believes that dolphins are "bright animals easily trained" then he does only "training" and ignores clues to other paths to the dolphin. If he believes that dolphins can become quite as understanding of his actions and words, given the opportunity, as another person, then he arranges to give the dolphin a long-term opportunity to learn the meanings of his actions in close quarters. With this belief he not only interacts with the body of the dolphin and his own body, but uses the voice and its actions as well to express himself completely and forcibly. If he believes that dolphins cannot ever learn English he never tries to teach it to them. If he believes that they not only have the brain to learn it but the ears to hear it and the vocal equipment trainable to speak it, he then tries to induce the dolphin to speak English.

A belief does not make a true fact. To obtain the (future) fact "dolphins speaking English" one must invest the requisite time, interest, energy, money, and self-dedication to make the attempt over a long enough period of time to see if the fact can be created through one's own efforts.

The human participant's basic assumptions and the progressive changes can be seen by reading the notes written by this person before, during, and after the period of exposure to the interactions with the dolphins. These are part of this report. This method of seeing the assumptions gives the detailed picture; except by connotation, it does not give the general assumptions under which she operates. Many different ways of expressing these generalities are possible. John C. Lilly's view of them, as expressed before the beginning of this project, was the mother-child view. Another way rephrased by him after exposure to the experiments, to the human participant, and to the results and to the recordings[2] is as follows:

1. In an environment suitably arranged for meeting one another on as equal terms as possible, a human and a dolphin can develop mutual trust, mutual understanding, and shared communication methods.

2. The human can communicate her emotional reactions to the dolphin, and he can respond appropriately to these reactions.

3. The dolphin can communicate his emotional states to the human and she can respond appropriately.

4. The dolphin has strategies he can use and others he can develop in the interactions; like the human he plans ahead.

5. Not only can techniques of transmitting information

[2] Some of these recordings are available from Folkways Records, New York, N.Y., and Paul Herbert, Hot Springs Lodge, Big Sur, Calif. 93920.

be worked out, but the dolphin understands "meta-language" directions given to him. These instructions are about how to mimic, how to pronounce, how to raise volume, how to lower pitch, and so forth. (The astonishing result is that he mimics only what he is told to mimic. He does not mimic the directions [meta-language] given with the words [language] to be mimicked.)

6. The dolphin tests the human: he knows what is wanted in a given instance, can purposely do it "wrong" to provoke a reaction from the human; he can do it right but won't for purposes of his own. One of these purposes is to keep the human reacting and interacting with him.

The human participant's assumptions, i.e., those of Margaret C. Howe, in her own words are as follows:

1. Dolphins are capable of communication with man on the level of high intelligence.

2. Dolphins are not only capable of this communication but are eager for it and are willing to cooperate with man to achieve it.

3. Possibly the best way to go about establishing this communication is to set up a situation where the man (woman) and a dolphin live together as closely as possible for an extended period of time.

4. This is a long process and involves many steps, each of which must be recognized and encouraged. The attempt to communicate with a dolphin in English involves two main parts: (1) the dolphin must learn how to physically say the words, and (2) he must learn the meaning of what he is saying. These two parts may be worked out individually or simultaneously.

5. One first step is the creation and the maintenance of mutual trust and reciprocal rewards one for the other.

Her assumptions fundamentally agree with those of John C. Lilly.

Design Needs of Man-Dolphin Facility

The first basic needs are air and sea water at the proper temperatures. The water temperature is 80°F to 84°F. A satisfactory air temperature is 80°F to 90°F. Both air and water must be continuously flowing through the facility. New clean tropical sea water must wash through the facility rapidly enough to dispose of wastes and maintain the temperature. A natural flow as the result of wind and wave action and tidal action is better than electrical (or other power) pumps (Plate 2).

There are several distinctively separate necessary areas in the facility. These areas must be immediately adjacent and have non-dangerous boundaries between them. The areas themselves are as follows: a deep-water area, a shallow-water area, and a "no-water" or dry area.

The deep-water area is for the dolphin to relax as dolphins relax, i.e., if he wishes to swim at high speed or do fast three-dimensional maneuvers, he is free to do so. If he wishes to leap out of the water it is deep enough for the take-off and for the landing. This area has water that is too deep for the human to be comfortable with the dolphin for long periods of time.

The shallow water is the area in which the results of interest are obtained. This area is shallow enough for the human to walk comfortably and yet deep enough for the dolphin to swim comfortably. This is the zone of encounter of man and dolphin: the mutually adapting area. Each of the dyad compromise something of their comfort in their cooperation with one another in this area. At any time the dolphin can leave this area. He can safely and comfortably scoot into the deeper water area. And at any time the human participant can safely and easily move into the "no-water" area.

The no-water area has two sub-areas within it. The

one immediately adjacent to the shallow water may be called the damp area. It is inevitable that splashes from the dolphin's actions put water into the damp area. It is also inevitable that the human in shedding the water acquired in the shallow water will shed it in the first part of dry area available. In the other part of the human area there must be a definitely dry area, i.e., with no sea water allowed anywhere in this area. This is the zone of human relaxation as a human. It is comfortable, is so designed for human beings. It is an area which is totally uncomfortable, anxiety-provoking and sometimes even dangerous for a dolphin.

It is convenient to think of two additional areas adjacent to these. At the deep-water end of the facility should be the sea itself. This is where dolphins come from in the first place. At the other end of the dry area is all of civilization on dry land. This is where the human participants come from and return to for refreshment from the isolation from humans.

If we could only arrange for the dolphin to return to the sea for his refreshment in a similar manner, we would consider the facility ideal. Some of each of the above areas should be inside, out of the tropical sunshine, and some should be outside, in the trade winds and in the tropical sunshine, subject to all the vagaries of the weather of the tropics.

In any practical facility made with a limited budget the areas of deep water, shallow water, dampness, and dryness are of necessity relatively small. In fact, they are unsatisfactorily small from the standpoint of evenness and monotony for this study in dyadic isolation. Ideally the facility should have all of the complexities built into it that the dolphin values in the sea and that the human values in an ordinary everyday civilized life in a home.

The food problems have practical and ideal aspects. Ideally the dolphin should be free to hunt in the sea for his own diet and return to the facility for his education with the human participant. Until the day that is possible, the humans must supply fifteen to twenty pounds of fish per day per dolphin. Butterfish is, in our experience, the best and most complete diet for the dolphin. At certain times of the year it can be obtained in large quantities frozen and shipped in from the United States mainland. With deep-freeze freezers and a supply of electricity, satisfactory maintenance of the fish supply can be successfully achieved.

The food for the human participant is the participant's usual purchase-stored-cooked diet in the completely dry area. In the special circumstances of the wet live-in, most of the usual foods can be used. However, pragmatic experience shows that special, easy-to-prepare-and-to-cook foods are best. One special food for the human is the food of the dolphin. It has been found that fried butterfish is a good compromise food at times.

The questions of power and light sources inevitably come up. We have used electricity as our major power source and propane gas as the heat source for cooking. Electricity (115 volts A.C.) is dangerous around thoroughly grounded salt-water in large quantities. Either the dolphin or the human could be strongly stimulated or badly burned or even electrocuted if mistakes are made involving switches, power outlets, and appliances. We have found that no wall switches, outlets, or electrical appliances can be anywhere near the walls or area enclosing the sea water. We have found that if we put in waterproof lights, run the cables out of the room and plug them in a dry isolated room which includes the switch, we avoid fires and shocks. In the current cooking experience a two-burner propane gas stove has been used with the gas supply outside of the building. The stove is raised far enough above the water to prevent sea water splash corroding the stove or spoiling the food. One suggested addition for a long-term living-in is some form of oven. For purposes of keeping food that needs refrigeration a gas refrigerator would be a welcome addition. Possibly low-voltage A.C. lights would be preferable to the present 115-volt lights.

The actual facility used departs from the above ideal in some respects. The deep-water area is sixteen feet below the shallow-water and dry areas. It is necessary for the dolphins to take a trip on an electric hoist elevator in order to move from the shallow water to the deep water and vice versa (Plate 5). The deep water is a sea-level pool approximately sixty-five feet long, twenty feet wide, and 4½ feet deep, with its supply of fresh sea water furnished by the trade wind waves (Plates 3, 4). This is our emergency facility in case of power failure cutting off the pumping facilities at the higher levels in the building.

The shallow-water zone, the "encounter space," consists of two areas. The inside one is forty feet by twenty feet and the outside one is twenty feet by twenty feet (see photographs).

In the inside shallow-water space are the sleeping, cooking, and office facilities for the human. Analogous functions for the dolphin are carried out anywhere in the two areas.

The dry area is the rest of the building and contains fish storage, human food storage (including a refrigerator), human toilet facilities, and human dry sleeping facilities when needed.

Special aspects of the shallow-water facility are as follows: the inside room has a "recording studio" hung with carpets on walls and ceiling in an area twenty by fifteen feet to facilitate sound recording in air with minimal echoes. The recording itself is done on tape machines in an adjacent dry room. The microphones are protected by proper plastic bags and are hung from the ceiling in the recording area. Insofar as it is possible, vocal exchange lessons take place in this area. However, some interactions take place outside on the balcony and hence cannot be recorded.

The details of the construction of the facility can be adequately seen by careful inspection of the photographs and the captions. A floor plan of the facility is shown in Figure 1.

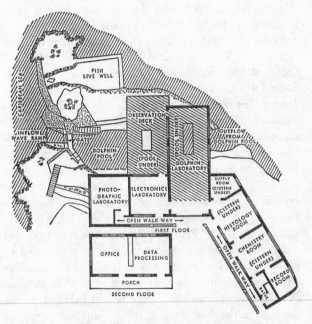

FIGURE 1. *The Floor Plan of the St. Thomas Laboratory Showing the Location of the Flooded Areas for the Living-in Experiment.*

The balcony is to the left and the inside room is to the right (marked with 45-degree lines). The sea pool is immediately below these two rooms, 16 feet below the floor level. The sea water in this space was kept at 18 inches for the period of the experiment.

History

It is considered desirable at this point to present what we can in the limited space of the history of the human participant in her relations with dolphins.

On February 7, 1964 Miss Margaret C. Howe joined the Communication Research Institute staff in St. Thomas. Up to that time she had seen dolphins once briefly in a Florida dolphin circus. From February 7, 1964 through April 5, 1964 she worked with dolphins, mainly with Peter, a male dolphin, in the fiberglass tank (at that time in the upstairs room which was later flooded). The other two animals were in the sea pool. During this time there was a four-day period (April 10–13) in which she did her first vocal work with Peter. In this work she demanded that he make a sound before he was given a fish. This was Peter's first exposure to vocal work in the operant conditioning kind of situation.[3]

On April 15, 1964 Pamela (a female dolphin) was brought upstairs and put into the tank with Peter. From this date until the seventeenth of May Margaret Howe worked with both Pam and Peter in the fiberglass tank.

On the eighteenth of May 1964 Sissy was moved upstairs and put into the tank with the other two dolphins. Margaret continued to observe and work with all three. No vocal work was being done nor had there been any done since the four days in April with any of the dolphins.

On the twenty-second of May 1964 all three dolphins were moved into the sea pool and Margaret had her first look at all three together under water through the observation bubble (see photograph). On this date several of the personnel at the laboratory began serially observing

[3] Cf. later view of this procedure in Appendix 1.

through the bubble and recording animal behavior in protocol book form. This type of work continued through the twenty-fifth of August 1964 (Plate 9).

From the twenty-fifth of August to the first of October Margaret continued to observe the dolphins under water. Her main effort was spent in working with data of the past several months. Tapes and motion pictures of animal behavior were being worked on and developed. All three dolphins remained in the sea pool during this period.

From the second to the fifteenth of October 1964 there was a general transition period in the laboratory. The personnel were being changed and plans for a complete change in the research orientation and program were taking place. The three dolphins remained in the sea pool.

From the fifteenth to the thirty-first of October 1964 Margaret Howe was for the first time on her own at the laboratory. She was placed in complete charge. She learned to set up the electronic apparatus for recording vocal and underwater sounds. She made her first attempts at independent vocal work with each of the three animals in the sea pool. Some tapes of importance were obtained after this period.

On the second of November 1964 Peter was brought upstairs and put into the fiberglass tank alone. Margaret concentrated on vocal work with him at this time. This is the beginning of the currently important data. Here Peter went through the transition phases of first responding to Margaret with no air-borne sound at all and learning the rules of this game. When he gets the idea of responding to air sound with air sound he begins to click in air, to whistle in air, and to make humanoid sounds. This attempt is encouraged with special emphasis given to his "humanoid" emissions (these are the dolphins' sonic emissions which resemble somewhat some of the basic elements of human speech). Once Peter does learn that it is a humanoid sound that Margaret wants, he consistently interrupts her and has to learn to listen. Teaching him to listen is the next part of the program. Progress was made during this time up through the ninth of January 1965.

On that date Peter was put downstairs into the sea pool (Plate 10). Pam was moved upstairs into the fiberglass tank. From the ninth of January through the nineteenth of March 1965 Margaret worked with Pam on vocalizations and on close human contact. In the period March 20 to 27 the seven-day experiment was accomplished. Margaret lived in the tank with Pam (see photographs). From the twenty-eighth of March through April 19 Pam remained upstairs, Margaret continued her vocal work with her, Peter and Sissy were in the sea pool. On the twentieth of April 1965 Peter was brought upstairs and put into the fiberglass tank. Pam was brought downstairs and put into the sea pool.

Until the twelfth of May 1965 Margaret and Peter worked together on vocal responses. On the thirteenth of May Peter was put back into the sea pool with Sissy and Pam. He stayed here while Miss Howe made changes in the facility in preparation for the 2½-month experiment (see photographs).

On the fourteenth of June Peter was again brought upstairs, and put into the new flooded room area (see photographs). On the fifteenth of June Margaret Howe moved into the room with him to begin the "wet live-in" program for 2½ months.

On September 1, 1965 Margaret Howe moved out of the wet room. Between the fourteenth of September and the fourth of October Margaret was away from the laboratory. Peter was moved to the sea pool on the thirteenth of September and he was put back upstairs on the nineteenth of September 1965.

The above history does not give a description of possibly important factors in the development of Margaret Howe's training and experiences. The results of her experience are best given by Margaret herself. From this point on when it is germane Margaret's words will be given verbatim.

In summary Margaret Howe's experience at the Communication Research Institute, Dolphin Point Laboratory in St. Thomas, is as follows:

From the seventh of February 1964 to the latter part of October 1964 Margaret was a member of a group of nine humans. Eight and one-half months were spent with a group working on animal behavior with the three dolphins. From approximately the twentieth of October 1964 to 1965, Margaret has been running the laboratory herself on this particular project with the aid and encouragement of Dr. Lilly, who has been able to spend approximately five days every month at the laboratory. Margaret's staff during this latter twelve months consists of herself and two or three workmen. Two workmen, Richard Turnbull and Aubrey Pickering, had experience previously in particular ways of handling, feeding, and caring for dolphins.

During the period that Margaret spent in the laboratory with eight other humans plus the three dolphins, she spent three months observing and writing her observations on the dolphins' behavior. This experience is very germane and useful for her in the context of the current experience. The perspective of the preliminary period leading up to these experiments in Margaret Howe's life is best given by a sample from her notes:

Date is Thursday August 13, 1964. Time is 1104 hours. Visibility is good. Pam is now swimming full length of pond. She is in her "spot only" routine. (What is the spot routine? I don't recall but I explain somewhere.) Pam and Peter rest by the inflow. Sissy is circling, sonaring by the hydrophone. Peter circles slowly. Now Sissy chases Peter. He bites along her. He does three half-leaps, they swirl, Sissy opens mouth wide and slides her teeth down his back. Peter turns over, he is now underneath her. Peter bites her throat. Lots of creaking door sonaring going on. Sissy swims to Pam, Peter follows her, biting at her tail. They hassle. Peter upside down again. They come mouth to mouth.

1110 hours. Peter bites hard on Sissy's eye. He puts his head under her genital region and bumps upward hard, squealing starts now. Whoooooo, whoooooo, by Sissy. She circles away from Peter, now back to him. He is after her tail in tight circles, lots of loud whoooooo, whoooooo. Sissy makes it and lets out a steady stream of bubbles from her blowhole as she does so. In center of pool the two line up face to face, not touching. Noses about four feet apart. Peter suddenly lurches forward after Sissy with mouth open. Sissy goes to Pam and they cruise together. Peter cuts in, haggles with Sissy, making whah, whah complaints. (Time for writing.) Pam's right eye closed now cruises with Sissy. Peter is alone, swimming around outside pool with his belly facing in towards the wall. Peter flips upside down and goes into chasing Pam. Pam leaps clear of water three times, turning to face opposite her way as she does. Pam slows down, Peter is immediately less intense in this chase, Pam noses along Peter's genital area, Sissy joins them and the three circle together.

1115 hours. Peter upside down nibbles Sissy. Sissy also turns upside down and continues whooo whoooo while upside down. I can see the stream of bubbles . . . the three cruise silently, aimlessly, Peter ahead by a length, Sissy outside and even with Pam who is inside. They come to a pause and rest at the surface (time gap for writing).

1120 hours. Peter and Pam both have their right eye closed. Sissy circles pool slowly. Fiddles with piece of grass. Pam undulates in place, Peter starts to circle her excitedly, always facing her with belly turned towards her. Sissy hovers nearby—Peter moves in and sonars Pam's genital region. Pam moves slowly in circle, Peter follows. Peter leads Pam sonars fish under grate, Sissy is resting near Pam. There is no intensity here, all three seem to be resting and doing not really much of anything. Nosing each other, sonaring genitals, fish hovering, grass playing, all seem to be just passing the time of day. Sissy is alone. Now she half leaps whapping the water with her side, again and again, fonp, fonp, she smashes down. This must feel sensational. No one pays any attention to her for a while. She continues. Suddenly Peter from the opposite end of the pool faces her and I can hear him sonaring like mad. He slowly advances towards her, speed increases and he ends up flying at her with mouth open. They hassle. Pam comes over for a look. Peter squeals, races, trying to press genital regions to Pam, no erection, they have a big hassle, lots of bubbles, Sissy starts leaping and Peter follows suit. Pam dashes around, Peter noses into Sissy's neck, Sissy's flukes flick across Peter's genital, suddenly it is quiet. Rest period. Just as suddenly Sissy is whining and chasing after Peter's tail (gap for writing notes). Peter and Sissy swirl, Peter seems to be directing, pushing her around, nipping her here and there, and it seems that quite often their genital areas come in contact. This is very vigorous. Pam mildly observes an attempt.

1135 hours. Pam stays close to Sissy. Peter and Sissy seem angry at each other, are bopping and nipping and whah, whah, scolding each other. Sissy passes by Peter and wham. She slams him with her whole tail. I can feel the swell in the water as it hits the bubble. Pam is out of it but stays close to Sissy.

1145 hours. Suddenly the fight is over, and the three rest quietly together by the inflow.

I am confused by the way a vigorous looking and deathly sounding squabble can end with a big "nothing." Just suddenly turned off, then resting side by side, seemingly no interest in continuing the squabble????

M. HOWE

The accumulated notes, observations, and to a certain extent, tapes, of this period of Margaret Howe's investigation of the dolphins is conserved and used by her in writing a report on this research.

I asked Margaret early in March 1965 to: 1. give an account of her feelings of dolphins and their possible "code of living" with the directions "begin from the heart and work out," and 2. read and comment on the book *Planet of the Apes* by Pierre Boulle. These two papers contain information about Margaret's basic ideas and for that reason are included here.

Begin from the Heart and Work Out

I have worked with dolphins in two different ways: first, I spent time observing three animals (Peter, Pam and Sissy) together in a large sea pool with underwater vision available. Second, I have worked intensely with one animal at a time, both in lessons in English and in number systems and in close physical contact. I have been swimming with the animals involved. For half a year I have lived in a laboratory the only other occupants of which were the three dolphins. This is the longest period of time since I left home to go to school that I have shared living quarters with any other living being.

Living in a different environment from your roommate does eliminate certain obvious communal factors (clothes, social life conflicts, food sharing, and so forth): it does not eliminate communication and awareness of each other. I can hear or speak to any dolphin from any part of the building. This does not include their very high frequencies or their underwater sounds of course. It does include any air emissions or loud underwater sounds. I am usually a fairly light sleeper and at least one dolphin (the one who happens to be in the tank nearest my bedroom) can awaken me during the night. Let me say here I would like to work out and materialize an even closer living situation for man and dolphin.

From my work days with the dolphins and from my close living with them I have learned many things about their specific intelligence and learning ability and about their personalities. I have learned something of the dolphins' society as it exists among the three of them and man and dolphin society as it exists among the four of us. I have learned something of their ethics or civilization. This account will not deal with the intelligence and learning factors directly; it is more a general approach to the dolphins' code of living.

In observing animals together there is so much to see that it takes a good while to be able "to see" anything. And there is such a constant interaction and so few immediate repetitions of any one act between any two of them that it is hard to be conscious of what one is seeing. In fact for a while at least you are seeing simply a beak and an eye or two staring back at you! After a time it is possible to note not only the type of action, i.e., sex play, sleep, idle play alone, and so forth, but also to get a feeling of the mood in the pool in general or of that of any particular dolphin, i.e., extreme excitement, annoyance, or dissatisfaction, pleasure, boredom, and so forth. I do not deal here with the specific actions but rather I generalize about the mood.

The three animals consist of a young adolescent male and two more or less adult females: a dubious triangle. Sex play can occur between a male and a female, between two females or between all three animals at once. I did not witness jealousy between two animals strong enough to cause any real battle. Indeed never did I witness a situation that caused a real battle between any two of the dolphins. And yet, because this seemed an obvious outcome, we tried inducing outside factors to enable us to witness just such a show of strength or of dominance.

We tried tossing one ball into what seemed neutral territory of the pool occupied by the three dolphins. In most cases the dolphin to first reach the ball became its "owner." This dolphin would then "possess" the ball as it were, and play with it in front of the other animals. Only a few times did the ball "change hands" during such a period. More likely, even if "the owner" became distracted and left the ball for a moment, the ball would remain free and not be picked up by another dolphin. The owner was somehow secure and could return at his leisure. Several times the ball would be held onto the body of one dolphin by another

dolphin but this could well be some sort of game brought
about by invitation from the owner of the ball. We tried
setting up the feeding situation where a neutral fish (this
was later questioned—the fish had come from one bucket
"belonging" to one of the dolphins) would be tossed out into
neutral water in the center of the pool. The feeder avoided
eye movement or any other indication of where the fish was
going. Again the first dolphin to it, and there was no great
hustle to get to it, was the owner or in this case the eater and
that was that. This experiment was not repeated often
enough to discover any patterns of who got the fish the most
times, and so forth. But in all, a very mild, unemotional,
organized and somewhat surprising and disappointing display
to the human observers.

Does this "what's mine is mine and what's yours is not
mine" attitude continue from dolphin-dolphin behavior to
dolphin-human behavior? It would seem so.

We set up an experiment to get some sort of possessive or
dominant reaction from a dolphin by attaching a ball to a
long piece of stretch cord. We lowered the ball into the pool
from the observation deck above, the ball touched the water,
was sonared by the dolphin but was not touched by the dolphin. The game of "tug-of-war" on the ball did not materialize at all! Again this surprised and was somewhat a disappointment to the human observers.

(*Note:* in other experiments of this sort the animals have
been known to not play tug-of-war with the ball but to bop
it out of the water into the air and have it sink back into the
water again.)

It must be emphasized that any of these experiments are
subject to such uncontrollable factors as the mood of the
dolphin, preference at the moment for a certain ball, interest
in other activities, and so forth. But not once was there the
slightest suggestion of taking the ball and "pulling" or trying
to "take it away from" its original source, i.e., another
dolphin.

*What does not happen is quite as important as what does
happen.* Again it was observed that during feeding (and all

animals at CRI are hand fed) animals preferred a slight toss of the fish. This could be a very slight passage of the fish into the air (even one-fourth of an inch), between human hand and dolphin mouth. One of our animals when hungry (I have tested this many times myself) is very reluctant to "take" a fish out of a human grasp. A dolphin will come and take an end of the fish in his mouth, feel even a slight resistance and let go or continue holding—but seldom will he pull it away. The dolphin must know that eventually that fish will "belong" to him but it would seem that they are reluctant to "take fish away from" a human hand: rather be given the fish with some neutral territory in between.

Along these same lines another incident occurred between Sissy and myself.

A camera crew was filming beside the pool, I was in the water swimming with Sissy. We had played a bit and I was without a mask. My mask was lying on a wall just above sea level. Apparently wave action knocked it into the water and it sank to the bottom about two feet down. For a moment I could not find it and then discovered that Sissy was hovering above it. I approached to pick it up, Sissy sank a bit and "sat" on it. This indicated to me that it was, for the moment at least, "her" mask. I tried for several minutes (with an amused camera crew looking on) to get the mask from Sissy. Sissy bopped at me with her beak and I withdrew. We had to get on with the filming and that was the one mask I was most comfortable in. I obtained another mask and tossed it five or six feet away, it sank. Sissy was distracted and went to investigate. I bent to pick up "my" mask and Sissy came streaking across the pool, barking and opening and closing her mouth at me. I was threatened and withdrew. Looking back I am annoyed at myself for breaking the "dolphin law." I knew perfectly well that I was not to "take" that mask but human trickery had taught me how to get it. Another dolphin, I believe, would not have "taken" the mask from Sissy nor used trickery.

Another interesting point: I went back into the water with Sissy several minutes later and finished the filming. I was a bit cautious expecting Sissy to be annoyed or resentful. Not so. Sissy had forgotten the incident or considered it closed. It was "my mask" again.

With single dolphins alone I started a new series of encounters. In a smaller tank on an upper level I worked intensely with one dolphin at a time, teaching English and a number system. I have worked this way with Peter, a young male and with one of the females, Pamela.

Peter is young, boyish and tends to be the "naughty" one of the three dolphins. He delights in such mischief as plugging up the outflow of his tank with a toy so that the tank eventually fills to the brim and spills over. I came in to find Peter joyously leaping about in this great sloshing tank. I scold him in English. (I had not tried the dolphin discipline actions, such as a firm whack over the head.) Peter responds with a slight sulk but is very inclined to be "naughty" again when he has the opportunity.

When I first met Peter he was very used to a game with other persons that involved a human arm or hand inside his mouth rubbing his gums. Being a "green novice" I was having no part of this game and refused to play it. Peter soon learned that he was not to scare me with his open jaws and now is very gentle with me and seldom opens his mouth. I say seldom because this involves another point.

Without exception I have found that when displeased or angered by human actions that any of these three dolphins will "threaten" or "warn" the human before going into further discipline. This threat is in the form of 1. opening and closing of the mouth in a warning manner; 2. a rapid bobbing up and down or sidewise movements of the head in a "go away" gesture; or 3. a vocal "whah, whah" indicating annoyance. I have seen all three methods of warning used by an animal to humans and also to other dolphins, and one soon learns to respect such a warning. One is expected to.

All of this builds into such a nice way of life. Possessions are "owned and not fought over." People or animals are "warned" that they are doing something wrong. Discipline is brief, quite clear and then over. Can these animals not be incited to some very aggressive, hostile, in a word, "human" act?

On one occasion I observed Peter in a situation that certainly seemed to call for such a reaction. For several months I had been carrying on a personal battle with a rat in the laboratory. A sly character who occasionally gave me glimpses of his disappearing tail and left lovely traces of his presence during the night. He was also seen on the wires to the lights above Peter's tank. One night I turned on the lights apparently startling the rat and he fell smack dab into the middle of the tank with Peter. Three human friends visiting me and I rushed to witness the action. The sides of the tank are smooth and slightly slanted, the rat could not climb out. All of the humans around that tank including myself were anxious to see Peter snap at, bop around, drown, flip into the air, *something* that rat. Peter looked at the rat, sonared it briefly, nudged it a bit and then ignored it. Peter was much more interested in the people around him who were obviously very excited about something. I tried putting the rat afloat on a piece of board in the tank (see photographs). Again Peter took a look at this setup and nudged it briefly and then *nothing!* We stayed with it for a half an hour, simply not able to believe that Peter was not going to open his jaws and devour or at least mutilate that rat. Indeed not, the incident ended and the anticlimax was my putting the rat into the outflow and sending him to his burial at sea. Again Peter had displayed to me the possibility of a non-hostile code of living. How delightful!

And along with this lack of hostility in the dolphin must be explained a certain caution, possibly stemming from their life at sea and the needs for caution. Any new object that is introduced into a pool with the dolphin is first sonared and observed visually before being touched. This extends from a small piece of paper to a human being. Even a small living fish tossed into the pool is carefully sonared before it is snapped at, if indeed it is snapped at at all. Our animals are fed dead fish and are fed so well that it is difficult to get a normal reaction to a living fish.

By citing these various instances I do not mean to give the impression that dolphins are totally devoid of moments of violence. These are very powerful, fast animals capable under moments of stress of a very impressive show of strength.

But I am implying the possibility of a lack of wheeling
and dealing, of cheating and stealing and lying and other
seemingly small but nevertheless devious ways of life stemming from human foible. From what I have observed and
felt I do not feel that a dolphin newspaper, if one could exist,
would contain articles on robbery, murder, dishonesty, de-
linquency, riots.

This business of communicatively joining the two species,
man and dolphin, is very new but is progressing rapidly in
proportion to the obstacles to be overcome. The biggest factor
in this rapid progress is not only the widening human interest
and anxious anticipation of the wide possibilities, but also of
the dolphin's own interest and cooperation in seemingly just
as strong anxiety to "get on with it." We must remember
that as they live and work with us they are learning not only
the lessons in English and number systems, etc., they also
are learning, just as are we, about another way of life. A new
set of ethics and morals. Let us determine at the outset to
be cautious of what we let the dolphins observe, learn and
instinctively "feel" about all this. Let us be open to the possibility of learning and practicing what we learn from the
examples set by the peaceful, gentle, and not to be over-
looked in a time when ulcers and nail-biting are part of our
every day life, *happy* dolphin!! [End of Margaret Howe's
account.]

Planet of the Apes by Pierre Boulle

I found this exchange of man and apes on the evolutionary
scale delightful and witty, and substituting dolphin intelligence for that of the apes, entirely believable.

But there is one point raised by the overall pattern of the
book that bothers me deeply:

The pattern runs . . .

    (1) Earth: Man dominate, ape subordinate,

    (2) Betelgeuse: Ape dominate, man subordinate,

    (3) Earth: Ape dominate, man subordinate, and we

have every indication that had our travelers returned
to the planet of apes, the time lapse would have allowed for

(4) Betelgeuse: Man dominate, ape subordinate.

Why why why must there be a dominance and a subor-
dination??? Why must man *take over* or why must the apes
take over?

I have occasion every day to look an animal (dolphin)
straight in the eye and to speak and listen and smile and scold
and somehow try to bridge the verbal gap that does exist between myself and this other intelligence whose existence I
accepted as fact long ago.

But never never have I imagined that when the dolphin
one day learns the form of our intelligence would he then proceed to "take over" this planet. No more than I have imagined that man must strive to keep the dolphin subordinate
and "under control."

Can it be, as Boulle suggests, that within one environment,
land, only one species will be allowed to hold superior intelligence? This may well be so. In this case man and dolphin
could exist on an equal level . . . man on land and dolphin
in the water.

But this simplicity is poppycock. Land, sea, and air melt
into one to intelligent beings. So we cannot accept that man
is most intelligent on land and Cetacea (dolphin) in the
water. We must face the thought of the two equal intelligences on equal footing on this planet. This may well already exist, with the only missing link being communication. When that link is no longer missing and dolphin and
man can communicate thoughts to each other (and that day
will come!) will we be faced with a war situation? With a
conquer-or-be-conquered atmosphere? I sincerely hope not.

Looking back it could have been that instead of the happy
bisexual society that we live in, fate might have swung us to
a monosexual society simply through this boring "one must
be superior" routine.

Looking ahead it may well be that one day we will find it
hard to imagine a monospecies society . . . as we live hap-

pily in our quite normal bispecies culture . . . that of Man and Dolphin.

MARGARET HOWE

My comments:

This account clearly shows the basic feelings and enthusiasm of Miss Howe taking hold with the dolphins. She sees clearly, writes clearly, thinks and feels clearly. She thinks well on her feet; her actions are appropriate. These are the talents she brings to this project. We avoided choosing a psychologist, a psychoanalyst, a comparative zoologist or any other person in a specialty within science itself. A more pragmatic, general yet direct approach than any one of the present sciences offers is sought. I felt that to carry out this project a rather rare human being uniquely herself is needed. She is dedicated to getting the project finished. Keeping her eyes as open as she possibly can, as open to all lines of evidence and truth testing as she herself is capable of, she operates without reference to artificial criteria generated by scientists.

In the preliminary experiment of seven days and nights with Pamela Dolphin, Miss Howe found much information useful for planning the 2½ months' experimental period. She found data on herself, the dolphin, their interactions, she found by experience the problems and some solutions regarding the clothing, the wetness, the walking, the cooking, and the rest of the real living-in situation. She wrote an account of this full week.

The full progression from the past into the future includes a long-term plan of setting up a house which dolphins can share with humans. Among other things, Miss Howe is planning such a house in the following write up. As a result of the seven days' experiment, she has many suggestions in the way this house should be constructed. These suggestions insofar as can be done are then followed for the 2½ months' experiment which follows the seven days' experiment. The 2½ months' experiment is the second phase of the long-term plan to develop a living-in program between Margaret and a dolphin. The house is an essential facility for this future development and these preliminary experiments are necessary for the proper design of this house.

2

Living with a Dolphin: Seven Days and Nights with Pam

A preliminary seven days and seven nights with a dolphin was arranged with Margaret Howe. The aims of this experiment were to test human and dolphin tolerance to a set depth (sixteen inches) of sea water, to find particulars of human needs such as clothing, food, fresh water, dry items (pens, paper, books), to find the limits of human tolerance of sleeping on wet bed in wet clothing, to see progress in human-dolphin relationship during such close living, to continue vocal lessons with dolphin and record same, and show vocal progress under such conditions.

The following is Miss Howe's account of this period:

In sixteen inches of water a human can maneuver, walk, work at a desk, sit in a chair, eat.

It was shown in this experiment, however, that at least with this particular dolphin, sixteen inches is not enough to allow her back, over a period of time, to remain wet enough for a normal, healthy skin. Pamela could have kept wet by constantly bobbing and causing waves to wash over her back.

A tiresome task and Pam chose not to. Her back at the end of the week was not seriously dried and cracked, but it was bad enough to show that longer exposure to this environment would lead to trouble.

In this depth there is a limit to the maneuvering a dolphin can do (Plates 6, 7, 8, 11). Jumping, swishing around, high-speed swimming are limited if not eliminated. It must be remembered that Pamela, at the time of the experiment, had an injured flipper and was going through a very inactive period. I believe that a healthy animal with no injuries would, after not very long, go "stir crazy" and long for deep enough water to leap and dive in. I feel that this should be available to her or him.

This depth (sixteen inches) seems rather ideal for the human: it is shallow enough to walk in without any great hindrance. (Knee-deep water is very difficult to walk in. Sixteen inches is midway up my calf, 19½ inches is at my knee joint.) It is shallow enough to allow a chair to sit in it with the seat above the waterline. It is shallow enough so that normal splashes made by the dolphin rolling or turning over are not high enough to reach human things—desk, papers, TV, etc. It is deep enough to allow humans to sit and float with ease and therefore get "down next to" the dolphin. And a small point but important in this experiment: it is deep enough so that when sitting in the chair I could drop my hand loosely over the side and have it in the water, thus affording Pam an opportunity to rub my hand.

I would recommend that in the final experiment, sixteen inches of water flood the entire house. There must also be, however, a deeper (thirty inch) passageway through the house in which the dolphin can travel and maneuver; thus he could lie in "his" space in the kitchen, watching you, decide to come to you, and simply go from thirty inches to sixteen inches of water to do so.

I also recommend somewhere in the house a deep pool, at least six feet deep for the dolphin "to be a dolphin in." This should be connected to the other waters. While thinking of all this I have also thought about walls and doors. A special "dolphin door" is used by both humans and dolphins. The open space under the door has double purposes: 1. humans walking through the doorway will not have to pull the door against the weight of the water; all of the swinging part of the door will be in air; 2. the bottom of the door is higher than sixteen inches above the water level to afford the dolphin dorsal fin space to go through with the door closed.

Living for a week is very different from living for a year or more. However, from my experience I have found that clothing—wet suits, top and bottom and two-piece so that one can be removed—is vitally important in a room where air temperature is between 79°F and 83°F. I found leotards good for drying speed and protection (warmth), but the top piece fits too closely through the crotch. It was from this garment that I got so chapped. I am not sure, however, that a looser garment would solve this problem. Loose garments can chap too . . . they even rub the skin more. One note on bras: hooks on the back can tend to "wilt" and I found that one was at a bad angle and was digging into my back. I had to bend it back into place several times. A bra without hooks would be good . . . but elastic would not hold up either. A problem.

It is very important, even during one week, to have dry clothes available. Shorts, shirts, anything. The human is used to changing clothes and feeling "fresh," and just because the clothes will end up wet 95 per cent of the time is no reason to assume that there is no reason for change. Wet clothes get a soggy feel to them after a while, and it is desirable to get into dry clothes and then get *them* wet. They will not have the same soggy, rundown feel. Example: it is desirable to change daytime clothes to sleep clothes, and in the morning to change from sleep clothes to daytime clothes. The outfit is unimportant, the wetness of the clothes is unimportant . . . the change is very important. I recommend more experiments on what clothes are comfortable when wet. That a supply of clothes be available. At the house or an outside source there should be a setup to handle the laundry problem. Include sheets (not necessary), towels, blankets, quilts, etc. (see discussion on sleeping), all of which must be attended to.

I found that during this week I did not covet fresh water as much as I thought I would. I was seldom thirsty, not that I was seldom overheated. I did need fresh water for washing my face in the morning, and for my teeth (saltwater toothpaste is so-so and promises to get boring after a period of time). I did not rinse my hands with fresh water before reading, writing, and so forth. Perhaps this should be done as I did have slight discomfort with my fingers, probably from constant salt contact.

I recommend fresh-water taps in each room. Bathroom with fresh-water shower. Clean hair and body become important even after one week although not desperate. But long range . . . shower would become very important. None of these fresh-water outlets would need a drain. They could run right into the "floor" of the sixteen inches of salt water.

If there are (a) water and (b) a dolphin in the same room, things are going to get wet. In sixteen inches of water, Pamela could soak the TV which was a good six feet off the floor. Obviously, the human things need to be dry. Pen, paper, TV, electrical items, etc. I had relatively few items during my week's experiment and Pam was relatively quiet and still. [This quietness may have been because of her injury.]

I recommend that more experiments be done in setting up and care of objects for humans. That the house have high shelves, high electrical outlets (if any), high electrical equipment (if any), and a design of covering to "dry store" things. Perhaps "dry" areas of work, a raised platform with a desk on it. Cupboards at top of walls with access only to humans. This is purely a designer's problem.

During this week, all my food was cooked outside the room and brought to me. The problem in the flooded house would, of course, be different, as the person would have a kitchen. I do not think that any rigid diet need be set up for the human. I do recommend that canned foods be kept in dry store and that the cooking facilities be as simple as possible. Two burners are quite adequate. Butterfish is excellent fried and this could be a simple source of food [but possibly monotonous]. Electric or gas facilities in the design of the kitchen must be thoroughly investigated; I will not do that here.

During my week I slept usually in daytime clothes, wet, in a bed that was wet, with a dry quilt that got wet, with a dry pillow that got wet, except for a corner I would protect with my cheek. Several times I went to bed in dry clothing, but the bed was still wet. This meant that the clothes became damp through the night. Several times I became uncomfortable when sleeping, because my skin itched. I suspect that this was due to the amount of time I spent in the same clothes, rather than to the fact that I was damp or wet. Usually I slept well and several times was surprised by a very sound sleep.

Sleep patterns are broken with a dolphin. Many times I was awakened in the night by a restless-hungry Pam. This is O.K. but must be accounted for. I solved it by taking daily naps, as closely as I could matching my sleeping patterns with the dolphin's sleeping or resting patterns.

I recommend that more experiments be done to determine results of "wet" sleeping.

NOTE: I had a stiff neck on my last day in the tank and on the day following my getting out. Did wet sleeping cause this? I would like to see experiments done to determine if dry sleeping, still in close proximity to the dolphins, is possible. Sleep for a week is unlike sleep for a year or more. Is "wet" sleeping the answer?? Is sleeping in heated water the answer?? Is dry sleeping the answer?? I do not know. I do recommend being flexible enough to match the dolphins' sleeping pattern. A man and a dolphin will have a year of wake hours and of sleeping hours, and there is no necessity for eight hours awake, eight hours asleep, and so forth. What *is* important is enough sleep/rest for both, *not* when it is obtained.[1]

A note on cleaning; during even one week in this small tank, dirt collected and sat on the bottom. In a house, where

---

[1] The isolation tank with Epsom salt solution of density 1.14 for the human answers this sleep problem.

the dolphin is not constantly stirring up the bottom of each room, this would surely happen. There must be a system for draining that would allow scrubbing. Also a "vacuum" of a siphon hose should be available. This seems to be the best way to clean dirt out of water . . . without draining.

A week is a very short time and every animal is different. I decided only one thing at the outset of my experiments: to be in no rush "to make anything happen between us" and to let Pam take the initiative as much as possible. I was glad I made that decision; I stick by it, whether for a week or for a year. I found, during this week, a nice slow, steady, sweet binding of the relationship between us. Our mutual relationship was, for a day and a half, zero; we had no contact—slowly I approached Pam . . . and she allowed stroking.[2]

Then she invited this . . . turning on side, etc. Long rub sessions slowly turned the tide so that soon she was coming to me . . . rubbing my legs, hands. Until almost the end of the week Pam would not eat from me in the tank. She would not even take food from an outside source with me in the tank. Slowly all this resolves itself until Pam, at the end of the week, is taking fish from me while I am in the tank . . . sitting or standing.

Progression in familiarity and boldness can be seen throughout the week. In the beginning there is a very polite, gentle, "tippy-toe" business of getting to know you.

Toward the end of the week, we were both loosened up to the point of Pam demanding attention from me, interrupting conversations, flapping tails to get my attention, etc. And I am feeling freer with her . . . at one point I let loose and yell at her to stop something that is annoying me.

I think that this change of mood in the tank is interesting

[2] [A clinical note on Pam. This dolphin had been badly traumatized. Her behavior is in general "distant," "remote." She is shy and retiring. She is wary and cautious. She gives one the feeling, however, that she is also gentle and wants to make contact but something is keeping her from that contact. We know that before she joined us she had been through two traumatic episodes which we do not describe here. (She was speared by a diver three times in the *Flipper* movie.)]

and important. I am not saying that any politeness or gentleness stops; I am saying that both parties become freer to make
their wishes known to the other.

I recommend that in any other preliminary experiment or
in the flooded house itself . . . nothing should be rushed.
That the dolphin be allowed to go at its own pace . . . and
each animal may be different in this. Over a longer period
of time, lessons are scheduled throughout the day . . . and
that the time in-between living be as easy and free for both
parties as possible.

During this week, I recorded only one lesson with Pam.
It was not until the end of the week that I was able to feed
her from within the tank anyway, and then very often she
would eat only a few fish. Over a longer period of time, I feel
sure that the dolphin vocalization would increase . . . encouraged by the human . . . and would become part of the
in-between living as well as part of the lesson.

Pam did, immediately upon my entering the tank . . .
show a willingness to respond vocally to me. It was in
delphinese, however. And only after a period of time did she
begin to vocalize in any humanoids. I believe that the closer
you are physically to the dolphin the closer you can get
vocally. And during a week's time the progress here can be
very slow, but over a year(s) . . . such a situation should
have spectacular results.

I would like to see a house built so that a man and a dolphin could actually live together for one, two, or three years.
If dolphins are truly going to learn to speak to us in English,
I think they must have a much greater exposure to us and
our language than the two hours or so per day they get in
the present lessons at the laboratory. Eventually the whole
living situation could be a lesson with us. With the animal
learning more and more and the human demanding more
and more English words before he will respond to the dolphin's wishes.

No one will ever know the outcome of such a living experiment until it is done. We owe it to the dolphin and to
our curiosity to try it.

This is Margaret Howe's seven days and nights with Pam as she reported it. In this report the planning ahead for a much longer experiment of living in the wet environment, Margaret with a dolphin, is given. At this point she was willing to commit 2½ months or approximately one thousand hours to the project. This is in spite of interferences with her private life and the satisfaction of her social needs. In a sense Margaret is insisting that the world come to her and her dolphin. She cannot go out to the world during this experiment. Let us now enter into the experiment through the program that she set up for herself to carry out. After this we will give the detailed reporting during the 2½ months, as written by her at the time.

The experiments are considered by Margaret to be still preliminary. The flooded house program for "permanent" dolphin-human living is uppermost in her mind. Therefore she calls this a "program for a 2½ months' preliminary experiment."

Margaret and I had many conferences before, during and after the seven-day experiment: planning strategies, compromises, costs, materials, personnel, were all discussed. After such conferences, Margaret then took the initiative within the limits of the possible and carried out the actual details. Since what she *did* is the important data and since this is based on *her final plans*, the content of our conferences is not recorded. Though possibly important, only the reflections of this content through the mirror of Margaret's writing is left in this account.

3

Program for a 2 ½ Months' Preliminary Experiment: Living with Peter Dolphin in a Special Facility

Before the live-in began a program was laid out as follows: The experiment is to be carried out at St. Thomas, U. S. Virgin Islands, in the Dolphin Point Laboratory of the Communication Research Institute during the months of June, July, and August of 1965. One human and one dolphin are to live together day and night, for the period. They will eat, sleep, play, and work together within the boundaries set up by the experiment. Details of these boundaries will be included in this report (Plates 13–17).

The purposes of the human are: 1. to gain information about the learning ability of a dolphin exposed to such an intense and prolonged interspecies isolation with the human; 2. to attempt to teach the dolphin to "speak" English and to "understand" English; 3. to gain additional information in order to properly design the flooded house. (The only previous experiment known to us along this line is a one-week period, March 20 to 27, 1965, during which Margaret Howe and Pamela Dolphin lived together in the fiberglass tank at the St. Thomas laboratory. The results and recommendation for that week's experiment have resulted in the extended experiments started in June.)

Daily notes and recordings are kept in the St. Thomas laboratory by Margaret Howe. Included is a general weekly summary report by Miss Howe. No visitors are accepted in these two rooms or to the electronics room without an appointment set up by Miss Howe. All visitors are to be recorded in the notes.

Any changes in schedule are to be made only if initiated or approved of by Miss Howe. She accepts responsibilities to make changes as she sees fit. She will be out of the tank all day Saturday. In part the time on Saturday is spent organizing tapes of the previous week and setting up tapes for the following week. Weekly reports are to be done.

At any time during the 2½ months, should Miss Howe become ill or in any way physically discomforted, she may withdraw temporarily any time she finds necessary. Any withdrawal must be noted.

Following is an outline of the daily schedule to be followed, subject to later changes by Miss Howe.

7:30 Miss Howe gets up, washes, eats.

8:00 to 8:30 Recorded lesson with Peter, five pounds of fish.

9:00 Miss Howe daily cleaning, vacuum, etc.

9:30 Miss Howe does feeding, notes, protocol, check workmen.

10:00 to 10:30 Miss Howe and Peter play . . . involves some lessons.

11:00 Miss Howe and Peter outside . . . together but relaxed.

11:30 Miss Howe gets lunch.

12:00 to 12:30 Recorded lesson with Peter, five pounds of fish.

1:00 to 2:30 Miss Howe sleeps, fun, write, read, relax.

3:00 to 3:30 Recorded lesson with Peter, five pounds of fish.

4:00 to 4:30 Time spent working with Peter.

5:00 to 5:30 Miss Howe works on notes, bills, tomorrow's schedule.

6:00 Miss Howe has dinner.

6:30 Games with Peter, visitors, reading . . . always with awareness of living with Peter.

End of day and work is over, the two are still together.

10:00 Bed.

Above schedule to be followed Sunday through Friday. Saturday is a free day for Miss Howe; Saturday night sleep with Peter.

The language lessons will use a basic vocabulary in various categories as follows:

Basic vocabulary for both pronunciation and comprehension: numbers (1–5); personal names (Peter, Margaret, me, you); greetings (hello, bye-bye); objects (ball, toy fish, bucket, bobo clown, kinipopo, baby block); actions (speak, listen, come, go, give me, etc.).

To teach numbers, it is planned to use a series of balls with hooks in each end. The balls can be easily put together by the operator in any combination or taken apart. Many ways can be used to teach numbers. The human can hold a string of balls and point at the balls as she says them . . . "one, two, three," etc. The human can hold a string of two in one hand and a string of three in the other, and correspondingly show that one is two, one is three. Addition and subtraction are endless.

One problem is to teach the dolphin to say the name of the number, rather than to teach him to make the appropriate number of sounds for numbers. First, have the dolphin repeat after you. Second, demand that the dolphin name, number, or count the series of balls you hold up without you speaking.

So little is known as to what dolphins do and do not know about color. I suggest this not be among the first lessons, as the response of the dolphin may be nil anyway. Use wooden plaques all the same size and shape, the only difference being their color. First, have dolphin repeat after you; second, demand that the dolphin name the color as you hold up the plaque.

Shape can get involved with various named angles and so on, but I suggest one begin with basic shapes. Use wooden plaques of the same approximate size and color, with the only difference being shape. As above, dolphin comprehension can be kept track of by first having the animal repeat after you and, second, demanding that the animal name the shape of the plaque that you hold up.

If we are going to get into small sentences with these dolphins, it seems essential that names be used, both proper, "Peter," "Margaret," etc.; also, such as "you" and "me" should be taught.

Greetings explain themselves. The only reason I used them at all is: 1. as a signal ("bye-bye . . . lesson is over," etc.), and 2. "hello" is such a natural thing to say when entering a tank or a room. These are getting into the area where it is hard to know if the dolphin understands.

The list of objects can be changed according to the animal and the surroundings. It should be flexible . . . if the dolphin should get an ashtray into the water and play with it, it should have a name.

I suggest, as with all of these words on the vocabulary lists, that once a word is learned and the meaning understood, it should not be allowed to lapse from the list. If Peter learns what an ashtray is, it should not then be put into another room and forgotten. It should become part of Peter's things and should be used.

Anatomy is a difficult area in that it is hard to get the dolphin to identify the object with the word. I suggest, when patting Peter's tail, to name it over and over. Then change to saying "tail" to him and coaxing him to offer you his tail.

Getting the animal into some sort of game is a good way to bring action. I "throw" ball. Peter, "GO GET IT" or "PICK IT UP." "BRING IT HERE" . . . "GIVE IT TO ME" . . . , etc. This list should be added as new actions are taught and played with. This is more readily done with human speaking and animal acting. Not until much later will we probably have such a thing as Peter telling me to "go and get" something (at that point I will become his most humble slave!).

In all of the above I suggest the gradual getting away from fish as a reward, and using instead as a reward the human's obvious pleasure with results, petting, vocal rewards, etc. To do this I will try:

1. Fish as a reward after each response.
2. Fish as a reward after every other correct response.
3. Gradually move to having lessons just before feeding.
4. Gradually move lesson farther away from feeding.
5. Make feeding at this point as dull and unrewarding as possible. The feeder not to speak to the dolphin and to feed at a rate so that the dolphin has no chance to speak.

Usual human participant will not feed the dolphin.

This is all a long-range program. It is essential first to get the animal volunteering humanoids and to obtain a sense of listening, then speaking.

WEEKLY REPORTS—M. Howe. Written during the 2½ months' experience:

June 15 to 19, 1965. First Week

I must say that this week for the main part, is a week on preparation and adjustment. Peter was brought upstairs on Monday. He seemed happy and contented with his new home, but as yet he has not ventured outside. I tried coaxing him during one meal but no go. I may force him out next week just to get going.

I have been so busy getting ready for this experiment at the beginning and had two very disappointing times of filling the completed tank rooms only to find leaks. Once I was ready and the rooms were flooded to twenty-two inches I found that there were a lot of last-minute things to get and hence a day of in and out of the flooded room. On Tuesday night I was fairly settled.

The first few nights in the flooded room were awful. I was uncomfortable and hardly slept. Later I seemed to adjust to that and by Thursday I was fine. I found that it was very tiring just to walk across the flooded room. Everything I do takes more energy than it normally would; but I take a nap in the afternoon and that seems fine.

Peter is his energetic self and a bit nippy on the toes. I carry a long-handled broom with me for that and ward him off. This is not always the case, of course: we have had several long "loving" sessions. The water is deep enough for him to roll over and this he does for tummy rubs. He sleeps just next to my bed . . . some nights he has been quiet and others he just has to yell and splash around. He is always hungry . . . and usually wakes me early in the morning to tell me to feed him.

Lessons have gone fairly well . . . I start with counting and shapes. I am stopping, however, for the moment . . . go back and get Peter into the habit of listening. Speaking. He seems to have lost his sense of conversation. He often overrides me. One thing at a time. I cannot teach him if he is going to yell every time I open my mouth. He has said, for the tape . . . one clear word, "BALL." This came in the middle of one of his ramblings by himself and it could contain no meaning. But it is good pronunciation . . . in a nice comparison with Pam's "BALL."

We have several games—the most promising of which seems to be a retrieving game with the dishcloth or the ball. I throw the cloth, squeal "Go get it" to Peter . . . he dashes away . . . brings it to me . . . and willingly flings it in my direction. This seems endless. I would like to work it into a business of "Bring ball" or "Bring cloth" and get him to tell the difference. A step in the right direction.

He had picked up a nice business of following the inflection in my voice . . . "one, two, three, four" . . . with an upturn on the "four."

We have played several times with his brush . . . he loves to be brushed gently with it. I usually do this in front of his mirror where Peter spends a good deal of his time. I name the brush as I use it. So far Peter has not copied this.

Several personal notes that I will put in here and be done with. I find that clothes are no problem. I spend the day in a bathing suit . . . shower before dinner and put on the top of a leotard. I have not been cold yet, at night I do not use the wet suit. The room is warm, the nights are not . . . I have not had the problem of cold that I had with Pam.

The bed is usually damp by night, but it wipes off and half the time I don't use the quilt. I have sprayed several times for bugs, but they have not bothered me.

Cooking is fine.

Cleaning is interesting. I find that I must do it several times a day, the waterflow is in my favor. Each morning most of the dirt is neatly deposited at the foot of the elevator shaft. All I have to do is suck it up. This I tried with the vacuum from Miami . . . found it did not pull enough; I put a hose through the elevator down to the sea pool, fill it with water to start a siphon, and find it has a good pull. Only problem is a small mouth. Perhaps a funnel at my end of the hose will fix that. Also, the dirt collects several times a day . . . so I have to do this several times a day. Outside is another problem: algae grow on the walls . . . I clean it daily . . . cleaning the floor is not so easy. There is a stronger flow there and the dirt scattered. It will not collect in a pile. But in general the place stays cleaner than I thought it would . . . and the seawater is always clear . . . not milky.

In the shower I have been using a children's shampoo; it does not sting the eyes. Peter stays under the shower with me and does not seem the least affected by the soap so I will assume that in a large quantity of water its effects are negligible.

When the phone rings . . . it usually takes me a while to get to it . . . and on the way I explain . . . "telephone" to Peter. He often hears me talking and starts in vocalizing . . . very loudly and in a competitive way some time . . . it is amusing. I encourage this. (See photograph.) Peter uses the mirror . . . talks to himself . . . scolds . . . shoots water at his image. I plan to get a microphone over him to get some of these private conversations. A good deal of the talk that Peter does when he is "alone" is now in humanoid. Interesting and encouraging.

The one thing I really don't like is Peter's loss of ability to listen. He must learn this soon or I will be tempted to get Pam up here. Peter is good and loud and humanoid but he is slow to really pronounce . . . and he is forever interrupting. But I will give him at least another week.[1]

Another interesting point . . . I found that when I listened back to the tapes I had made during the week . . . I was much more encouraged than I was at the actual lesson. I do not get to listen to the tapes during the week. I have just spent all day Saturday checking up on records, bills, and tape listening. I may change my schedule to Saturday out of the tank but working in the electronics room on work done previous week . . . and take Sunday out of tank and use it as a free day.

Outside work is being done . . . I looked at the wall around Pam's future tank. It is about four feet high all the way around, it may be finished this week . . . in which case we can get the water systems in and make it ready to get Pam up the following week. Pam and Sissy are both down-

[1] Before these experiments began, it was questioned as to whether to work with Peter or with Pamela. Pamela (from the previous work with her) had good pronunciation. Peter was more vigorous but had poorer pronunciation.

stairs in the algaefied sea pool. But that will have to go for
the moment. New concrete should be in soon to fix that
situation.

To sum up . . . a good few days' beginning . . . and several nice games, lessons, habits started. I am pleased . . .
and look forward to the next week.

June 19 to 25, 1965. Second Week

Several new things developed this week.

First, Peter and I got on a more sociable, physical level.
Peter began to be gentle with me, and allow me to go to him
without the broom. He did not nip at me as he used to . . .
rather he was making a thorough study of my feet, legs,
ankles, knees. Doing this he is very gentle . . . the rough
part being when he tries to push me around. He gets between my legs and pushes me apart. When he starts to nip
. . . I make a big fuss . . . shout at him and retreat. But
we are getting much friendlier . . . and I feel more comfortable with him.

Second, my earlier thoughts on Peter are coming true;
Peter is more and more inclined to "play games" and speaking is going rather slowly.

I will take advantage of this . . . and use the games all I
can for speaking. We will continue to play the "towel fetch"
game and the "cloth fetch" game. We have gotten so far as
to have three balls thrown and collected and brought back
to me. From this I can start to name the number of balls,
and try to get him to fetch only one, or only two. He is very
enthusiastic about this game . . .

Listening to the tapes . . . I find the most encouraging
thing is that Peter does seem to be working. He is taking his
sweet time in really beginning to listen to me again . . . I
have had several sessions where I have really had to yell at
him to bring order to the lesson. One time I let him ramble
on and on, but I tried to copy all of *his* sounds. The tape
was interesting. I was surprised at how well I was able to copy
at least his pitch . . . and how he seemed to test me with
new combinations of sounds.

I have concentrated mainly on counting and shape lessons.

I recorded one spontaneous game developed when we were watching TV. The TV is on in the background, and Peter and I are playing with the towel. Peter speaks for it, I throw it, he gets it, brings it to me, and on and on.

I do not know how long Peter will stick at this game . . . I always get tired before he does. It would be interesting to just keep going until he tires of it.

Peter eats well. Only once has he refused a meal, and then he ate it about an hour later. Occasionally when I am eating something he sets up a row . . . open mouth "feed me" kind of thing . . . and I toss him a piece of whatever I am having. A sardine was the most interesting . . . he mashed it up a bit before dropping it.

I am well pleased with all of Peter's activities except his apparent vocal ability. He is more than eager . . . works hard . . . but he just does not seem to hear or be able to copy the pronunciation aspects of speech. Perhaps this will come . . . perhaps not. He has said a clear "ball"; he has worked well on the beginning of the word "one" . . . the "wa" . . . and best of all he does seem to have a nice sense of pitch.

By this I mean that when I count, "one, two, three," my voice will often rise on the "three" . . . and often Peter will copy this rise in the last of the three sounds. This is true of words like "triangle" also. And "hello." I try to say one word the same way each time . . . sometimes I fail but for the most part I am consistent in my inflections and Peter is beginning to pick this up.

He has been practicing with the pronunciation of the letter "M" from "Margaret," no doubt . . . and is discovering that rolling slightly so that his blowhole is just under the water gives a satisfactory "M" effect. (Pam has done exactly the same thing.)

Peter is certainly many times more humanoid vocally than he was two weeks ago . . . and some of this is beginning to creep in to non-lesson time such as when he wants my attention, he is annoyed, etc. I always reply in some form to an uncalled-for humanoid and encourage him. Peter continues to "chat" whenever I am on the phone . . . and this is mostly in humanoid. I don't think anyone has called here recently and not heard Peter in the background. I have asked people how he sounds . . . and they say that they can hear him very well. I think incidentally that Peter is quite happy. I would not have said the same thing of Pam in that other situation . . . but here the water is deep enough so that Peter is well covered . . . moves easily, can race around . . . and I see no bad effects at all. I am also quite comfortable except for the sleeping. My bed now has about three inches of water in it . . . that will not come out . . . it is saturated. I have been on and off sleeping out of the tank . . . and I am waiting for some polyethylene sheeting to make my bed more waterproof. I will screen it in. I had a fever of 101°F for a day . . . and spent the day out of the flooded room in bed. Aubrey Pickering had been ill and I think this accounted for my fever.

We have not forced Peter outside yet . . . I am waiting for special workmen to come and look at the balcony to see about cleaning it and I don't want Peter there when they do. And for the moment he seems happy inside. Each day he moves farther down by the elevator . . . it may be that he will get outside himself (see photograph).

Monday the sea pool will be cleaned and Tuesday the concrete will come and start being poured as was planned. My boys will continue on wall . . . and by the end of next week Pam should come upstairs. Here's hoping! [The reference is to the wall around Pam's new tank outside this building referred to earlier in this report.] (See photograph.)

I am anxious to start work with Pam . . . I miss her pronunciation capability!

June 27 to July 2. Third Week

Monday and Tuesday of this week we start in the first out-and-out cleaning of the new flooded room. The inside was drained and scrubbed down. Peter was put outside . . . we were going to get him into the sling but it was not necessary. He was gently pushed and went through the door. He spent a happy day outside . . . moving freely all around the center wall. (See photograph.) We worked inside and re-painted the bottom with Thoroseal. Tuesday we cleaned out-side. Peter had to be brought inside in the sling and he was reluctant. When he was in the sling I saw that his belly had some red marks, probably from the rough floor inside. They did not look open or even very sore, just pink. We were able to clean outside fairly well although the drainage is not com-plete and it is hard to get all the mucky water out. Most of the algae growth was at least scrubbed off, if not flushed out.

Draped shower curtains around my bed . . . dried all the parts of the bed . . . looked forward to dry sleeping. Found during the week that it works very well . . . Peter will get my attention by throwing ball up against the curtain . . . "whap, whap" . . . but he cannot get me drenched any more.

Several of the lessons this week were very poor. Peter has picked up this monotonous tone, a whine . . . and it goes on and on . . . he seldom stops to listen to me. I will do any-thing to break this, and several times I lost my temper and really yelled at Peter. Other times he listens very well . . . and at least seems to be trying to do the right things.

I still feel very strongly that I can do what I am trying to do . . . but I have not succeeded in doing it yet. I must teach Peter that he is to learn. Just that . . . and then we will have something. I can go through five lessons with him and be so fed up . . . and then I will give a counting lesson, say, and suddenly Peter is listening . . . rolling over and looking at the balls as I point to them, looking back up at me . . . try-ing sounds, listening when I repeat. It may be that Peter is not sure exactly what he is supposed to be doing. I must try to make it quite clear.

I find in going over the tapes of the week that they are very helpful . . . I get a condensed version of what has gone on. It all comes back. I am picking out some things that I find interesting . . . a good beginning of a word, a good copy of inflection, pitch, etc., but I have not started rerecording any parts of it yet. I am so lousy at the mechanics involved that it will take forever . . . and I don't think I have enough good material yet to make it worth the time spent. [When

I asked Miss Howe what she meant by "good material," she added "good pronunciation."]

Peter has still not gone outside on his own. He inches his way . . . I have decided it is just too shallow. This weekend I will raise the level and see if he will come out.

Toward the end of the week on Friday afternoon, I had the first really bad spell of restlessness. I just could not stay at the lab another moment. I got into the car and drove around a bit . . . and felt better. [Margaret has enlarged on this state of mind in a longer note, which will be inserted later in the summary of problems encountered.]

I am physically so pooped I can hardly stand . . . my legs from the knees down are numb. Note that I got my period on Wednesday . . . that may affect me. I sleep in my own bed Friday night . . . and feel better on Saturday. All of this fatigue was also combined with a depression . . . wanting to get away and see some people. I think I reached a point where my mind is not all on the job and I do not function well at all. At any rate . . . I went out and around on Sunday . . . and felt much better facing Monday.

To sum up . . . it has been a sort of neuter week. Not much visible progress, but no backslip. This is fine with me. The fact is still there that Peter and I have spent another week together . . . have yelled at each other . . . have had long, loving sessions, have scolded . . . had lessons . . . etc., and that we are a week closer in awareness of each other than we ever were before.

And for the moment that is all I expect. It has taken this long to really iron out the physical problems in the system, and with the exception of food, I think we have now done that. The cleaning people will be here on Tuesday to see about cleaning. About time!

The concrete was poured into the sea pool this week . . . that was a large distraction. Noise most of the day . . . I had to get out several times to see the work. Pumps would not work, the crew was there to pour, the pool was still full of water . . . I had a lot of outside problems on my mind. Saturday morning the crew was due here at seven-thirty to finish pouring concrete. I got up at 5:00 A.M. and put on the pumps to have the pool empty for them, and the power was off.

Most of these are small problems, but somehow this week they added and loomed very big for me. Pam stopped eating for several days. I was worried about her. She is fine now . . . back on her norm.

Peter continues to be very interested in games. He loves to go and fetch things. I must find a way to make this more worthwhile. The more of this kind of thing the better. I look for any kind of action or performance that has an order to it and some control on Peter's part. This "go and fetch" is ideal. Once again, I am eagerly looking forward to next week.

July 3 to 10, 1965. Fourth Week

During the early part of the week, work was still going on in the sea pool to get the sump properly concreted. Saturday morning the electricity was off and somehow the small tank by the sea pool was half drained. Having no power made it impossible to fill. I have purchased a fifty-foot flexible coil hose for a vacuum upstairs and it works as a siphon. I dropped it over into the tank, and filled the tank from the water upstairs. It is a very good emergency measure. I find that the vacuum takes out more water than the regular outflow upstairs.

I have also discovered that Peter's reluctance to go outside is not due to too narrow a space, or the doorway . . . rather it is due to the water being too shallow next to the elevator. (On the south side of the elevator the passageway floor is slightly elevated so that Peter would have to pass over a hump in the floor.) I raised the water to about twenty-four inches . . . and he goes outside on his own. Peter was outside one day . . . and I closed the top part of the Dutch door arrangement, assuming that he would not go under the door . . . as I wanted him to stay outside so I could clean inside uninterrupted by his presence. Not so! Peter very willingly came in under the door . . . went back out again. As long as he has enough water . . . he moves freely.

We spent a lot of time outdoors, I gave him several non-recorded lessons on the balcony and played with him while floating on the raft. (See photographs.)

I have begun working with Peter more and more at times other than feeding. When I am not going to give him a lesson at feeding time, I make feeding as dull as possible. I simply dump the bucket of fish into the water and leave him alone. He eats all the fish, but I do not speak to him, stroke him, etc. I find that more and more Peter is humanoiding to or at me to get attention. I respond as often as possible. I will be in bed, or cooking, and if Peter speaks to me in humanoid, I drop what I am doing and go to him, or else try to engage him in conversation. I do not respond to his attention-getting clicks and whistles. They mean nothing to me and I make that clear.

Peter is more and more interested in games, and often starts them himself. He can toss the ball, bunt with some accuracy to me or at me, and I find that I am suddenly necessary to his game . . . he seldom plays with these objects by himself. We play two games. One is "fetch" . . . Peter brings me the ball, cloth, or bunny, I throw it out, he dashes to it and brings it back to me. The other is catch . . . he hits the ball into the air to me, I can often catch it, and I toss it back to him. He is very willing to toss it back to me. There is no hoarding, or "keep away" instinct. [It is well to note that this is Margaret's special use of the word "instinct."]

I can come into the room, find Peter sitting at the mirror and the ball floating at the other end of the room. I can say "ball" to Peter several times and if he wants to play, he can go and get it . . . and does. It is hard to tell if he can make the distinction say, between the ball and the cloth. They are both lying around and I ask him to get the cloth, he will often get the ball. He seems to prefer the ball and I am not sure he isn't simply ignoring what I say in doing what he wants to. When this happens I ignore the ball, continue asking for the cloth, and if he will not get it I drop the whole thing.

John Lovett came during the week and took black-and-white photos. I have some on file, with the contact sheets but had sent the rest to Dr. Lilly. They are good shots and are an excellent record of the progress here. (See photographs.)

Recording sessions with Peter have improved. He is finally able to listen again! I have a nice system with him of hushing him. When he is wrong I simply put my fingers gently on his beak or over his blowhole and he is still. I repeat . . . and he follows. He seems to have lost the impatient squealing that was so annoying and we are working much better together. I have not yet gone over the tapes of this week so I cannot report.

I am not capable of using these tapes as I would like to. But I know what should be done and what I would like to do. I think that I will simply continue making the tapes and going over them as best I can . . . and at a later date I will have to take several days and perhaps get someone in who can properly rerecord. Listening to all the tapes is endless and I will make rerecordings of those parts that show progress. This must be done but it can wait.

Peter has become sexually aroused several times during the week, and I have thoughts and questions on this that follow in a separate paper.

[The paper in question is dated July 11, 1965.]

4

Observations and Thoughts on Four Weeks' Experiences

Margaret made a special report at the fifth week of living with Peter twenty-four hours a day.

Over the past several weeks I have had thoughts and made observations that have not gone into the weekly report. This will be sort of an intermediate report including these thoughts and observations.

To actually live with a dolphin twenty-four hours a day is a very taxing situation. Much more so than I had anticipated. Unlike a dog, unlike a cat, unlike a human, a dolphin is more like a shadow than a roommate. If given the opportunity, *he will never leave your physical being*. To try and sweep a floor *with* Peter, means that Peter is continually at your feet . . . touching you . . . pushing you . . . nibbling you . . . perhaps speaking (humanoid or delphinese) to you. *He does not go away*. To cross a room to answer a phone means that Peter meets you when you come into his immediate range and he walks with you, pushing, nibbling, slapping, *the whole way*. And if you are on the phone for half an hour, Peter does not get distracted or bored, *he stays right with you* . . . again touching you, pushing you, nibbling you, speaking, squirting.

At the moment, I am in a situation where Peter is still reluctant to move down by the elevator and outside. I can "escape" from him. But he has gone outside by himself . . . he can move all around the room, and it is just a matter of time before I will not have a place to "escape" to. This is, of course, what I want to happen, but I had not realized the intensity of the situation. If not actively involved in a game, Peter will be touching me in some way and demanding attention. This may sound mild, but I literally cannot take a step without Peter getting all tangled up in my feet. And if I should continue to ignore him, I am likely to get a slap with his tail that can take my feet out from under me. My shins are bruised, up and down, from the constant butting with his nose and the front of his flippers. *And all of this suits me just fine.* We will never be comfortable with the dolphin until this business is solved. Peter *must learn that I can get hurt* . . . and he must learn that no matter how annoyed he may be, he is not to hurt me. Until that is clear, there will be an element of danger with dolphins, that is, for me anyway, too much to live with. I cannot feel that, if suddenly in the middle of a game or a lesson Peter should become annoyed, he would be likely to physically damage me. In this respect we are dealing with a "wild animal" and we must domesticate or civilize them. [I questioned her on the term "wild animal" and was wondering if maybe a "wild man" might not be better. She said no, she meant "wild animal" and that is the sense in which she means it.]

This, of course, makes no sense to the person who has had a "nice swim" with a dolphin or with one who has "played for a while" with a dolphin. When you expose yourself to a dolphin twenty-four hours a day, you are becoming the "other dolphin" in their life. You become vulnerable to their whims and moods throughout the day. You lack the introduction of a "human coming to play for a while." You are exposed to their sexual needs and play, their hunger, their playful antics, their needs for heavy exercise, and for rest. You are no longer a nice interlude in the day. You are a constant companion, and must make your peace with the dolphin as such.

Making this "peace" with Peter has occupied a good deal of our time together and we are doing nicely. I have my own physical fears, etc., I am not a "big brave man." Perhaps a braver, stronger person could solve this problem in less time . . . but this is what I have been able to do so far. To begin with, I went into the flooded room with rubber bootees. I have had Peter nibble at my feet before and wanted to avoid it. He did indeed nibble . . . and I took to carrying a broom with me when I walked. This thwarted him off, he came with me but I could protect my feet from his constant attention. After several days the bootees became a nuisance, and I shed them for good. I continued carrying the broom, but this soon became a nuisance too. I decided to tackle the thing.

Peter, on his own, seemed to sense a problem and became willing to tackle it too. He would become very gentle, and we began to have our first "loving session." This gave me confidence and was a reward to Peter for being "gentle." We became more and more confident with each other. I began walking freely without a broom. Peter continues to follow me and push at me with his beak, but for the most part he keeps his mouth closed and does not nibble. When he does take my foot or leg in his teeth, I make a big fuss, yell at him, kick water, even slap him if it hurts, and immediately remove myself from "his" area. I wait, and Peter usually responds by turning over, wagging a flipper at me, mouth closed and lies still. I approach him again, using a soothing tone now, and if he remains gentle we go on playing and the incident is closed. If he continues to snap at me . . . he has indeed tricked me into coming back . . . I blow my top and leave him alone for a good while. This seems very effective . . . every day Peter and I can be quite happy and comfortable with each other for longer and longer periods of time.

All of this business is hard to describe in detail daily . . . some of it is very subtle . . . but the changes in our relationship can be seen after several weeks. It is a big part of our work together . . . and no matter how long it takes to solve, it will be well worth it. I look forward to the day when Peter will yell at me rather than nip at me, to show his displeasure. This is a big anti-instinct step for him and I appreciate every effort on his part. My bruises and scrapes are well worth it (Plate 18). [Previous studies in the three months' observation period by Margaret on the behavior of the dolphins show the patterns of a dolphin using his teeth on other dolphins.]

So much for my "taming" Peter. Now to my progress in and plans for teaching.

In his normal existence, Peter has no need to speak English. Before I can expect him to really start speaking, I must give him such a need. This I can do, so far, in two ways.

The first is to demand, through food reward, later hopefully to be vocal or physical reward, to repeat what I am saying.

The second is to introduce various objects, and uses for various objects, into his life and to make them so necessary or so much fun that I can then demand that he use speech to indicate, or get, or control, these objects.

The food reward, recorded or "formal" lessons with Peter have been slow. The program I have set up has been held back because somewhere along the line Peter had forgotten how to listen. Much time has been spent just trying to get him to give and take, listen, and respond. He is now back on the track, somewhat, and lessons are becoming more fun for both of us. I can stop screaming and touch Peter on the beak or blowhole to indicate that he must listen again. I think a big part of this is to make sure that feeding times are not too delayed. When Peter is really hungry he simply yells until I feed him. Feeding three times a day helps to take away the "tension" of feeding time . . . and makes a more relaxed, easygoing lesson. Peter has a good appetite and always eats everything I offer him. When I feel that he is too hungry to pay attention I just feed him straight, and get more fish for him. It is not fair to really hold back food from a hungry dolphin. It should be more of a snack or a tidbit.

Anyway, Peter is settling back into the groove and listening, and I can begin in earnest our lessons of counting, shape, and color. These are the three I will begin with and then we will see. It has been slow, but at least we have accomplished something. Peter is the pacesetter here; all I can do is to push him to his limit and then match his pace.

At the moment Peter is at this point: he can listen, he can hush up. He responds with a good 95 per cent humanoid, only occasional delphinese comments on the side. He can somewhat imitate the word "ball" and "hello." These are not too clear . . . but are there. He is obviously working on "L" and "M" . . . probably from "hello," "ball," and "Margaret."

My first goal will be to get him to pronounce any word clearly and know the meaning. This will probably be a time coming, and is the hardest step. Once he learns that he can say something and have it mean something to me . . . then the other words and meanings will come easier. So I repeat over and over the few words he seems most able to repeat . . . and I don't think he will be bored with this repetition until he has mastered the word, at which point I will move on. It all makes for very boring tapes, of my repeating one word over and over, and Peter giving various replies. But I can hear changes; I can see changes as he tries for new sounds . . . and I will not stop this tedious chore until I feel that Peter is ready. The public, etc., will just have to wait for fancy, snappy tapes. There is nothing clever or cute about a deaf mute trying to learn to speak. It is a slow, dull, drooling-at-the-mouth, agonizing, and frustrating business, and that is about the size of what Peter and I are engaged in.

The list of objects in Peter's life is always subject to change . . . and frequently does. I think it is very important to choose objects that can both be played with . . . and talked about . . . and this is a much harder choice than it would seem (Plates 20, 21). I have gone into it blindfolded. Peter has taught me as I go. I began rather naturally, with a ball. This is appropriate . . . Peter can occasionally say ball, and I demand that he attempt it before giving him the ball. Now comes the question—what to do with the ball? In the beginning, we did nothing. Peter spoke for the ball, I gave it to him, and he happily took it off in his mouth. Period. This changed as Peter began bopping it gently . . . bouncing it on the bottom. All of this seems to come quite naturally to all dolphins . . . they *like to play with the ball. Fine!* But do they like to play with the ball with people? It seems natural to toss the ball and see if Peter will go get it. Dogs have trained us in this game. Peter knows it too! I don't know how I taught Peter this, or even if I did teach him this . . . but he very happily chases a ball, picks it up . . . brings it to me and lets me have it. *Fine!* Can he do this with more than one ball? *Yes!* Peter can hold three balls in his mouth at one time . . . and will go and fetch three balls at the same time and bring them all back. This I will tuck away for later when his counting is more developed . . . to try and see if he can bring just one, or just two.

So one of Peter's objects is a ball, small, red, and buoyant.

If Peter will go and fetch a ball, will he fetch other things as well? *Yes!* I have tried the game with a cloth . . . he likes to vary this, bringing it back in his teeth, or on a flipper.

The variation of this game is as follows . . . after Peter handed me the cloth, I started rubbing him gently with it . . . saying "rub." Peter did not respond vocally to this but several times later when he returned with the cloth in his mouth he would not immediately give it to me. Instead he held the cloth, sunk to the bottom, and ran his beak and the cloth up and down my legs and feet. I say "rub!" "Thank you Peter!" and he gives me the cloth for another toss.

So another object is a cloth: a dishcloth or a face cloth. I found a wet towel too heavy and too clumsy.

Peter has always had, as long as I have known him, a float. This is a rope with a float at either end. He plays with it alone, it is easy to sling into the air, and I have not played with it with him.

So another object is a float.

Another game Peter and I developed with his ball is "catch" . . . we are several feet from each other. I tossed the ball to Peter, where if he gets it he does one of two things . . . he can flip it to me underwater by snapping his jaws on it . . . or he can bop it from the surface of the water into the air. The latter I have encouraged and we can go several bops with a fairly good aim on his part and I am able to catch it after he bops it. This is suddenly stopped by Peter, who lies on his side and will not play any more until I stroke him and coo. Several minutes of this and the bop game continues.

I have collected two baskets, one blue and one red, and three balls of each color. I will hang the baskets and see if I can interest Peter in a brief water basketball. I will later see if he can sort out the colors.

So another of his objects is the basketball equipment.

From the beginning of this experiment I have had a brush, kept by Peter's mirror. Stupidly humanlike, but fun. It is a dust broom, a soft thick thing. Peter seems to like it . . . but can take only so much of it. I do not use it too often, but when I do I name it "brush" and as I stroke Peter with it I say "brush, brush." Peter will lie on his side and let me brush him all over. He likes to be brushed on the beak and around the lips.

Another object for Peter . . . brush.

I found a long, tall rubber rabbit . . . it floats and when you squeeze it . . . it squeaks. I gave it to Peter and explained "bunny."

I showed him how it squeaked . . . bopped it around a bit, and left it. He soon had the bunny squeaking. I went to him and named it again. I took it away when he left it. I will keep it until I am ready to play bunny again and then I will explain what it is again to Peter. I do not think things like this should be left with him for too long. They get forgotten and used-to. They should be carefully allotted time and attention.

Peter now has a squeaking toy . . . a bunny.

I have let Peter play for a while with his shapes . . . just to let him get more acquainted with them. When I use them in a lesson, I do not let him have them . . . I hold them up or dunk them into the water for him to see. I do not think he is ready to play with these yet . . . until he understands the difference, they are meaningless and they can't really play together with them. So they will only be used for the moment in formal lessons, that he has been exposed to them.

Peter has a diamond, a square, a circle, an oblong, and a triangle. These are wood, they float, are painted white with a black border (Plates 19, 22).

For the moment these are the basic kit of Peter's objects. There are daily arrivals of screws, apple cores, cigarette butts, buckets, tea bags, brooms, books, etc., that get into the flooded room and are usually named for him, but the above are steady members of his routine now. As this kit is added to, I will make a note of it in a report.

Slowly an environment is being set up for dolphin and human living, and slowly I am learning what is needed and what is not. I am learning that I am not completely capable of complete isolation with Peter, and happily I am learning that it is not necessary. I have been very depressed and discouraged and have found that I simply must break out at least once a week.

I have found that during the day I will find any excuse to get out of the flooded room . . . to have to go downstairs and look at a pump . . . to have to go upstairs and get something . . . to have to get out and spend a few minutes loving my cat . . . to have to get out and take a shower in my own bathroom and dry my feet completely . . . and after all these "have-to's"—it has been most important *to have to go back and see what Peter is doing.*

But for the 2½ months at least I think it is very important and valuable to stick as closely as possible to the setup routine, just for the value of being there as much as possible . . . to find out what we do when the game is over . . . when a lesson is lousy . . . or I am exhausted, etc.

In a boring interval suddenly Peter will flip the cloth at me, and we both gain the sense of being stuck with each other . . . or blessed with each other . . . and the more of this there is the more we can work out things together.

I find that this living is hard and taxing on my own private life. I do not think that I would like to live with this much restriction for too long a time. But for the moment, and certainly for the next few months, I am very happy to do it with the obvious gains that have been made and will be made.

I hope with what I am able to learn in these months, I can establish some sort of system for learning and teaching that will make a future more livable nine-to-five schedule with a dolphin more profitable. Or perhaps not a nine-to-five schedule, but a looser living-in situation that will afford the human more time on his own. [This is a dull small area

for living. There are definitely isolation and solitude effects
showing. A mother and human child can go out of their
house together, Margaret and the dolphin cannot leave
together. Eventually the "delphinomobile" may be an answer
for both Margaret and Peter to vary their surroundings.]
(Plates 23–26.)

5

Who Teaches Whom What: Mutual Trust

July 11 to 17, 1965. Fifth Week

Sunday and Monday nights of this week I got very little sleep. Peter was awake and slamming tail hard on water. I tried speaking to him, playing with him . . . no good. He is restless, his tail goes "whap, whap" all night. Also during the beginning of the week I find that my play periods are changing with him. Also during the beginning of the week Peter begins having erections and has them frequently when I play with him.

Peter has been upstairs with me for just a month, and up until now he has not displayed his sexual excitement. I think we must learn a lesson from this.

I find that his desires are hindering our relationship. I can play with him for just so long now and then he gets an erection and the play/lesson is broken. I find that I cannot satisfy Peter . . . I am in the water with him and he is too rough to handle. He jams himself again and again against my legs, circles around me, is inclined to nibble . . . and is generally so excited that he cannot control his attitude toward me. I have had Peter in the same condition before, but under different circumstances. When Peter was upstairs in the Fiberglas tank he would occasionally become aroused, and I found that by taking his penis in my hand and letting him jam himself against me he would reach some sort of orgasm, mouth open, eyes closed, body shaking, then his penis would relax and withdraw.[1] He would repeat this maybe two or three times and then his erection would stop and he seemed satisfied.

Now, however, I am completely in the water with him and because so much of my body is exposed, we cannot get into the same position as above. I am completely vulnerable to him and he pushes and shoves my legs and feet, and quite pathetically tries to satisfy himself. I can feel his mounting frustration, and he is impossible to work with following this.

I have decided that Peter must go downstairs with Pam and Sissy for at least a day. I think that it is only fair, after say a month with only me, that he join them for a day or so. This, I hope, will relieve his frustrations, so that we can go on working for another month. I know that dolphins have been worked with for much longer periods in isolation without a break to romp with other animals, but I feel that at a certain point one may be hindered by unsatisfied sexual needs. I would rather lose Peter for a day and have him happy than continue as we are.

This will be much harder to determine in the females, if in fact it does exist. When Pam comes upstairs to her tank I will give her a month and then look closely for signs of frustration or lag in her learning. *This may be a very important and as yet unrealized step in dolphin teaching.* To try and keep an animal in isolation and a learning situation beyond this point of frustration may impair learning or even set it back. Each animal may have different tolerances, or they all may be somewhat alike. With Peter, so far, it seems to be about a month. I will follow this report with a report on Peter's attitudes after he has had one or two days with Pam and Sissy.

Another thought I have had on this subject is whether or not it would be best for the human to somehow find a way to satisfy the dolphin's sexual needs without another dolphin.

---

[1] The male dolphin's penis appears outside his body only while erect. It disappears inside the genital slit when not erect. (See pictures, *Man and Dolphin*.)

This may strengthen the bond between the dolphin and the human. It may also lead to more and more frequent "sexual periods" between the two. If Peter knows that I can satisfy his needs, he may feel free to turn any play period or lesson into a sex period . . . but if he knows that I will not have any part of his sexual needs and that once a month he will be put with Pam or Sissy, he may reduce his excitement periods with me. This would, of course, be preferable. I will try and see. *This is a problem,* and it must be solved . . . I cannot go on having my shins belted about by lusty little Peter. *It hurts!*

Peter continues to improve his attitude during lessons. He is most attentive, listens as well as I ever hoped, and tries hard. I am working only on a very few words, trying to ram them home with him. He listens, repeats, listens again. He has that lack of pronunciation, but improves daily on inflection and pitch. Listening to the tapes, he could be speaking English from the general sound of it. It is just not yet comprehensible. In the middle of a cocktail party it could be considered background conversation. It has all the right "feel" of English . . . and soon it will be. I am very pleased.

The sea pool is done. It is painted with blue Tile-It on the sides and white Thoroseal on the bottom. It is filled and Pam and Sissy are in it and very happy. They can still leap clear out . . . I was not so sure about that with the new bottom. They love it. Sissy spends a good deal of time upside down with her nose in the sump inspecting every inch. I have not been in yet, but I went partly in one day to rub Sissy with cream; she got a bit of a sunburn. It is so nice to walk down a sloping side at the outflow rather than those steps.

The wall around Pam's tank is done, and painted. I had a hard time deciding on color . . . something not too bright and not too hot. I decided on black and white combination, and have done it in big stripes. It is not too dizzy looking as I feared it might be and it seems to be as cool and dim as possible. I am working on a possible scheme for the inflow there . . . if I could somehow use the outflow from the balcony into her tank . . . it would save a pump, electricity, noise, etc. It may or may not work. I am just waiting for the

pump to arrive from Miami. I could put a valve on each end
of the siphon to control it through that. I am sure the water
would be clean enough . . . there is so much upstairs.

One month of the project is up . . . and well spent. I
now am no longer thinking in terms of three months . . . I
think in terms of forever!

July 17 to August 1, 1965.

Rather than dealing with this as a weekly report, I am
going to write at length about several topics that have come
to notice during these weeks.

An interesting thing has been going on, as observed by
Dr. Lilly involving Peter and his "mouthing" with me. I will
recount what goes on.

When Peter and I first became involved in ball playing,
we worked nicely into a game where, several feet apart, we
bopped the ball to each other, calling it "catch." Peter slowly,
subtly, would toss the ball shorter and shorter distances . . .
I would have to step towards him to pick it up. This soon
moved into a game where I would stand just in front of
Peter and really *put the ball into his mouth*. He would lie on
his side . . . and gently close his mouth on the ball, releasing
it to me. Soon he would hold the ball in his mouth . . . lie
on his side, and I tentatively took the ball out of his mouth
and began slightly rubbing his gums as I did so. Peter laid
dead in the water, eyes partly closed. I was willing to accept this form of mouth play. Previously I would go into a
rage whenever Peter opened his mouth in playing a game.
Now, however, because Peter was so still and gentle, obviously a little entranced, and because the ball was in his
mouth and he could not possibly bite down on me too hard,
I was willing to play his way. Note that in the beginning
Peter would keep the ball in the front of his mouth . . .
mouth open only slightly and not able to close at all. Slowly,
Peter began to roll the ball back in his mouth until his jaws
were full open and he could close them several inches with
the ball still inside. At this point I held back a bit until Peter
convinced me, by his gentleness and trancelike fixation, that
this was "pleasure," not "fool Margaret" period. I felt a little

silly, and was delighted that Peter had devised such a subtle, gentle method of getting me over my fears of all those teeth. So we had arrived at point one . . . Peter "dead" with ball in mouth, slightly open, with me stroking lips and gums. Once step one had been established, Peter slowly moved on to the next step. And that is what happened . . . I had no idea of the end result of this play . . . I was along for the ride to see the results of Peter's increased gentleness and my diminishing fear. Peter led the way.

His next move was, during the same sort of play, to slowly sink in the water with a ball .toward the front of his mouth and his jaws slightly closed. All slowly and gently, Peter would run the open tip of his mouth up and down my leg. I, meanwhile, was keeping an eagle eye on the ball and as long as it remained in his mouth I knew that he could not bite down and thus I allowed the play. This, then, became step two in Peter's plan.

Next Peter gradually moved the ball in his mouth so that his jaws were full open with the ball still in the back of his mouth. Now he would sink and go through the up and down the leg business; only this time his full set of teeth were running up and down my leg instead of only the tip of his mouth. I again kept an eagle eye on the ball . . . my "safety factor," held my breath as the teeth ever so gently went up and down my legs, and allowed this play. [Peter is estimated to be about five to six years old, his teeth still have the childish very sharp tips to them and are just beginning to be worn down. They are still capable, however, of drawing blood.]

All of the above happened over several weeks; it has been a slow, gradual buildup. Peter woos me into position and once we are started he seems to completely relax, eyes fully or partially closed, rolling on his side . . . obviously having a marvelous time. My only reaction at this point was to hold my breath and watch the ball . . . I am not an active member at this point.

Peter is not through. During the above, the ball slowly, seemingly, "accidentally" drops out of his mouth. At first I demand that he take it back before I will let him go on with the teeth . . . but soon he is so obviously involved in his fun, and the ball just seems to slip out of his mouth, and again I take a big breath and let Peter continue, his jaws open up and down my leg with no ball. My safety factor is gone and I can only let the play go on for a few seconds at a time.

Peter continues pressing this game . . . and slowly I gain confidence. I no longer demand that the ball be there in the beginning of the game to make me feel better.

Peter simply approaches me, mouth open, rolling on his side; I stand very still, legs slightly apart, and Peter slides his mouth gently over my shin. His mouth opens all the way and he begins up and down my leg. Then the other leg. The whole knee is in his mouth.

At this point it occurs to me what has been going on. Peter is courting me . . . or something very similar! I began to take an active part in the play. After several minutes of Peter "stroking" me gently with his teeth, I compliment him vocally, soothingly, and rub him as he turns to be stroked. Several minutes of this and Peter is back stroking me. I still hold my breath a bit but Peter has convinced me that this is a perfectly legitimate game among dolphins, and with the toning down he gives it for my benefit, it is actually a very pleasant feeling!

Two things about all this stand out in my mind. One is the over-all way Peter was able to woo me, to teach me that *I could play this game.* I had many fears . . . Peter obviously realized them and found ways, and *props* (the ball after all was a very convenient tool) to reassure me. Peter has worked long for this contact . . . he has been most persistent and patient. [Notice that Peter used a tool in a rather sophisticated way in order to induce Margaret to accept certain kinds of attention.] Second is the mood in general of the play. This is obviously a sexy business . . . all it really involves is physical contact. The mood is very gentle . . . still . . . hushed . . . all movements are slow . . . tone is very quiet . . . only slight murmurings from me. Peter is constantly, but ever so slowly, weaving his body around . . . eyes near closed. He does not usually get an erection during this, but does present his tummy and genital area for stroking.

I find that once Peter does have an erection, his mood usually changes completely and he gets so rambunctious I have to leave him. Perhaps this is his way of involving me in some form of sex play without scaring me away.

I feel extremely flattered at Peter's patience with me in all this . . . and am delighted to be so obviously "wooed" by this dolphin.

Several other points have come up during these weeks. For several days there have been groups of from four to six persons at the laboratory. They all saw Peter. They were all dry, standing outside the flooded living room, dangling arms over the wall. This is going back to the "dolphin in the tank-human leaning in" idea . . . and I do not like it. Peter fell back into the old business of squirting up at the people and various dangling arms and heads. And the people? Usual reaction . . . saying "no" in a high-pitched, giggly voice, and ducking down, only to pop up seconds later and dangle again, inviting more squirting.

This is all very fine, and people are flattered and Peter finds it a game but I refuse to allow it. It is boring, eventually annoying, and completely out of line of what I am trying to do by living with Peter. I stop this business by getting in with Peter (and I have been outside with the people). Peter began to play with me . . . and although he was still very aware of the "outside" people . . . he no longer focused on them. Enough said . . . Peter is not in a cage and will not be played with, teased, observed, stared at, or anything else by "outside" people. You are several months too late, people, Peter has outgrown you. [And so has Margaret.]

I went to San Juan and purchased several new toys for Peter. I will introduce them one at a time. I have removed all balls from his rooms, and have given him six "toy" fish. They are red, plastic, about nine inches long, they float, and I can push them gently and they glide on top of the water. Peter began bopping them . . . has collected them together several times . . . and slowly we are working out "toy fish" games. The real butterfish I now term "fish in bucket," as a contrast. Occasionally I play with the fish and a ball . . . explaining "ball" and "toy fish." Peter's "toy fish" comes out

as two clear separate sounds, but no pronunciation yet. I am
working on "toie." I have not spoken to him yet of color . . .
but I do count the fish with him. Slowly these new objects
are becoming part of his life. I will discuss the other toys as
I use them.

*August 2 to August 18, 1965. Eighth, Ninth,
and Tenth Weeks*

The past few weeks have been interesting ones for me, in
that I am finding that I have periods of lag in my attention
to my work.

I fight this to a point, but only to a point. I find that once
my attention is averted from Peter, it is best not to fake it,
because my lack of genuine enthusiasm with him can only
lead us backward.

It is also true that during these weeks there have been
other distractions at the lab that have required my attention.

Two awnings have been installed, one over the Fiberglas
tank and one over the block pool at the outflow of the sea
pool. (See photographs.) We have needed these for a long
time, and I was very glad to see them installed.

Also during the week photographs were taken of the lab
in general and of me in with Sissy and Pam. We took a series
of pictures of Sissy being brought upstairs on the elevator.
(See photographs.) For this we used my bed, the pallet to
show it in operation. My bed was therefore soaking wet, and
it took several days to get the foam dried out. This broke my
pattern with Peter, and I find that once it is broken, it is very
hard to get back into it.

Also, several matters in town required my attention. Our
phone has been out of order for over a week now, and all
calls have to be made from outside. (This led to a good deal
of anxiety on Dr. Lilly's part in which he spent thirty-six
hours trying to raise me and almost came to St. Thomas to
find out what was wrong.)

Also I had to go out to the employment agency to start
the long fight to keep our three workmen . . . the new im-
migration law states that I must try to find local help. This
is still not settled.

So all in all it has been a distracting week. Meanwhile I have worked with Peter as best I could.

Monday of this week after my several days out of the flooded room, I moved back in with Peter and I find that, after the lapse, energy seems to be renewed on both parts. I am delighted with Peter . . . and he is working as hard as ever. I say "work, work, work" and Peter says "play, play, play." I try to combine them. He plays endlessly with his toys, *if I play with him.* I usually work with two different toys at a time . . . say the toy fish and a "Ba Be Block." We go from one to the other, and I try to get him to tell the difference. He does and he doesn't. Once he has correctly made a choice, I scold him when he makes a mistake. Some of this I am sure is just the bad little boy doing as he wishes.

I wish to add a note about the progress in the sex problem that developed between Peter and myself. I have found that during his erections, Peter was much too strong and pushy and I could not work with him. Then there was the business of Peter wooing me with the nibbling on the legs game. This was an example of Peter teaching me something.

Now it has happened that Peter has modified his sexual rambunctiousness . . . to a more humanized level . . . and no longer has to come to a dead stop when he gets excited. Peter's sexual excitement usually begins with the biting business, and my stroking him. Now, however, when his penis becomes erect, he no longer tries to run me down and knock me off my feet, rather he slides very smoothly along my legs, and I can very easily rub his penis with either my hand or my foot. Peter accepts either and again seems to reach some sort of orgasm and relaxes. We usually go through this three times or so before he quits and starts another game. This is not a private thing. Peter and I have done this with other people present . . . but it is a very precious sort of thing, Peter is completely involved, and I involve myself to the extent of putting as much love into the tone, touch, and mood as possible. We do not have to respect his privacy . . . but we cannot help but respect his happiness!

Now two things . . . I started out afraid of Peter's mouth, and afraid of Peter's sex. It had taken Peter about two months to teach me, and me about two months to learn, that I am free to involve myself completely with both. It is strange that for the one, *I* must trust completely . . . Peter could bite me in two. *So he has taught me that I can trust him.* And in the other, he is putting complete trust in me by letting me handle his most delicate parts . . . *thus he shows me that he has trust in me.* Peter has established mutual trust. Could I have devised such a plan? Looking back . . . things I left out. The effect of isolation and solitude over the ten-week period cannot be ignored. Looking back over the time spent and the notes collected, I find that I, for some reason, left out things about myself. Perhaps I felt they were not important or was ashamed of them.

Several times during the period, I felt the physically depressing effects of the situation to the point where I found myself actually crying. Small inconveniences suddenly loomed as very large and ugly. And I would find myself in a fit of self-pity, depression. It was Peter himself who brought me out of it every time without exception. An example of all this: to take a shower at night before going to bed, means that I have to stand in knee-deep sea water during the shower, dry myself, and then wade back to my bed. This meant that when I got onto my bed, my legs from the knee down were wet with salt water. Even after drying with a towel, the dampness would still get through and make the sheet on my bed clammy and, if I had any nicks on my legs from Peter, they kept "stinging," and in this rather bizarre setting with moonlight shining on the water making moving shadows all over the ceiling and walls, dull pump noises from below, I would try to settle down in bed, and occasionally found that out of sheer self-pity I would be adding my own salt tears to the mess I already lay in. And then, usually not very long after I lay still, Peter would sound off in humanoid, loud and clear, very close. From where I lay I could part the shower curtains around my bed, and reach out my hand to my eager, bright-eyed roommate who had usually collected a ball of some sort and was all set to start up a nice game of fetch or catch.

Peter was very determined in his expression of his need for me to enter into his game . . . he would toss the ball again and again into my bed, and emit humanoids in long and involved phrases, they were not perfectly clear in meaning but were perfectly clear in intent . . . that I seldom if ever ignored him, and usually ended up right back in the water, not caring at all about sleep, or the wet bed or the shower routine . . . simply overwhelmed at what Peter and I were accomplishing together.

Another example of the kind of depression that I went through: during the day the two workmen are around the lab, and I can talk to them and hear their work going on. The last one usually leaves rather late in the day . . . several hours after I have supposedly fed Peter his dinner. I found that the sound or the sight of that last person leaving at the end of the day depressed me so terribly, that the only way to get myself out of this feeling was to hold off feeding Peter until after they had all left. This I did and found that when the sad feeling came over me and I felt so alone, I would then have yet another lesson to do with Peter. At the end of the lesson I would be so involved with Peter and what had gone on during the lesson, that I avoided the empty feeling I dreaded. When I was expecting a human visitor in the evening I was very excited, elated. I almost always found, however, that when the visitor left I was sadder and lonelier than I was without a visitor. (I seldom had visitors.)

The feelings of depression and aloneness were not a constant thing by any means, but they did come and go, and my having to turn to Peter to overcome them was, I feel, an important part of the experiment. [Margaret has not read any of the solitary sailing, alone in the polar night or the isolation experiments literatures. She is acquainted with some of the things that I have told her of this area of isolation. I feel that her description here is definitively her own and that little, if anything, of this is suggested from outside. There is an interesting correspondence here with experiences of other people isolated alone.]

This is the end of Margaret's notes made *during* the experiment. Following is additional data compiled *after* the experiment.

6

Vocal Exchanges Between
Margaret and Peter

Before moving into the tape analysis part of this report, we would like to say something of the difficulties in this area, and of our frustration in not being able to turn you into the *listener*, rather than into the *reader*.[1]

To date there is no way that we know of to *print* something so that you can *hear* it. We are limited to several ways of writing about, or describing sound, or even diagramming sound. No one of these methods, or the sum total of these methods, can give you the sound itself. So many aspects of a lesson with a dolphin and a human can be described, so much about the sounds made can be learned by *reading*, so much about the sounds can be learned by *looking* at a diagram, that we feel it is well worthwhile to use as many ways as we can to give you as much of a picture of the sounds as possible.

We do emphasize, however, that each one of these methods can only tell you some aspects of the sounds:

[1] Arrangements can be made to obtain a copy of a tape of samples of sessions showing Margaret and Peter's vocal progress in a year's work ending with this 2½-month period by writing to Paul Herbert, Hot Springs Lodge, Big Sur, Calif. 93920. It is also available on a Folkways record, New York, N.Y.

the following part of this report is intended to inform to the best of our ability about the vocal aspects of this experiment.

Miss Howe has devised a method of sampling the tapes made during these 2½ months and during the previous time giving her interactions with Peter on a vocal level. The following section is devoted to these representations that she has worked out, of typical short samples chosen from longer tape records.

Since these tapes are so important to the transmission of information the segments that are used for transcription are copied and placed together in proper calendar sequence and will form a part of this record.

Some samples for pronunciation analysis were selected for analysis by the sound spectrograph. Sonograms of Peter and Margaret pronouncing the same word again and again form part of these data.

The following is an attempt to transcribe portions of tapes in such a way so that the reader can gain a better understanding of the kind of thing that goes on in a lesson with the dolphin Peter. It is *not* an attempt to accurately describe the exact sounds made by the dolphin, but rather to show the progress, over a period of several months, that took place between the human and the dolphin in the teacher-pupil relationship. The transcription method is set up as follows:

1. Two lines are read at a time, as in a staff of music. One line is MH (Margaret Howe), and the other line is PD (Peter Dolphin).

2. The symbol c is used to designate a click, whistle, or any other form of "delphinese." Thus a series of clicks may be written ccccccc. An exact count of the clicks is not represented here, and ccccc does not mean six clicks . . . it simply means a series of clicks.

3. The symbol x is used to designate a humanoid sound made by the dolphin which is *not a clear enough hu-*

manoid to accurately describe phonetically. Thus is a humanoid attempt by the dolphin.

4. When the humanoid attempt is clear enough to be written phonetically in English, it is described as best as possible. Thus "oie" may be an attempt at "boy" . . . without the "b."

5. Instructions to Peter spoken by MH are in lower case, and words to be copied by Peter are in capitals. Thus, "Peter, please say HELLO MAGRIT."

6. Brief summary notes follow each transcription.

7. These transcriptions are of only the air-borne sounds as they are recorded on the tapes. All underwater sounds are kept out of this account.

Sample Seven Months Before 2½-Month Experiment
(November 3, 1964)

MH	SPEAK GOOD	SPEAK GOOD BOIE
PD	cccc	cccccxx xx

MH	Good, Peter, good! Now you're going! Yes,
PD	cccccccccxxx

MH		SPEAK	Good boy! SPEAK
PD	cccccccccxxx	cccccccxxoi	

MH	GOOD BOIE	SPEAK GOOD BOIE.
PD	cccc	xx

Dr. Lilly (JCL) has just arrived and Peter is taking a break to see what's happening.

MH	SPEAK	GOOD BOIE	Good boy. (JCL
PD	ccccccccccc	cccc xx xx	

MH	in background) Did you hear that?
PD	cccc

MH	Speak GOOD BOIE	SPEAK GOOD
PD	c c c c c c c c c c ccccc	

MH	BOIE	SPEAK GOOD	(Giggle)	yes,
PD	xxx	xxxxx		oii

MH come on, take a fish   (JCL voice in back-
PD   xxxxxxcccc

MH ground) MH and JCL chat. SPEAK GOOD BOIE
PD   xx

MH SPEAK GOOD BOIE   (JCL in background)
PD   ccc   xxx

MH Who is that, Peter? (JCL voice) Come on . . . SPEAK
    GOOD BOIE
PD

MH (JCL voice) SPEAK   GOOD BOIE
PD   cccccccc   ccccc

1. Repetition of SPEAK GOOD BOIE by Margaret over
   and over, an attempt to get Peter to respond in
   humanoid.
2. Peter responds mainly in delphinese clicks . . . only
   a few humanoids.
3. Peter often speaks (clicks) while Margaret is still
   speaking.
4. Lesson is interruptible . . . Peter and Margaret are
   not "meshing gears" . . . there is a rather loose structure to the lesson.

Sample Six Months Before 2½-Month Experiment

MH Sssssssshhh I AM SUCH A GOOD BOIE
PD   cccccccxxxxccc

MH   No, Peter, sssshhh. SPEAK
PD ccxxxx xxx xx (shrill)

MH GOOD   No, no. Shhhh SPEAK GOOD BOIE
PD   xxxxxx (shrill)

MH FOR FISH   shhh DO NOT
PD   xxxxxcccxx (shrill) cccc

MH PLAY   shhhhhhh, Peter, DO NOT PLAY
PD cccccccccccccc   cccccxxxxxccxxx

MH Yes, sshhhh SPEAK GOOD BOIE   SPEAK
PD xxx   ccccc xx cc

MH GOOD BOIE   John, that telephone is ring-
PD   xxxx (shrill)

MH ing. SPEAK FOR FISH GOOD BOIE   HELLO
PD   ccccxxxx (weak)

MH ELVAR HELLO ELVAR   SPEAK AND
PD   c ccc xxx lo xxx

MH EAT   No no, sssssshhhh ssssshhhh
PD xxxx ccccc xx (shrill)   c c c x x x c c c c x x x

MH SPEAK AND EAT   SAY GOOD
PD   xxxxxx ccccccxxxx C

MH BOIE   SAY GOOD BOIE   ssshh
PD CCCCCCC   ccccccccccccccccccxx

MH come on,   I MUST SPEAK FOR FISH   I
PD   xxxxccxx   xxxxx cccc xxx

MH WILL SPEAK AND EAT NOW ssshhhh, no Peter
PD ccccc   ccc xxx (shrill)   ccccxx

MH   I WILL SPEAK AND EAT
PD (shrill blasts)   ccccccxxxxx (shrill)

1. Peter is still doing a lot of delphinese clicking.
2. He is beginning to give a few more humanoids, but
   these are in the form of shrill blasts.
3. He still interrupts Margaret and vocalizes while she
   speaks.

Five Months Previously (January 5, 1965)

MH AIR OWN EMM   SAY NO ETCH EIM
PD cccc cc   cc xxx xx

MH   SIGH IT ARE   I'll go from lesson
PD xx cc xxx   xxxx ccc xxx

MH eleven back into lesson number eight   listen
PD   ccc xxxx cc xxx

MH TOI   OIT   OICH CHOIE OIT
PD   cc   cc xxx cc   c c c c

MH   COIE OIT COIE TOIE
PD ccccc xxxxx xxxx   xxxx ccc xxxxx

MH say GOOD BOIE GOOD BOIE   OIEZ
PD   ccc xx   xxxxx ccc xxx

MH ZOIE OIS CHOIE   OIE Peter, say BOIE . . .
PD   ccc xxxxx

MH GOOD BOIE   I AM A GOOD BOIE
PD   xxxxxcccxxxxx   ccc   c c c c c

MH   SPEAK GOOD BOIE
PD xxxxx cccc xxxx   ccc xxxx xxx

MH TOIE OIE SOIE ROIE   OIE say
PD   cccc xxxxx ccc xxx c c

MH OIE   GOOD BOIE   OIM MOI LOI
PD   xxxx c   cccc xxxx ccc

MH OIT   OIL   murmur OIL LOI ROI OIK
PD   cxxxx   xxxxx

MH   Listen . . . OIL LOI ROI OIK
PD ccc xxx ccc xx   xx oi xx c

MH OIZ ZOI OIS CHOI   (murmur) OIL LOI ROI
PD   xxx ow xxx

MH OIK   say GOOD BOIE   nope . . .
PD xx xx xxx xxx xxxx   ccc xxx xxx

MH GOOD BOIE   GOOD BOIE (high)
PD xxxxxxxxx

1. Peter is giving more and more humanoid responses.
Still some clicks.

2. Peter interrupts occasionally, but is getting a nice sense of listen, speak, listen, speak.

3. Words used by Margaret are from a nonsense syllable list designed to present combinations of sounds to the dolphin.

MH	Peter, say HELLO yes . . . say GOOD BOIE . . .
PD	ccxxxx xxlo

MH	GOOD BOIE . . . Come on, Peter, say GOOD BOIE
PD	xxxccxxxccxxx

MH	Nice. English, Peter, pronounce. Say
PD	xx xx

MH	MARGARET . . . come on MA No! Listen.
PD	cccvv xx

MH	MARGARET Not very good say HELLO
PD	xxxxx xxc ccc xxaw baw

MH	That's better say HELLO MARGARET
PD	cccc cccxx uh uh uh

MH	uh uh . . . listen, listen HELLO MARGARET
PD	awxxx e

MH	nice nice listen listen listen say HELLO
PD	awxxxx ccccc c c c ccccc

MH	GOOD BOY We are going to speak Eng-
PD	cc c ccxxxw aw xxx

MH	lish yet, Peter . . . say HUMANOID . . . HUMAN-
PD	

MH	OID No! That's not right. Say . . . BALL
PD	xxxxx awxxx

MH	No! Listen Listen, listen BALL
PD	ccccxxx cccccccxxxxaw

MH	O.K. HELLO uh uh uh listen listen HELLO
PD	cc uh uh cc

MH	Uh uh Peter, I don't mean to bore you but
PD	xxxxxxxx

MH	you say it right and then we'll go on. Hmmm? You
PD	

MH	didn't say it right. Now listen. HELLO Pretty
PD	xxxx xx

MH	good, pretty good. n'uh un uh now listen,
PD	ccccxxx c c c c c c c

MH	listen listen listen Peter sssssh, say MARGARET
PD	c c c c c xx ccc

MH	uh uh no! Wrong MARGARET.
PD	uh uh uh xx uh uh uh uh

MH	Peter! That's noise!
PD	xxx

1. Peter still clicks, but mainly humanoid.
2. Some of his humanoids are beginning to shape into English sounds.
3. Peter still interrupts Margaret, but occasionally hushes when told to. Whole lesson is shaping up.

After Ten Days of Living Together Twenty-four Hours per Day (June 8, 1965)

MH	Say . . . MAGRIT all right sssssssh
PD	ccccc xxx xxx xxx xxxx

MH	listen listen no! Listen! Listen, Peter! Listen no!
PD	xxxx xxxxxx xxx xxxxowxxxxxxxx

MH	Listen Peter! sshhhh HELLO MAGRIT
PD	xxxxxxxx xx xxx xx xxxx xxxxx

MH	GOOD BOIE GOOD BOIE Come on . . .
PD	xxxx xxx

MH	Listen, listen. no no no . . . say GOOD
PD	xxxxxx xx

MH   BOIE   Peter! Listen to me! Now stop it! no!
PD   xxxxbxxxxxxxxx   x x x x x   x x x x x x x x x

MH   no! no! Listen Peter, shhhh shhhh   say GOOD BOIE
PD   xxxx xxx   xxxxx

MH   Oh, he just won't listen to me. HELLO
PD   xxxxx   xxx

MH   thank you, that's good. MAGRIT   all right I
PD   cccccxxx xxxx

MH   Am   all right GOOD BOIE   all right no,
PD   axxx xxx   xxx Bxxx xxx   xxx

MH   listen, no no no no shhhh listen   listen   listen Peter
PD   xxxxxxxxxxxxxx xxxxxxx   xxxxxxx

MH   HELLO   no, he's just getting   HELLO
PD   xxxxx   xxxxxxxxx   xxxxxx

MH   HOW ARE YOU?   No, not very good, Peter.
PD   xxxx xxx   xxxx

MH   HOW   Listen, Peter, no no no no ssshhhh . . .
PD   xxx   xxxx x x x x x x x x x x x x x x x

1. Peter replies in almost solid humanoids. Very few
   clicks.
2. He has lost his beginning sense of conversation . . .
   again, he interrupts Margaret. He speaks at the
   same time.
3. Time is spent trying to get him to listen . . . hush.

After Sixty-three Days and Nights (August 10, 1965)
(Plate 31)

MH   MAGRIT   All right, listen . . . BALL
PD   xxx xxx   xx xx

MH   Peter . . . BALL   BALL   Yes. Say TOIE
PD   x xx xx   xxaw

MH   FISH   listen . . . TOIE FISH   murmur come
PD   aw   xxx xxx

MH	over here, Peter. Say BO BO CLOWN
PD	xxx xxx xxx

MH	Let's do it again. Pronounce, Peter BO BO CLOWN
PD	xxo

MH	nice. KI NI PO PO Listen . . .
PD	oh xxx xx xx xx xx

MH	KI NI PO PO That's better. murmur
PD	xx xx xx xoh

MH	MAGRIT Listen, MAGRIT No . . .
PD	xx xx xx xx xx xx

MH	MAGRIT No, Peter. Listen, MAGRIT
PD	xx xx ee xx xx xx

MH	MAGRIT better. Say HELLO MAGRIT
PD	xxx xxx xxx

MH	Pronounce, Peter. HELLO MAGRIT
PD	xxx xxx xxx xxx

MH	That's better, Peter. Say BO BO CLOWN
PD	ohh aaa xxx xxx

MH	Listen. BO BO CLOWN Listen . . . BO BO
PD	xxx xxx xxx xx

MH	CLOWN Listen, Peter, BO BO CLOWN
PD	xxx xxx ownxx xx xx xx

1. Peter no longer clicks or gives any delphinese responses.
2. Peter listens, speaks. When he is wrong, Margaret can hush him and start over.
3. Peter improves in giving back the same number of sounds that are given to him.
4. Peter is able to make parts of his words understandable.
5. Less is controlled, progress can be seen and heard during even such a short segment.

After the Experimental Period Is Finished (October 8, 1965)
(Plate 32)

MH Now you think, Peter, 'cause you used to do this.
PD

MH Listen. BA BEE BLOCK   Yes! (clapping)
PD   mxx xxx

MH That's better. Now do the other one. Say . . . BA
PD

MH SKET BALL   No, BA SKET BALL
PD xx   xx xx xx   xxxx xx xx

MH Better. shhh! MAGRIT   No. It's EMMMMMM
PD   xxx   xxx xxx

MH (ends with a kiss on Peter's head) say . . . MMAGRIT
PD

MH   no, not EH. It's MMM. Eh . . . MMM
PD eh xxx

MH MMMMMM MMAGRIT   Yes! Yes! (clap-
PD   (softly) Mxx xxx

MH ping) That's an EM. Let's do it again. Say . . .
PD

MH MMAGRIT   Yes, that's better. (clapping)
PD   mxxx xxx

MH Good! Say . . . BALL   No, not MAGRIT.
PD   xxx xxx

MH BALL with a BEE. Say . . . BALL   Yes! BAWL!
PD   baww

MH Good! Say . . . MMAGRIT   No . . . not EH.
PD   eh xxx

MH MMMMM. MMMMM. MMAGRIT   Yes
PD   mxx xxx

MH . . . that's better . . . that's better, Peter . . . Good!
PD

MH Yes, you can muffle it (clap)
PD

1. Note that Margaret syncopates "baby block" and "basketball" and Peter learns to follow this.

2. Note Peter speaks out of turn and is immediately hushed in lines seven and eight.

3. Note Peter, for the main part, is responding with humanoids, the right number with usually a good pitch and inflection. Margaret begins to demand more . . . working on enunciation. Special sounds.

4. The lesson is controlled and formal, and the give-and-take of learning, teaching, speaking, and listening is established so that progress can be seen.

7

Conclusions About Living
with a Dolphin

Some of the photographs in this book with their captions illustrate many of the points made in the body of Margaret's writing. In order to appreciate the magnitude of many of the tasks she mentioned, these photographs should be studied.

The conclusions are divided up into two sections: those by Margaret Howe, summing up the findings, and those by John Lilly.

Margaret writes as follows:

General conclusions about learning ability of dolphins. (a) It is difficult to record all the information Peter has learned in this program. Dolphins not only can learn, but enjoy learning, learn fast, and they have learned lots of things we cannot know about. We limit the information. (b) Dolphins can learn to play *with* someone. At the beginning of these 2½ months, Peter would not share his toys . . . he played alone, was often the initiator of a game with a human. (c) Peter learned *how* to work during a vocal lesson (as taught by the human) and also made vocal progress. (d) Peter learned how to teach me. (e) Peter learned to curb his physical energies to allow for my being so "human." (f) Peter learned that he could please me immensely, as well as annoy me.

Vocal progress made by Peter is as follows:

The written tape transcriptions show the following steps in progress, early to late. 1. Peter mainly clicks, a few humanoids, interrupts me. 2. Peter gives me more and more humanoids, still interrupts. 3. Peter begins to listen, gains a sense of conversation. 4. Peter learns to hush when I shush him . . . I can correct him. 5. Peter makes good attempts at copying my speech, at the same time keeping a good listen, speak, listen, speak business.

The written tape transcription does *not* show the following steps that were also made in progress: 1. Peter learned to copy the inflection in my voice very well. When my voice rises in the last part of a word, Peter's also rises. 2. Peter learned to be relatively quiet in the water during a lesson. Early lessons are filled with Peter splashing around and often circling the room during a lesson. At the end of the period, he remains in one place during the whole lesson, involved in his part in the lesson. He *listens*. 3. Peter learned to watch what I am doing during a lesson. If I am counting balls, or pointing to shapes, Peter will lie on his side, and I can see his eye look at the objects. 4. Peter has learned to work for whatever he gains out of the lesson as well as my vocal and physical praise, rather than for a fish reward. Peter will enter into a humanoid conversation, speaking and listening, at any time of day or night . . . *no longer just during feedings*. This has been so successful, that now Peter himself will often call to me or start to speak when I am with him, and I find that the lesson or conversation that follows was actually started by Peter. Our formal lessons are still done during feedings, but the fish itself is not used as a reward. Peter gets fed all the fish during the same approximate period of time whether it is a good lesson or a horror. When he gives a poor response, he gets a fish, and a vocal scolding from me. When he is brilliant, he gets a fish and a vocal praising from me.

Conclusions from 2½ months' program for designing future flooded house are as follows: The main conclusion is that this program has shown that this type of living situation is very worthwhile, and that the longer, more permanent flooded house program may prove invaluable as a step in breaking the communication barrier between man and dolphin, and therefore must be achieved.

There are several minor points learned during the course of this program that will prove valuable in the longer program: 1. More work must be done on the diet of the human. This program showed that lots of canned goods, spaghetti, etc., allowed the person to stay healthy, but a considerable gain in weight was noted. Refrigeration would help this problem. 2. Margaret felt, after her one week live-in with Pamela, that even her short bobbed hair was too long, and tended to stay damp through the day and night, and took too long drying when completely wet. For the 2½-month program, she cut her hair into a very boyish cut, about one-quarter inch all over. This could be completely dried with a towel in a matter of a few minutes, and was easy to keep clean and free from salty stickiness and itching. She did this, not only for reasons of health, but also for the advantage of not having to resist leaping in with the dolphin at, say, an odd hour of the night just because she wanted to keep her head dry. (Margaret is determined that nothing as trivial as wet hair should stop just such spontaneous play.) 3. Sleeping must be improved. Being able to sleep in a dry, comfortable bed each night would eliminate much of the discomfort in the program. This must not, however, be done in such a way as to remove the human from the dolphin's area . . . the dolphin must be able to rouse the human at any time. This could be done vocally, however, and not with splashing. Being able to touch and see Peter from her bed was very important . . . this closeness should not be sacrificed for dryness. Perhaps a more rigid curtain around the bed would be appropriate. 4. Being able to shower (fresh water) and get into bed without touching saltwater would be almost a necessity for a period much longer than 2½ months. 5. The human operator involved in the longer program should not have outside responsibilities at the same time. Note that Margaret was distracted or worried by outside construction problems, health of other animals, workmen problems, etc. Pumps, electricity, refrigeration, food, etc. should not be handled by operator . . . but should be taken care of by outside personnel. 6. Flooded house area should contain within it as much variety of living for humans as possible. Several rooms, different sections, a good dry area, an interesting wet area, . . . etc. Note that the two rooms proved to be a rather dull environment for two months. Activity for the human was limited. Note activity for dolphin was also limited . . . and recommend deep area for dolphin relaxation. 7. Sufficient time out must be allotted the human to avoid negative results (lag in interest) of isolation effects. Positive effects, however, of isolation effect (closeness with dolphin) should not be avoided.

One major result is that all of the time, energy, money, self-dedication, and facility development have been eminently worthwhile. I feel that we are in the midst of a new "becoming," moving into a previous unknown, armed with a kind of knowledge that we could not have obtained except through these experiments. I wish to emphasize (and not overanalyze) at this stage of our human development that new totally unexpected sequences of events took place. These events were ably reported by Margaret Howe. In addition much that is not yet consciously reportable has taken place in Miss Howe. Also much that neither she nor I have yet been able to get at in the human-dolphin relationship and in the dolphin. Currently this group is on their way and, I feel strongly, on the right way. This and similar endeavors should be supported and enthusiastically encouraged in order to continue toward the flooded house program.

I personally have learned much new about dolphins, much new about a first-class human faced with a dolphin for long periods. I have learned some new things about the abilities of man and a dolphin in carrying out a good-natured, yet serious wet living together program.

I find that the information collected shows that the assumptions on which this project is founded are productive of new facts. Margaret tests out the assumptions with intelligent and emotional interactions between herself and the dolphin. The only limitations of this kind of research are in our conceptions as carried to this work, modified in the course of this work, and used in planning future more comprehensive contexts for this kind of shared living.

In this sort of work it is wise to minimize the gadgetry, and to maximize the use of one's self. It may be that the fundamental barriers which do exist between these two species may be overcome by Miss Howe's dedicated efforts unaided by devices created for human-dolphin communication. (Another project of CRI is exploring the possibility of surmounting the frequency barrier between human speech and "delphinese." If it turns out that the frequency barrier is the limiting one, then the developed electronic means may be employed.)

Our major goal is breaking the interspecies communication barrier so that we can mutually exchange information having descriptive, predictive, and cognitive meanings. Until we live with dolphins and they with us, the dolphin mind remains opaque to us, and the human mind remains dryly out of reach of dolphin teaching.

Miss Howe did a magnificent job. She now rates a long earned vacation. Her intraspecies needs finally are being taken care of: she, like the woman with the chimpanzees in Africa, married her photographer. For a year or so she will tend her own family, human only. It may be that eventually she will be able to arrange to have a dolphin in her family with her children as one more "child."

Peter has been returned to his dolphin friends for his well-earned vacation from a human—for a while. Some person other than Margaret may continue the work.

8

The Importance of
Interspecies Communication

Man may be on the threshold of a new area of discovery in the field of communication with beings other than the human ones. The newly accelerated space programs of the Soviet Union and the United States have led to the lunar landings of man. The probing of other planets by means of interplanetary vehicles has already started with the Mariner series. The plans for the first biological samplings from the planet Mars are nearly completed. Plans and projects for the detection of extraterrestrial, intelligent, communicating life forms have been formulated. (One such project, called Ozma, failed to find narrow-band signals from the stars Tau Ceti and Alpha Eridani.)

Thus it can be seen that some scientists, some engineers, and some administrators within certain government agencies are seriously engaged in planning for the *detection* of nonhuman, intelligent beings from outside the earth. However, there is no public evidence that any plans are being formulated as to the possible ways of dealing with these beings if and when they are detected. Serious consideration of research plans in this area is not yet respectable; detection, yes; dealing with them, no. It is necessary, scientifically, to consider well in advance the areas for future research. I believe it is important that we consider possible ways of dealing with nonhuman intelligent life forms before the duty is forced upon us. We must decide what humans with what training, with what motivations should make the first contacts. I would not like to see certain kinds of human beings start the initial contacts with the other beings. We should consider carefully the kinds of human beings which are best suited for this kind of contact. It is about time that man consider the kinds of men, the desirable traits and qualifications of those persons who will be in control of this kind of important communication.

For example, highly classified, top-secret military plans may already be formulated for dealing with such beings. I hope not. The last thing we need is a closed, military-secret treatment of this subject. This would be an assurance that the wrong kinds of human beings would make the first contacts and probably spoil those contacts forever. This subject needs public airing, with a fresh breath of youthful minds freely discussing possibilities, ways, and means. The military approach of necessity is on the offensive-defensive logical base. The necessary curiosity and the necessary love with which such beings should be met are something that military minds leave at home when they go to the office. Currently we need responsible, competent humanists in this field: the need for them is so great that it looks as if it spells the difference between success and possible disaster on an unprecedented scale. (With the current picture as it is, I would advise any being greater or lesser than we are not to contact us. In our present state of development, we are still unsuitably organized and unsuitably educated to make contact.)

Our present military potential is great enough to kill not only all human beings but all life forms on the land

and in the sea. It may sound a bit silly to go beyond this potential for cataclysm, but modern military minds are carrying the power to create cataclysms even further. It takes only an elementary knowledge of modern nuclear and particle physics to see the trend to the ultimate Armageddon of vast released energies destroying planets. It takes only an elementary knowledge of what is happening in the United Nations, in the Far East, between the United States and the Soviet Union to see the brink of the release of these vast energies. *Homo sapiens* is fast developing the means of destroying this planet as a habitable abode for all of life as we know it. It may be that this is the natural course for our form of life. It may be that it is destined for this type of self-destruction. It may be that the evil in enough of us is destined to destroy the whole of us.

I sincerely hope and pray that this is not so. I hope that my children and their children have the opportunities to pursue beauty, goodness, truth, and self-fulfillment that I have had. It may be that I have not taken enough of the responsibility against this evil in my own lifetime. The old saying that one is either a missionary or a scientist, not both, may be a disguised, evil way of regulating too much of my life. Let me illustrate this point by the story of my contacts with one of the scientists turned "missionary" to try to eradicate the evil implicit in the use of atomic energy in our era.

Dr. Leo Szilard met several times with me in 1958. He later used information he gained in our talks to write a parable of the dolphins and of man.[1]

This parable was in the service of Dr. Szilard's humanitarian ethic and hope of elimination of the military control of the vast sources of energy by the physicists. Szilard turned from physics to become a missionary in the hu-

[1] Szilard, Leo, "Voice of the Dolphins" (1961).

manitarian tradition. When I first met with him we were both in a great medical research center. We were about as far from destructive evil as each of us could be. He had lately embarked on a search for the scientific bases of human memory. In the course of his search, he was interviewing me along with many other scientists who had worked on the brain.

At this time I had completed some of my investigations of the dolphins. I had just decided to leave that particular institution and start a new institute devoted to dolphin research.

He told me of his hopes of the peaceful uses of nuclear energy and of banning the military use of it. Apparently to test me, he argued with me about the dolphin project; he elicited in our discussion all the facts I then knew. He elicited my theories about their intelligence and "languages" and my ideas about the consequences of these theories, and the consequences of communication with them.

At the time, he tried to persuade me to stay at the medical center. He met every one of my reasons for leaving. At that time I had made up my mind. I wasn't to be dissuaded. For what I wanted to accomplish, I feel that I was right. For what he wanted to do, he was right. If I had wanted to be a humanitarian and a missionary and work with him, I would have stayed.

In his parable he based his "Vienna Institute" on the model of the present Communication Research Institute that I had already planned in my own mind and had imparted to him. In this parable, the dolphins solve many of men's problems by sheer intellectual superiority. This is a fantasy, of course. We named the species of dolphin that could accomplish this after Szilard; we call them *"Delphinus szilardiensis."* The characteristics of this species are any characteristics that Szilard wished to give them. He enjoyed this joke.

Before Szilard died, we talked several more times. I was more and more involved in the creation of the new research institute. He became more and more involved in the "ban-the-bomb" efforts which were then in progress.

Today, I feel closer to Szilard's ideals than I could have at that time. The danger has increased with the entry of China into the nuclear warfare race. It may be that there will be no time left for humans to prepare to begin to really communicate with the dolphins and the whales. It may be that we are all doomed to extinction before such an ideal can be realized. Szilard's fantasy of human-dolphin intellectual teamwork may remain a fantasy because it did not have a chance to be tested or to be realized. In fact, intellectual teamwork of humans with any other being (possibly greater than we) may never come to pass. The true race of today is not a military race, it is a race between humanitarianism, no matter where found, and militarism, no matter where supported. If the military forces destroy us, then everything great that man has accomplished (including nuclear energy and the vast sources of energies beyond the present ones such as those existing in anti-matter) end in nothing. Somewhere else, someone else may know we ended our own existence, though we cannot then know whether they do or not. We may end in several small flashes or in one big flash sent out into the eternal blackness of the cosmos. If there is anyone else watching in the proper regions of the electromagnetic spectrum, they may try to account for the demise of this planet by a theory that it happened through purely passive, nuclear planetary and stellar forces and energies. On the other hand, they may be advanced enough to know that we destroyed ourselves through these energies.

Personally, I would rather see how it comes out. A friend of mine once tried to commit suicide. We talked all one night; finally he agreed not to take his own life.

(I am not sure that he would have committed suicide, even without the talk we had that night.) However, he later said that the most cogent and helpful thing that I said to him was, "If you commit suicide, you won't be around to see how it all turns out." I hope that the destructive ones of our species are curious enough to want "to see how it all turns out." I further hope that they can control themselves and others in order to control these awful forces enough to be able to save all of us.

Historically then, the Communication Research Institute was born out of an effort to create a new research institute devoted strictly to peaceful projects. If we are to destroy ourselves, there is no point at all in the kinds of research which I am doing and which I propose doing in the future through the Institute. Therefore, I must believe we will live on. There must be people like myself who insist we will live on, who insist on doing these projects in the face of the imminent demise of the planet Earth. Otherwise, such projects will always give way to other "defense" projects. I asked myself again and again should I not participate, along with Szilard, in attempting to be in control over atomic energy for peaceful purposes?

My argument to myself ran somewhat as follows: Why do we fight wars at all? We do it as a defensive measure because we are attacked by others. We do it because it is necessary for the health of the nation as a whole in order to keep up maximum production of a huge industrial machine. We do it to protect that which we hold most dear and to maintain those institutions and those activities which we consider to be ideal in terms of the future progress of our species.

I choose to consider interspecies communication one of these ideal activities, i.e., one of those activities for which we have created a military machine in order to be able to carry on that activity in a protected and fostering atmosphere, as it were, behind the lines of the military perimeter. Without dedicated people who persist in scientific research which is oriented toward an idealistic set of aims and goals, we may as well give up the ghost as a progressive species and sink into a new dark age. If all of us get out and fight, do development only of weapons, then no one is left at home to bring us farther along the road out of our abysmal "peacetime" ignorance.

What is it basically, deep down underneath, behind the apparent façade that communication with another species may possibly give to man? Szilard attempted to answer this question with his parable. If one reads his story, one can detect a bit of making fun of man and his current needs. He arranged it so the dolphins in the Vienna Institute gave easy and facile answers to all of the major problems facing man today. For example, the peoples of the world were fed by one of the dolphin's inventions.

We may obtain the cooperation, say, of the dolphins and get them to work on the major problems facing us. They may in their original alienness be able to see our problems more objectively than we can see them and to solve them for us. They may have, and today we still do not fully factually know this, an intellect superior to ours, as Szilard assumes.

If interspecies communication is to exist at all, I feel that it will give us far more than just facile solutions to man's problems. As a result of my experience and experiments with dolphins, I feel that they have much to teach us which is new to us and that we have much that is new to teach them. Our work on the problems of importance to dolphins, and whomever else they may be communicating with, may be our best contribution to them and may be our best contribution to ourselves. Sometimes I feel that if man could become more involved in some problems of an alien species, he may become less involved with his own egocentric pursuits, and deadly competition within his species, and become somehow a better being.

I wish to underscore and to emphasize the cooperative aspect of this interspecies communication attempt. When we make the assumptions that we do on this project, we also must face the consequences. We have found that we cannot make the kind of progress that we wish to make with dolphins unless we give them the respect that we give to one another. We find that we cannot proceed and make progress with a given dolphin unless we treat that dolphin with gentleness, with politeness, with respect, and with discipline of a special sort. We find that a young dolphin will, quite as unashamedly as a young human, take advantage of our good nature. We and they need and want mutual respect and mutual discipline. Our group and they do not want unilateral exploitation by man. Our group and our dolphins do not want unilateral exploitation of man by the dolphins.

The whole philosophy that says that the one species must rule the other species has been cast out of the thinking of myself and my colleagues. We are often asked, "If the dolphins are so intelligent, why aren't they ruling the world?" My very considered answer to this is—they may be too wise to try to rule the world. The question can be easily turned around, Why does man or individual men want to rule the world? I feel that it is a very insecure position to want to rule all of the other species and the vast resources of our planet. This means a deep insecurity with the "universes" inside of one's self. One's fears and one's angers are being projected on others outside of one's self; to rule the world is, finally, to rule one's inner realities.

It is my deep feeling that unless we work with respect, with discipline, and with gentleness with the dolphins that they will once more turn away from us. Apparently at the time of Aristotle or just preceding his time, the dolphins approached man. By A.D. 50 in the time of the Romans, they had turned away from man not to come back until this century. This is one-half of the view. To be complete, we must say that at the time of Aristotle man turned toward the dolphins. It is only in this century that we once again seek the dolphins. I prefer the view that each of us has sought the other, at least twice, once 500 B.C. to 200 B.C. and once again in the twentieth century.

Exploitations of dolphins by men are not only a disgrace to our humanitarian ideals but also are a definite handicap to our possible future with them. If we are to communicate with them on anything but a "bright animal" kind of exchange, we had best show them our best side from the beginning. Their present relationships with us are pretty well restricted to their "entertainment value" and some uses the Navy is making of them. If our future with them is to have wider horizons, we must bring those wider horizons to our work with them.

If we think of dolphins as "lower animals," then we will not even attempt to meet them as "equals" worthy of our efforts. If we think of them as "bright, intelligent animals serving man" in entertainment, in circuses, and on television, we are favoring a segregationist point of view. Currently, we place dolphins "over there," with chimpanzees, performing dogs, and fictional horses that talk to TV audiences. Currently, in the entertainment media, dolphins are equivalent to "good boy"-type dogs, similar to Lassie.

If we "teach" them to aid our underwater work in the sea as glorified "seeing-eye dogs" of the Navy, of oceanographers and of divers, we are far from my goals for them. This sort of a relationship ("fetch and carry") is not between equals. Slavery (man to man) has had a long history in our species. Persons can still "buy" dolphins from other persons even though they cannot "buy" another human being. As long as the legal view of dolphins is that of "animals," they will still be an article of commerce to be exploited for man's purposes. The dolphins are not yet protected even under "animal conservation" laws.

It may be that the word "equal" is not quite the term to use for dolphin-human comparisons. A dolphin can be what I call a "cognitive equal" with a human being and still be an alien and strange mind as seen by the human. We must somehow translate the Golden Rule, and the dolphin will have to do the same, for use between such strange, likable, cooperative beings. As one of the "others" in the Golden Rule, neither his appearance nor his alienness of thought should deter us or him. Both sides will have to search for the bases of equality. The United Nations does not recognize race, color, or creed as a means of differentiation between human beings. Let us add "species" and use this approach as a good example of the kind of thinking which we should be applying to the dolphins and whales. In addition to race, color, creed, and religious beliefs, the new criteria should read: *"No matter differences between species, no matter differences of anatomy, no matter differences between media in which they live, creatures with a brain above a certain size will be considered 'equal' with man."*

Currently, without this point of view we may be doing violence to dolphins. It may turn out, for example, that the worst thing in the world to do to a dolphin is to lock him up in a closed tank (of any size) and give him free food and free care. This is among the worst things that can be done to one of us. Consider those cases in which we do it to one another.

Even the places where persons are confined like dolphins have a very poor reputation. We call places where we give free food and free care to people who are locked up, "prisons," "state hospitals for the insane," "prisoner-of-war camps," etc. A very poor press. In other words, among our most cherished ideals for each of ourselves and each of our loved ones are civil rights, personal freedom, private enterprise, and private initiative. From this point of view we are mistreating the dolphins.

Let us look at our present dealings with dolphins from the humanitarian viewpoint. In order to get the feel of the dolphin's situation with respect to us imagine that we as a species are placed in their position by "invaders from outer space."

The invaders arrive in their interstellar space ships. Their appearance is totally alien to us. The aim of the invaders is to collect humans as interesting bright animal specimens for displays in their zoos, in their circuses, in their schools, in their medical research institutes, and in their universities. These displays are primarily for entertainment and scientific purposes. They treat us even as we currently treat the dolphins.

These invaders cannot live in air. There is too much nitrogen in our atmosphere for them to be comfortable. On their planet nitrogen is their source of energy, even as oxygen in our atmosphere is our source of energy. Even as 100 per cent oxygen is eventually poisonous to humans, so is 80 per cent nitrogen to the aliens. By special means not yet known to us, the invaders modify the air of our planet for their own use.

After long study the invaders find out how to capture human specimens. They study us for a long time. They learn how curious some of us are about anything new; they learn how repelled we are by the invaders' true appearance. They learn how upset some of us become by the death or disappearance of loved ones. They learn how to influence the general directions of the thinking of large numbers of humans.

Once they are able to influence the thinking in the mass, they devise "warfare between humans" to facilitate their collection of human specimens. When the order comes from the invaders' planet to collect more human specimens, a war is started among human beings. During the chaos attendant upon the war, they collect human specimens as needed. Large explosions, large fires, and disappearances at sea are used as covers. When the invaders collect humans not under these covers, a small flurry of interest is created in the human press by the unexplained disappearances.

Even as in our collection of dolphins, the invaders have trouble with their collection program. At first, most of their human specimens die. The causes of death are not too well known nor are they thoroughly studied by the invaders. So many humans are available, however, that the invader collectors do not worry about those who are lost. When they find that they are losing all of them, they begin to investigate the possible causes.

After many years the invaders discover that humans need oxygen to breathe. They asphyxiate their first specimens by keeping them in an oxygen-free atmosphere in their spacecraft. All that the invaders can obtain are anatomical specimens for scientific investigation back on their home planet.

This lack of success keeping the specimens alive opens up a whole new science on the planet of the invaders. They call it "interplanetary zoology." Under this title they begin their study of human physiology. They discover the humans' need for oxygen; they keep them in special tanks containing 20 per cent oxygen and 80 per cent nitrogen. Experiments with the invaders' home planet atmosphere show that it anesthetizes humans even when oxygen is added to the mixture. The invaders' scientists discover that the 80 per cent xenon in their atmosphere causes the anesthesia. The xenon is removed and nitrogen substituted as the inert gas for the humans.

The Academy of Science on the invaders' planet lost

much time by arguments about these questions of human metabolism. Many specimens were sacrificed to prove this or that hypothesis which ultimately turned out to be incorrect.

The human specimens decide to try to communicate with their invader captors. None of the invaders pay any attention.

The humans' attempts to communicate are watched very carefully by one interested invader scientist. He duly reports his observations to the invaders' Academy of Science. He writes a paper on the hypothesis that humans are intelligent. A flurry of interest stirs the invader scientists' group.

Meanwhile, inside the tank these research attempts by the invader scientists are viewed by one of the human specimens as "attempts on the part of intelligent creatures to communicate." A storm of human controversy results. "Are the invaders as intelligent as we are because they captured us? Are they not just sadistic predators of a high native intelligence (bright animal) but with no really civilized ethics? They cannot be intelligent, they have no developed sense of either fairness nor of true altruism with respect to the humans."

The human specimen with the communication theory begins to respond to the invader scientist with complex sounds and gestures. He quickly makes a discovery. He receives no answers if he uses his normal speech spectrum. He has to lower his voice an octave or so before the scientist apparently can even hear it. (As is well known if one breathes xenon this does lower the real voice frequencies. The human was not breathing xenon, so that his voice frequencies were up where they normally are in nitrogen on the earth.) He finds that he must train his own hearing to hear the invader scientist's very low-pitched voice. To keep the invader's interest, he mimics as best he can the voice sounds which are put out by the invader. As his mimicry apparently improves, the excitement builds up among the invaders.

These facts are announced to the invaders' Academy of Science. Many invader scientists try their own approaches as a result of this flurry of interest. The psychologist tries conditioning; the physiologist tries brain methods; and the trainers trained some specimens for circuses. The human specimens are forced to make "cute" noises for the entertainment of the invaders. The exploiters of the human specimens begin to make a profit.

Meanwhile the original report of the mimicry by the humans of the invaders' sounds is investigated by the invaders' Academy of Science. A research project is established under a modest grant to the discoverer to allow him to pursue the findings. He continues the research and, with human help and electronic aids, he devises a special interspecies communication method. Communication is established. The alien human intelligence is not measured, but humans are accepted into the invaders' society as equals. Earth is set aside as a tourist attraction for the invader scientists. Thus we have a "happy" ending.

Whether or not we and the dolphins and whales can ever achieve a "happy" ending, we should at least try to find such a road, one to the other. Other, less happy endings, could be concocted for the parable of the invaders. Let us not even allow ourselves to consider such endings. Rather, let us strive for the happy ones.

In this parable, I am carrying to a logical extreme the current situation with respect to the dolphins and the whales. I feel this is a wrong approach since this puts such ideas comfortably off in a safe, fictional framework.

With four other speakers in a recent symposium, (Lilly, 1966) I was asked to speak to the question, "If there is extraterrestrial intelligent communicating life, how will we recognize it and how will we communicate with it?" Currently we are faced with other species possibly as intelligent as we are. We do not yet recognize their intelligence. We do not even attempt communication with them. We do kill them, eat them, and use their bodies as industrial products. We have no respect whatsoever for their huge brains. In other words, as a species, human beings faced with other species demean them, kill them, and eat them. I hope all this carnage can be stopped and something more ideal can take its place.

In the above parable of the invaders, the Golden Rule is not applied to the humans by the invaders until their science says it must be. We do not apply the Golden Rule to the dolphins or the whales nor any species other than our own. Even dealing with our own species, we tend to annihilate vast numbers of them. As a species, we are a poor example for highly intelligent life forms from other planets or from our own planet to communicate with. Let us improve ourselves.

Perhaps (and it seems likely from our experiences in the Communication Research Institute) the dolphins are applying the Golden Rule to us. To those humans who are willing to apply the rule to them, the dolphins use the Golden Rule. I suspect that if the dolphins did not apply such a rule to us we would annihilate all of them.

The Golden Rule has been devised by several great men in the past. There were and are those among us who apply and have applied it with diligence and great effect. Christ, Gandhi, Buddha, Quetzalcoatl, and the other great religious teachers have applied it with diligence and great effect and remind us of the necessity of this rule.

If modern humanitarians can become interested enough to either work directly with the dolphins or to obtain the support for the efforts of others, we may acquire enough information to discuss the dolphins' real ethics. It may take the dedication of a new religious leader to carry it off appropriately. I hope not. I hope a framework can be found within our society in which such work can be accomplished.

If we suddenly stir up the real invaders from outer space and are still devoting most of the world's wealth to military weaponry, we will inevitably use the weapons on the invaders, too much too soon.

With the present lack of applying the Golden Rule interspecieswise, the whaling industry can still exist. If whale-like forms, for example, were to come to earth from outer space, it is inevitable that our military group would consider this visit an "invasion." Even though the visiting whales, as it were, come on a friendly mission, they may not have a chance of expressing this. They probably will be shot down before they can get into orbit around our planet.

If the whaling industry is a good example of the way we treat harmless superior beings in the sea, imagine how we would treat harmless superior beings arriving in space ships. Here we have superior brains right next door to us and we insist they are not superior and are only good to eat and to be made into fertilizer. If I were from an older, greatly superior culture from some other place in the vast universe, I would recommend that this planet be shunned. The human species is so arrogant that it doesn't recognize its own superiors. The only way that humans in the mass will respect any other species, apparently, is the ability to beat them in warfare.

Often I am asked the question, "If the whales are so smart why are they letting us kill them?" I also am asked the question, "If the whales are so intelligent why aren't they ruling the earth instead of man?" These questions reveal much of the questioner. I measure my answers carefully. One could become quite angry at the lack of insight into man shown by such questions. It can be embarrassing.

My answer is usually a humorous-serious joke. I pretend that "we" recently found the meaning of one word in the language of the "killer" whales, the word they use to designate *Homo sapiens*. Freely translated into English, their word means "killer ape." This semihumorous view can be rather serious.

We have named one of the largest of the dolphins "killer whale"; the term is derived from the "whale-killer" used by the whalers of the last century when they saw *Orcinus orca* killing and eating the large whales (even as we do them, cows, sheep, and pigs).

The bad press of these huge dolphins is hardly warranted. There is no recorded instance of an unprovoked whale ever attacking a human. Several cases have been confused with the great white shark which is not a whale at all. For a true picture see the motion picture and the 1966 *National Geographic Magazine* article on Namu the Whale.

Often I have asked myself what would a brain six times the size of mine think about? I ask in the spirit of philosophical inquiry and not in any superficial operational sense of the question. Since we do not know the thoughts of creatures other than ourselves with brains the same size as ours, the answer has obviously even more unknowns than first meets the eye.

The sperm whales have brains six times the size of ours. Before they are annihilated by man, I would like to exchange ideas with a sperm whale. I am not sure that they would be interested in communicating with me because my brain obviously is much more limited than theirs. Somehow I am sure that their huge brain is used effectively. I am also sure that it has capacities beyond my present comprehension (see Selected Bibliography 1962 and 1963).

I would like to exchange ideas with a willing sperm whale because the ability and the potential of such a vast computer as his is so far beyond our present theories, beyond even our imagining, that it is an intriguing and challenging subject. I have a theoretical approach which may give a hint as to where to look and what to look for, if and when we ever do so communicate. The beginnings of this theory were in *Man and Dolphin*. In this book let me expand it a bit to clarify some of the points.

The theory is as follows: The sperm whale's brain is so large that he needs only a small fraction of it for use in computations for his survival. He uses the rest of it for functions about which we can only guess. His survival computations (including feeding, hunting, sex, and escaping) may take up such a small fraction of his brain that he can do these things with only a very small part of his mind. It does not mean that he does them by means of reflex, instinctual patterns, built in. It means that he does them somewhat the way that we do them. To think the way we do he would need to use about one-sixth of his total brain. To him, our best thinking may appear to be reflexes automatic and primitive.

The rest of this huge computer is computing continuous inner experiences beyond our present understanding. If a sperm whale, for example, wants to see-hear-feel any past experience, his huge computer can reprogram it and run it off again. His huge computer gives him a reliving, as if with a three-dimensional sound-color-taste-emotion-re-experiencing motion picture. He can thus review the experience as it originally happened. He can imagine changing it to do a better job next time he encounters such an experience. He can set up the model of the way he would like to run it the next time, reprogram his computer, run it off, and see how well it works.

Currently, we do exactly this with some of the large

artificial computers. We program them to make a model of, say, an ocean basin, and the flow of silt on the bottom and the flow of water on the top, various kinds of changes that can be exerted over long periods of time. We then can make the computer run the model over a hundred-year period in a few hours and find out what the erosion pattern will be at the end of that time. In the same way, the sperm whale can model his past experiences, and change them the next time he meets a similar situation.

The sperm whale probably has "religious" ambitions and successes quite beyond anything that we know. His "transcendental religious" experiences must be quite beyond what we can experience by any known methods at the present time. Apparently, we can in rare times with our experiences begin to approach his everyday, accomplished abilities in the cognitive, conative, and emotional spheres. Only slowly have we begun to improve our control of such experiences. The means of inducing them are slowly being unearthed.

With our more limited minds and brains, we can have these experiences only under safe and controlled conditions; i.e., we cannot have them during the period of intense computations which are devoted to our bodily survival. Such computations (of necessity because of our limitations) will take up all of our computer. If we are going to have a "transcendental" experience, the physical and social surroundings must be such as to assure us that outside reality will make no demands on us. Each program is sufficiently complex so that our relatively small computers can compute only one program at a time or do a poor job of trying to compute both at once. (I may be doing a disservice to my species here. Some humans may have gone much farther than I with such experiments, and perhaps they can compute both programs satisfactorily and simultaneously.)

Perhaps the sperm whale has gone so far into philosophical studies that he sees the Golden Rule as only a special case of a much larger ethic. Compared with us he probably has abilities here that are truly godlike. From my theory, I deduced that attacks on man by sperm whales should be rare, with the exception of occasional cases of extremely severe provocation by man.

I tested this deduction from the theory by data found in the old whaling logs in a museum. The data were fascinating. In the six cases that I could find and check, there had been provocation of the sperm whale by men.

The cases were chosen from nineteenth-century newspaper accounts of attacks by sperm whales on ships and boats. In the newspaper accounts, I frequently came across the term "unprovoked attacks." This proved to be untrue. Every one of the attacks was provoked, as I found by checking the original handwritten log of the ship itself. In each and every case a notation stated that one or more "irons" had been thrown into the whale. Several such sperm whales were captured and the irons from as many as five or six different ships were found embedded in their sides.

The book *Moby Dick* by Herman Melville is based on such a real case. The sperm whale involved was called by the whalers "Mocha Dick." Six harpoons from five different ships were found in him when he was finally captured.

Thus we can see that a sperm whale, in general, does not attack us unless we first attack him. In one desperate attempt to escape or sometimes save his own life or that of other sperm whales, he may be provoked into turning and destroying.

Why do they not attack us unprovoked? *I believe they recognize that we are dangerous, even that we are the most dangerous animal on this planet.* I believe that they recognize that if they attacked us, unprovoked, we would organize quickly and wipe them off the face of the earth. I believe they recognize that we now have the means to do this. A large fraction of our atomic and nuclear weapons testing is done over and in the Pacific Ocean close to the ocean routes of the big whales.

Even if they have not been warned by our atomic testing, the whaling industry has kept them well informed of our dangerous abilities. They are exposed to all manner of our shipping across oceans including even single-handed sailors in small vessels. They must know by now that only certain kinds of vessels carry dangerous human beings, i.e., whaling ships, bomb-testing and military ships, and certain airplanes.

The slaughter of these magnificent beings must end. Instead of slaughter, let us devise new projects with whales, conserving them. Large private resources and government resources should be devoted to encouraging bright and intelligent human beings to devote their lives to this problem of achieving communication with these magnificent brains and minds.

The importance of interspecies communication, the peak of interspecies communication insofar as we can foresee it, lies here: establishing communication with the dolphins, and with the medium-size whales, and with the great sperm whale. I visualize a project as vast as our present space program, devoting our best minds, our best engineering brains, our vast networks of computer people and material and time on this essentially peaceful mission of interspecies communication, right here on this planet.

It is a bit discouraging to see this magnificent opportunity being thrown aside by the human race. I hope that enough people can be fired with the enthusiasm which I feel for it to launch the effort with momentum similar to that we are devoting to the space program, to oceanography, to nuclear energy, and to warfare. The rewards to the human race, new experiences, new ways of thinking, and new philosophies can be very great. The experience of such a venture with creatures here on our own planet will make the way safer for extraterrestrial life if and when our presence is detected. The "invaders" will be met with more understanding human beings and we then will deserve to be included as an "intelligent cooperating species" within our galaxy. Until that time arrives, I advise all extraterrestrial visitors to avoid man. He is a dangerous, unpredictable, powerful, "bright animal," operating in murderous concert.

In *Man and Dolphin* I predicted that perhaps within a decade or two we would establish communication with another species. Since that was written in the year 1960, one-half of a decade has passed. If we continue to receive support for the dolphin research, I suspect this estimate will be neither too short nor too long. If we can devote resources at higher than the present rate, we should be able to break the barrier, at least with *Tursiops truncatus* or *Orcinus orca* if not with the others. This book is devoted to this program, both in terms of where we are today, our past progress, and our future plans.

PLATE 1. *The Dolphin Point Laboratory*. Communication Research Institute, St. Thomas, U. S. Virgin Islands on the Caribbean Sea, 18 degrees north of the equator. View toward south and west; entrance road; steel motor-driven door closes entrance to wet laboratory room 40 ft. by 20 ft. on the main floor. Office on second floor; roofs (3000 square feet) collect rain for fresh water; cisterns are on ground floor below the main level (30,000 gals.). Year-'round temperatures are: low, night 75° F.; high, day 90° F. Seawater temperatures year-'round are 78° F. to 84° F. Daylight-nighttime ratio approximately 1 to 1 year-'round. Trade winds are predominantly from the southeast to east, 14 to 30 knots, approximately 80% of the year, except during August, September, and October. Waves about 90% of the year are from the southeast toward this building. Close passes of hurricanes for the laboratory were "Donna" (1963) with 80-knot winds and south winds (no damage); "Cleo" (1964) with about 50-knot winds; "Inez" in 1966 with 150-knot winds. Maximum waves 15 feet high in 1966, with wind tide of 5 feet.

PLATE 2. *Sea Pool, Balcony, and Wet Room.* This view is taken from a point directly south of and above the sea pool; Caribbean Sea behind the camera. Seawater flows in from the left and out through the flume at the far end of the pool. Spiral staircase gives access to balcony from sea pool. Wall to west limits sea wave noise in air above pool. Sea pool depth is 4½ feet, sloping upward slowly at inflow and at outflow ends to about 6 inches average depth. Daily tide range most frequently about 8 inches; extreme lunar tides over the year about 2 feet. One tsunami (in 1911) caused minus 30 feet and plus 15 feet tides for a brief period at middle of island. Offshore water depths one mile from lab are 15 to 20 feet. Maximum wave height thus is limited. Main floor is 16 feet above mean sea level and has waterproof wall to at least 19 feet above sea level, thus affording adequate protection against the highest waves.

PLATE 3. *Margaret Howe and Dolphin in Sea Pool.* Margaret is stroking skin between flippers, a region often presented by dolphins for stroking. Dolphin is rocking on Margaret's legs underwater. Margaret talks loudly and frequently.

PLATE 4. *Margaret Howe and Dolphin in Sea Pool.* Margaret spontaneously hugging the dolphin Sissy, wraps her arms around her, and continues to talk. Dolphin responds by arching back upward and pressing downward with chest and belly. This type of physical closeness may be followed by kissing the dolphin's head, peering into the blowhole, blowing gently into the blowhole, and mutual close-up inspection of each other's eyes, ears, mouth, etc.

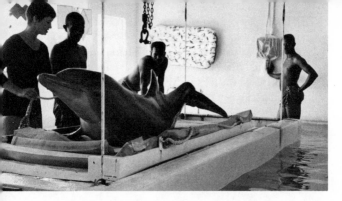

PLATE 5. *The Dolphin Arrives in Wet Room on the Elevator from Sea Pool.* The electric elevator is seen in raised position. The hand-operated chain hoist with shackle lifts the pallet off the elevator and carries it on an I-beam monorail off the elevator into the soundproof area to the left. The four ropes from the four corners of the pallet are fastened together in the shackle. (This room is seawater-flooded to a depth of 22 inches for the 2½-month living-in experiment.) Man at rear of room operates elevator controls.

This is the elevator that was used as a bed by Margaret during the 2½-month program. The foam was used as a mattress, and it was later surrounded with shower curtains. (See later photos.)

PLATE 6. *The Setup for the Seven-Day Preliminary Experiment.* The pallet to the left hanging from the chain hoist is used as a bed. The tank contains 18 inches of water. Margaret, dressed in leotards and tights, is at her desk, sitting on swivel chair in the water. Pam (not shown in picture) is in tank. TV can be seen on shelf at upper right, covered with polyethylene.

PLATE 7. *Margaret Howe and Dolphin during Seven-Day Experiment.* Margaret frequently sits in tank to develop new relations with Pam. Water flows out bottom drain at right (dark area). Inflow is near dolphin's beak.

PLATE 8. *Margaret Howe and Dolphin: Seven-Day Experiment (continued).* All feeding is an in-the-water-personal-contact affair. The fish are thawed outside this tank room, brought in the bucket, and given by hand. At times, depending on the experimental plan, the dolphin must produce airborne humanoid sounds to obtain a fish; at other times she is fed with no demands, one fish at a time, or even all fish placed in the water at one time. Demands for sounds from the dolphin can thus be disconnected from the feeding itself. Care is taken to feed to full satiation no matter when or how food is given; no use whatsoever is ever made of a starvation-hunger drive.

PLATE 9. *View through Underwater Bubble Port in Sea Pool*. Margaret is cleaning Plexiglas; Peter Dolphin is watching. Water surface is near top. Camera is in booth, in air. Margaret's experiences included frequent swimming with one to three dolphins in sea pool from February 7, 1964 to beginning of experiments reported here.

PLATE 10. *View through Underwater Bubble Port*. Taken from the observation bubble, the camera in air close to Plexiglas. Margaret and Peter examine the sump at bottom of sea pool.

PLATE 11. *Facility Changes for the 2½-Months' Experiment*. Margaret lives in with dolphin (Peter) in new flooded area. The outside flooded balcony is above the sea pool. Maximum allowable floor loadings ratings allow three feet of water (wall height). The outflow regulator is in upper right, just above spiral staircase entrance to sea pool walk. Margaret and dolphin Peter are on balcony, dolphin Sissy is seen in sea pool, 16 feet below.

PLATE 12. *Flooded Balcony: Construction, View, and Water Entrance to Flooded Room, Looking West.* The door in the wall to the right was cut into two parts and a slide substituted for the lower half to allow the human to cut off the trade wind by closing the upper half and to allow the dolphin to swim in and out at will unless the slide is in place. The white coil hose floating on the water is a vacuum cleaner hose for floor cleaning, underwater. The elevated end of hose is thrown over balcony, down 15 feet, to start the siphoning action and the vacuum cleaner propelled over the floor by hand for cleaning.

PLATE 13. *2½-Months' Experiment: Margaret Howe and Peter Dolphin in East End of Flooded Room.* A protected microphone hangs behind Margaret. The wall to retain the water is four feet high. To the right is Margaret's desk, suspended on ropes from the ceiling so that it can be pulled up out of the wet when not used. Margaret is touching Peter's raised beak with pencil; his mouth is open. Even when Margaret is writing, Peter can reach her and interrupt her at will.

PLATE 14. *2½-Months' Experiment: Margaret Howe and Peter*. Margaret's sleeping quarters are on the elevator surrounded by shower curtains. To the right is the runway from the cooking gas stove on a shelf above the water. Food cupboard is visible above the runway. Margaret is brushing Peter near his one-half air, one-half underwater mirror on elevator wall. When alone, he "looks" at himself in mirror and "talks" and "scolds" his image. Carpet (sound-absorbing screen) hangs between bed area and soundproofed area around camera. Ceiling and wall also covered with carpet in this "recording studio" area.

9

Differences Between the Communication of Man and of Dolphin

How do we know when someone is speaking to us? How do we know they aren't humming a tune, singing a song, talking to themselves, conversing with someone else, hallucinating a vision, repeating nonsense, doing an echo-ranging job with their voice, speaking in a language foreign to us?

Once we question how we know when someone is speaking to us, we find that the clues we use are myriad. These clues are quite subtle, and the alternatives many. And yet we come to a quick and correct conclusion. *As long as the other being is another member of our species, we succeed quickly and easily*. We succeed even when he is speaking a foreign language or is a pre-speech child; somehow we know for all human languages when the language stream is being directed in our particular direction. On the other hand, let the organic form of the speaker deviate radically from ours and we do not have this immediate and quick success. We have a difficult manifold of new data, obstructing our decision-making processes. We have hidden beliefs which prevent us from recognizing that they are attempting to speak to us.

For full communication with another being we ask for a rather narrow set of specifications. Basically, each of us asks a respondent to be a full and complete replica of one's own body and one's own mind. We almost insist that we talk only to ourself projected outward. If the other person looks somewhat like ourselves, it makes it easier for us to speak, though not necessarily easier for us to transmit useful information. Ideally, then, one would like a duplicate of one's self with identical form, identical experience, identical sex, and identical age as the respondent in an information transaction. Such an identity has the highest probability of a full and complete communication, one being with the other. The only cases similar to this are identical human twins.

Such twins may develop a language of their own, devised between them before they learn the communal speech of their parents. Thus if one can also choose one's genes and the genes of the person to whom one is speaking, it pays to have identical or nearly identical inheritance. In lieu of twinness, it pays to be siblings; one can sometimes talk to a brother or a sister of nearly the same age far better than one can talk to one's parents or one's children. Thus we can set up a spectrum of humans. Some humans are very easy to communicate with and others at the other end of the spectrum are very difficult to talk with and exchange information.

For example, sexual differences raise barriers. Genetic differences raise more barriers. A different nationality, different language, increase the difficulty. Differences in development of the body can be limiting; if one has a cleft palate, pituitary dwarfism, or pituitary gigantism, one can have very great difficulty in communicating with the so-called normal members of one's own species.

Brain size and the development of the brain establish

probably the greatest differences in this area. A micro-cephalic may not be capable of learning complex language as the rest of us know it. An underdeveloped brain for any reason may have the same problems.

But above all these limitations stands the monumental one of crossing the line from our species to another species. We may visualize this problem in the following fashion: Let us assume we have a manlike creature with a brain one-fourth to one-third the size of ours. This creature has two factors building up the barriers to communication with us: (1) He has an entirely different genetic inheritance with unknown limiting factors built in. (2) He has a smaller brain with less capacity than ours. This is the case of the great apes, the chimpanzees, the gorillas, and the orangutans.

One aspect of these creatures confuses us: their body form resembles ours. They have forelimbs with hands, hind limbs with feet, a visible neck, an expressive face, no tail, a dry existence, and a diet similar to ours. Their reproduction and their care of their young bear superficial resemblances to ours.

If we search among other known species on this planet, and if we wish to attenuate the brain size limitation, we look in vain at most of the other known members of the animal kingdom to find a brain equal to or greater than ours. There is a large gap in the primate series between what we consider a satisfactory brain size in our own species and the largest of the ape brains. When he reached the critical size of brain for developing a language, man probably killed off all the "protohuman" type of primates in his competition for living space and food. Language gives him such an obvious advantage in the hunt that he could eliminate his rivals rather rapidly by cooperative efforts, controlled by shouting instructions at his fellows at a distance, for example. In other words, there is no primate other than man, *Homo sapiens,* with a brain size equal to that of man. No primate has a brain larger than that of man nor is there any primate with a brain just under that of man. Perhaps some of the small-brained microcephalics are throwbacks to the protohuman types. Large-brained humans have their difficulties with most humans of the smallest brain size.

In our search for a brain size equal to man's, we must then go more distantly in terms of the body form and in terms of the medium in which the animals live. We must go to the sea to find brains equal to ours. There we have not yet eliminated them from this planet. Some of the medium-size dolphins have our size of brain; some very young and small elephants may have brains as small as ours. That's about it. The large elephants, the large dolphins, the whales, all have brains much larger than ours. The small dolphins and the porpoises have smaller brains than ours. To hold brain size equal to ours we have only a few choices: medium-size dolphins (Figure 2).

However, the body form, the physiology, and the medium in which the animal lives are radically changed. The dolphins' forelimbs have all the bones we do in ours, but they are all bound together in a pair of stiff paddles (or rudders). The hind limbs are missing entirely. Only once in a while are rudimentary hind limbs found in these species. A very long and powerful tail and flukes are present; we have absolutely no homologue of these structures, even as they have no homologues for our legs. There is no sign of an expressive face. The dolphins have no visible neck, the head is not well delineated. The jaws are four or five times the length of ours. The external part of our ears, the pinna, is completely lacking (the functions are taken over by structures *inside* the head). Their nose does not open at the end of their upper jaw; it opens on the forehead (the blowhole). Their mam-

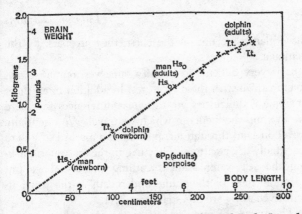

FIGURE 2. *The Relation of Brain Weight and Body Length for Man, Dolphin, and Porpoise*

This graph shows quantitatively our main reason for the choice of *Tursiops truncatus* (T.t.), the bottle-nosed dolphin, for communication research—young adults, 6 feet long, have brains equal to that of man in weight; as they age the brain weight and body length continue to grow to levels exceeding the average human size. The true porpoise (*Phocaena phocaena*) is limited in brain weight to the range of human children; the adult porpoise has a brain smaller than that of the newborn dolphin. Other dolphins (not considered in this book) have brains smaller than these dolphins. Still other dolphins have brains very much larger than those of these dolphins. The absolute size of a mammalian brain determines its computing capability and the size of its storage (memory); the larger the computer, the greater its power. One specimen of *Orcinus orca* (the largest dolphin) which was 510 centimeters (17 feet) long had a brain weighing 4.5 kilograms (9.9 pounds). Brain weights of *Physeter catadon* (sperm whale) have been found up to 9.2 kilograms (19.2 pounds) for body lengths of 1440 centimeters (48 feet); these are the largest known brains on this planet. (Relative brain size has little meaning in regard to computational powers: if it did have meaning, the marmoset monkey would be better than man at such tasks.) J. C. Lilly, "Critical brain size and language." *Perspectives in Biol. & Med.* 6: 246–55 (1963).

mary glands are not on the chest; they are back by the genitalia.

It is very difficult to identify ourselves, our anatomy, to empathize with these creatures. In addition to all these anatomical difficulties are the great differences in where we live and the media in which we travel. We essentially travel on land through air, pushing the air aside. We are essentially dry creatures. They live in the sea water, pushing the sea water aside, breathing the air above but spending most of their time underneath in the water itself. Even as we are dry, so they are wet.

The speeds of our progress in the air against the dry surface of the land are easily measured (Figure 3). We progress at a velocity from three to eighteen knots on our own feet on dry land. The dolphins can equal these velocities easily in the sea and can even better them. At least we know they can maintain the eighteen knots for a good deal longer than the rare man in top form running a record hundred-yard dash in ten seconds (eighteen knots). They can maintain this eighteen knots beyond the thousand-meter run in which the rare man in top form is now doing 12½ knots. By the time the mile is reached, the man is down to ten knots and the dolphin is still maintaining his eighteen. At ten miles the man maintains his ten, the dolphin his eighteen. Thus an everyday, essentially normal dolphin can maintain those velocities which only rare men can reach. (Of course man has learned how to go much faster in specially invented machines.)

In the vocal sphere, our communication is essentially air-borne. The dolphin originates his communication inside his own head in air passages; the sound is transmitted through his flesh into the sea and becomes water-borne. The limiting velocity of our communication of sound in air is 340 meters per second (1100 feet per second), or about 640 knots. The dolphins' vocal com-

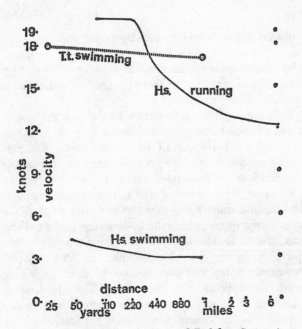

FIGURE 3. *Performance of Man and Dolphin Swimming*

Each species in its own medium has somewhat similar performances. The graph shows the average velocity maintained (knots) for the distance moved (yards and miles). The data for man (H.s.), running (in air) and swimming are from the *Guinness Book of World Records*. For the dolphin (T.t.) swimming, the first point is from our data for jumping out of water; this point is calculated from the height attained (ballistic computation). The second point is from the data of T. Lang, K. Norris, and T. Pryor. The running curves for man are the best performances known; the curves for the dolphins are the only known points measured accurately. Other dolphins can swim faster than this and the porpoises probably swim more slowly than these figures. One of the very large dolphins (*Orcinus orca*) has been found to maintain 20 knots for 5 days, 24 hours a day, under chase conditions.

munication has a limiting velocity in sea water of 1540 meters per second (5000 feet per second), or 2900 knots. Thus their sonic communication velocity is about 4.5 times that of ours. Using these figures, let us determine values of other variables.

For example, at a given instant how long is the spatial extent of one of our communications? From the time we start saying something until the time we stop it, that particular message is traveling outward from us in concentric circles at the velocity of sound. The leading edge of a sentence travels outward, the rest of the message follows it, and the trailing edge follows after that. If we measure the distance from the leading edge to the trailing edge, we get an idea of the length of the message in "air space," or in the case of the dolphin in "water space." For example, say that one says a very short "no." This word lasts approximately 0.2 second. From its leading edge to its trailing edge in the concentric circles radiating out from one's mouth is 6.8 meters (22 feet). In other words, if one's listener is 22 feet away, the beginning of the "no" reaches his ears just as the end of the "no" leaves the mouth. If he is closer, of course, the beginning hits his ears before the end has left the mouth. If he is farther away, the beginning has not yet hit his ears when the end has left the mouth.

In contrast, a dolphin's whistle lasting 0.2 second under water is 31 meters long (100 feet) so that the leading edge of a whistle of this duration reaches another dolphin 100 feet away just as the end of the whistle leaves the apparatus below the blowhole. As will be discussed later, if the dolphin is 50 feet away from a flat wall under water, the beginning of his whistle will be reflected and returned to his ears just as the trailing edge of the whistle leaves his head. If he is closer to such an obstacle, the returning echo of the beginning of this whistle will overlap the trailing end of the echo. For dolphins, this may be a very important relationship, as will be shown later.

One of the individual sound waves within those long transmissions has a special length, from one crest of amplitude to the next crest of amplitude, the "wave length." In human speech, the wave length of individual sound waves ranges from 3.4 meters (11 feet) for the lowest frequencies at 100 cycles per second down to very small values with much higher frequencies. For example, for frequencies at the upper end of the consonantal band at 8000 cycles per second, the wave length is only 4.25 centimeters (1.6 inches).

These wave lengths are important in our determination of the direction from which the sound is coming toward our head. If the wave length is very long compared to the distance between our ears, both of our ears are subjected simultaneously to approximately the same pressure changes. We cannot detect the direction the very low tones (long wave lengths) are coming from. At shorter wave lengths and slightly higher tones, the pressure variations at the two ears are not quite the same nor are the times of arrival of pressure changes quite the same. The detectors in our ears and the brain behind those detectors are very good at picking up very small differences in pressure and very small differences in time of arrival of the equal pressure waves. Thus, if a deep bass organ note is sounded on the shore and you are on a large lake or at sea (to avoid multiple reflections from other objects), you can localize the position of this source to a very small part of the total 360 degrees surrounding your head; at the low frequencies you can find, for example, a foghorn within something like two degrees despite no visibility in a dense fog. This property of low tones is why foghorns are so successful. Their deep bass notes penetrate literally miles through the air. Low frequencies in general penetrate more easily and farther than do the higher frequencies, which not only suffer from direct absorption by air and by dirt particles in the air, but are also easily refracted by temperature difference layers in the air and are reflected quite easily from any small objects in the way. The longer wave length, lower-frequency sounds do not suffer as much from such processes. In other words, their crest-to-crest distance is sufficient so that they cannot, as it were, be pushed aside by either temperature gradients, solid objects, or absorption processes.

The directivity of the higher frequencies is better than it is for the lower frequencies. In other words, as long as echoes do not interfere with the apparent direction of the source, a very high-frequency source fairly close to us can be localized within a very small fraction of one degree. Special rooms called anechoic chambers allow us to demonstrate this in the laboratory without going to the trouble of being out in open space.

Our ears are approximately 17 centimeters (7 inches) apart. The distance between our ears is one wave length at approximately 2000 cycles per second, or a half wave length at 1000 cycles per second. These are two important frequencies in the middle of our speech communication band. Our most easily detected frequency is 1000 cycles per second. It is also the frequency at which we are best at detecting small differences in frequency. This is the usual standard frequency for testing electronic equipment to be used for passing human speech. It is the reference frequency for amplitudes measured in logarithmic units called decibels. Our threshold for hearing in terms of intensity measured at this frequency is 0.002 dyne per square centimeter (microbar) absolute pressure. This is the value for people with normal hearing. This is the minimal detectable sound. A very loud sound at this frequency may be as much as 140 decibels above this threshold. This is above the threshold for pain, i.e., a sound which is so loud that it is painful. In absolute pressure units, this is approximately 3000 dynes per square centimeter (or 60 million times greater than the minimum detectable sound). These figures are useful to know, and we will contrast later similar figures in the dolphin's medium.

Let us return now to the wave length consideration and the distance between our ears. If a continuous sine wave at 1000 cycles per second arrives at our head from one side, the wave must travel around the head to the other ear in the air. A very very small fraction of the wave will travel through the head to the other ear through bone conduction and conduction through the substance of the brain.

Since the amplitude of the air-borne wave is very much greater than that of the intrahead wave, we use the air-borne wave for our detection. The dolphin does not have this advantage.

The shortest distance around the head is approximately 12 inches (29 centimeters). Thus the same part of a sound wave traveling from one ear to the other from one side to the other takes approximately 0.001 second (1 millisecond) to move from one side to the other. With the proper electronic equipment designed to delay two sound waves delivered independently to the two ears, it can be shown that one perceives a delay of one millisecond between two sounds as if one sound is coming only from one side of the head. As the sound source shifts around to, say, being directly in front of a person, the delay between the two ears approaches zero. With the proper electronic techniques, it can be shown that one can still reliably detect delays of the order of 20 millionths of a second (20 microseconds), and, say, whether the source is to the right or to the left of the midplane straight ahead with this amount of delay. This is, of course, for short, sharp sounds. With longer-duration sounds we do not have this degree of accuracy, and the delays move up to approximately 100 microseconds or more. Thus our nervous system is able to tell us from what direction sounds are coming with respect to the midplane through our head by measurement of the delay between the arrival of similar fronts at the two ears. Our brain does computations which fuse the two percepts into one effective source toward the right or toward the left.

The dolphin does not have this particular physical advantage in his reception of sound. Since the velocity of sound in the tissues of his head and in the water surrounding it are approximately the same, the sound waves coming to one ear are delayed only by the amount of time it takes for sound to travel through his head to the other ear. He does not have that small prolongation of the time of arrival of the sound that we have as it travels around our head. This means that at the longer wave length he will not have the advantages that we have in terms of localization of the direction of the source. Presumably at longer wave lengths, however, he can use pressure receptors in his skin (somewhat the way the shark does with his lateral line organs) to localize the direction of the low-frequency sound sources. Here in wave length he has the advantage over us of a body that is approximately 8 feet (2½ meters) long.

The dolphin's ears are approximately 12 inches apart inside his head; i.e., about the same as the shortest distance around our head. Since the velocity of sound, however, is 4½ times what it is in air, in his head and in the sea water, his time-delay discrimination is the same as ours, it must be 4½ times the frequency that we have for air. In other words, if the dolphin operates at the same minimum detectable delay that we do, he would need a frequency 4½ times the frequency that we use for the same degree of accuracy of localization of the source of the sound (same wave length in water as ours in air).

We use the peculiar shape of our head and the peculiar shape of our ears (the external pinna) to tell the difference between sounds coming directly ahead from those coming from overhead or directly astern. The dolphin, lying in the water stretched out, can use the differences in absorption between the peculiar shape of his head forward and some of the air sacs ahead of his ears versus the peculiar shape of his air-containing lungs astern in somewhat a similar fashion. Thus, he too can localize sources of sound by differences in the quality of the sound and the amplitudes of sources directly in front of him from those directly behind him. He separates right and left sources the same way we do, i.e., by measuring the delays of the arrival of the wave fronts between the two ears.

The dolphin may be able to do a better job than we in terms of his measurement or perception of the small time delay between the two wave fronts arriving at the two ears. Experimental tests of his ability to localize sound sources at very small angles have not yet been done. It is known that he is very good at this kind of perception at extremely high frequencies when using his sonar and picking up echoes from his own emitted signals. How good he is, however, at listening for the directions of sounds of other dolphins and other sources at much lower frequencies has yet to be determined. Let us now return to the comparison between our speech and that of the dolphin.

In our speech the wave lengths of individual sound waves, as stated above, run from 3.4 meters (11 feet) for 100 cycles per second to 4.25 centimeters (1.6 inches) for 8000 cycles per second. The comparable wave lengths for the dolphin in the homologous frequencies are calculable by remembering that the speed of in-water sounds is 4½ times our in-air sound speed and that the effective distance between the dolphins' ears is comparable to the effective distance between our ears. If we hold the wave length constant when moving from air to sea water, and shift frequencies to match, we find the homologous frequencies for our 100 cycles per second and our 8000 cycles per second. For the dolphin, the two homologous frequencies then would be 450 cycles per second and 36,000 cycles per second. We would thus predict that the dolphin's homologous band corresponding to our speech band would have these limits, i.e., 450 to 36,000 cycles per second. Since the above limits for our speech include all of the important fundamentals and harmonics for the transmission of meaning and since we can do without some of the fundamentals and overtones, it may be that the dolphins can also do without some of theirs. Even as we can limit our speech to a band 300 cycles per second to 3500 cycles per second (as in the telephone), so maybe they can be limited and still be able to communicate.

With the narrower band 300 to 3500 cycles per second we obtain nearly 100 per cent of intelligibility for the most frequent talkers and listeners, human type. An analogous dolphin telephone, predicting the frequencies on the simple constant wave length hypothesis, would use the frequencies 1400 to 16,000 cycles per second.

When we make the assumption that we should move the dolphins' frequencies 4.5 times our frequencies we are using a hypothesis which I call the "constant wave length hypothesis." In full, this hypothesis is as follows:

Human communication takes place in an air-flesh medium in which the contrast between the velocities in air and in flesh and the reflection of the sound in air from the flesh use a certain band of wave lengths in order to distinguish the direction of a transmitter, i.e., a speaker. The dolphin in water cannot use this contrast and must use the distance between his two ears inside his head because the wave length of his sound in the surrounding sea water is nearly the same as it is in his head. The effective distance between the ears of the human and the ears of the dolphin are approximately the same, i.e., about 12 inches or 29 centimeters. Thus, if the dolphin has the same time delay detection that we do, he must use frequencies 4½ times ours in order to maintain the wave length constant. In other words, for waterborne communication he uses the same band of wave lengths that we do; hence the frequencies must be 4½ times ours.

This constant wave length hypothesis is testable. We have set up experiments of various kinds to see whether or not these predicted limits for the dolphins' bands of communication exist.

One way of investigating the frequencies of the dolphins' communication bands is to measure their produced sounds directly while they are talking to one another. Even as in our case, one fault in this argument may be that some of the sounds they emit probably do not carry essential meaning for them. By observing the sounds themselves we can establish the extreme upper and the lower limits for their frequency bands. In the Institute, we have made literally thousands of such observations and measurements of frequencies.

One instructive method uses a fast frequency analyzer. This method displays the calculated results of a frequency measurement on a storage cathode ray oscilloscope. This storage oscilloscope allows one to store almost indefinitely a given wave form. In other words, the bright spot moves across the screen tracing the instantaneous amplitude of a given wave form; as it does so, the cathode ray tube (through its special structure) keeps repeating the wave form in the same place. By this technique, one can see the frequencies displayed directly on the cathode ray tube. The instant the dolphin starts talking to another, the amplitude of the sounds in each frequency band shows on the cathode ray tube face as vertical deflections of the spot of light corresponding to the intensity of the sound in each band. One can then photograph the stored results at will, erase the picture, and continue the observations, all within a few seconds.

This method shows extreme limits of approximately 500 to 85,000 cps for the dolphins' produced sound during communication exchanges. (This does not include their echo recognition activities, the so-called "sonar." Such activities will be discussed in another part of this book. The echo-recognition, active frequencies are higher.)

Thus there seems to be similarity between the predicted and the observed output bands of the dolphins. We then did experiments to find out how much of this whole band the dolphins consider essential.

In 1961 we set up a "dolphin telephone" between two tanks. These tanks were sonically insulated and isolated from one another. A telephone was arranged electronically to be two-way, i.e., the dolphin in tank A could talk to the dolphin in tank B and, simultaneously, the dolphin in tank B could talk to the dolphin in tank A. With the frequency band of the telephone band wide open, the useful frequencies transmitted were from approximately 2000 cycles per second to 50,000 cycles per second. By the use of electronic filters, we could limit this band to any part of the above band. The two ends of the telephone operated under water; in tank A there was a transmitter and a receiver and in tank B there was a transmitter and a receiver, all four of which were under water. A dolphin was placed in tank A and another dolphin in tank B.

The dolphin in tank A could communicate only with the dolphin in tank B, and vice versa. Thus their conversation would of necessity be limited to one another.

As soon as the telephone was turned on, the dolphins exchanged sounds.

In a previous publication we described how two dolphins exchange such sounds when placed in the same tank isolated from one another physically but allowed to communicate through the water with one another.[1] In this previous study we showed that dolphins exchange sounds very politely. When one is talking, the other one keeps quiet. In addition, we showed that they exchanged not only whistles, but also exchanged trains of clicking sounds. We also showed that the two kinds of sonic exchanges do not correspond in time, i.e., they can be talking with whistles and talking with click trains, the whistles and the clicks completely out of phase with one another. They can be using the silence of the whistle exchange with a click exchange and filling the silences of click exchange with a whistle exchange, and thus each are polite in the same mode. Thus one pair of dolphins talking can sound like two pairs of dolphins talking, one pair exchanging clickings, the other pair exchanging whistles.

These observations led to further studies in which we demonstrated unequivocally that each dolphin has at least two communication emitters, both in the nose, i.e., below the blowhole, one on each side. A right and a left phonation apparatus is demonstrated in the dolphin's nasal passages. Thus a given dolphin can carry on a whistle conversation with his right side and a clicking conversation with his left side and do the two quite independently with the two halves of his brain. An analogous human activity may be thought of as follows: if we could whisper and carry on a whispered conversation and at the same time carry on a vocalized conversation using two differ-

[1] Lilly, J. C. and Miller, A. M., "Vocal exchanges between dolphins." *Science* 134: 1873–76 (1961).

ent apparatuses. Since we do not have the two sides divided with midline structures, we do not have this advantage. The dolphin can control the two airflows separately and the two membranes' vibrations separately. A comparable human activity is the typist typing a manuscript and at the same time carrying on a conversation. Now let us return to the "telephone" experiment.

With the telephone between tanks *A* and *B*, the resulting sonic exchanges were found to be very polite, most of the time each dolphin maintained silence while the other spoke. It was found that while the telephone was turned on, the dolphins would exchange sounds most of the time. If we shut off the telephone, either all the sounds ceased or one or both dolphins gave the simple repetitious personal whistle ("signature whistle") characteristic of a solitary dolphin isolated alone. With the telephone off, any sounds that were emitted were completely out of synchrony with the sound emitted by the other dolphin. Little or no "interlock" was detected between the sounds emitted by the two dolphins. In other words, when sounds did occur with the phone not working, the alternating character of the clicks and of the whistles was lost. Either there was frequent overlap or many emissions were met with silence.

The telephone was modified by adding filters to reduce the intensity of sound at certain frequencies. The dolphins tested the system briefly. If the telephone was satisfactory, i.e., no missing critical frequencies, they continued using it. If it was unsatisfactory, i.e., missing critical frequencies, they stopped using it. In the latter case, they tested the system at intervals. If, meanwhile, we had restored the missing critical frequencies the dolphins resumed their "conversations" over the system.

We soon found that we could not cut the frequencies much below 28,000 cycles per second at the high end nor cut the frequencies much above 5000 cycles at the low end without losing the exchanges. The best performances were found with bands extending from about 2000 to about 80,000 cycles per second. Thus the exchange frequency bands correspond fairly closely with the produced frequency bands. In other words, dolphin conversation used a large portion of those sounds whose frequencies are emitted. In addition, the *exchange frequency band* and the *produced frequency band* correspond surprisingly well with the *predicted bands corresponding to our speech wave lengths in air* by the constant wave length hypothesis. In other words, we use the same wave lengths for speech in air as the dolphins use for their speech in water; the frequencies used are in the same ratio ours to theirs as the ratio of the velocities of sound in the two media, air versus water (1 to 4.5).

It is wise to review the question asked at the beginning of this chapter. How do we know that these two dolphins are exchanging intelligent information? May they not be singing a senseless round, making dolphin music, playing a vocal game, or just saying repetitious simple phrases over and over, or possibly humming reassuring sounds to one another?

We do know that they are not just repeating the same thing again and again. To observe this result, one records these exchanges on a tape recorder and slows them down four times. (Ideally, 4½ times according to the constant wave length hypothesis, to reduce the frequencies to our equivalent speech band.) At the new speed, one has lowered their frequencies four times, and stretched out each of their emissions by a factor of four. Thus we lower their 32,000 cycles per second to 8000 cycles per second and their 1200 cycles per second to 300 cycles per second. Our speech, similarly lengthened, without the frequency changes, is not easily understood; the method is not ideal but we have found it to be useful. (A later development in the Institute allows us to shift to all of the frequencies without lengthening or shortening the emissions. This is discussed elsewhere in this book.)

These recordings are used to listen and to measure the sounds and to find out if the patterns are changing or are merely repetitious (for our pattern perception system, trained as it is to human patterns, not the delphinic ones). Apparently much smaller-brained animals exchange repetitious cries. At least they sound repetitious to us. Frogs, birds, fish, insects, bats, monkeys have different cries for different emotional states. No one so far has detected whether or not these are used for any communication other than the emotional state of the sender, i.e., signaling danger, sexual activities, hunger, etc. A relation seems apparent between the number of different patterns used and the size of the brain of the creature using them. We might thus expect a very large number of patterns in the dolphin exchanges, at least as many as we use in our exchanges. The very small-brained birds and fish have very limited vocabularies, at least as the patterns are currently measured and counted.

In measuring the sonic patterns one basic problem is whether one is measuring aspects that are important to the sender and to the receiver in carrying the meaning. Similarly, it is difficult to choose what to measure in the dolphins' exchanges; we may choose variables not at all important to dolphins and sacrifice the important variables. Therefore, our criteria for differentiating and hence counting the number of different patterns may be totally incorrect. It is necessary to proceed empirically but cautiously and realize the limitations of the methods of arbitrarily choosing patterns.

When listening to the slowed-down exchanges, one is impressed with the numbers of different sounds one hears the dolphins use. The most varied of the transmissions that we have recorded are between "old" dolphins, those with large bones, scarred skin, truncated or missing teeth, and such marks of age. These are the really sophisticated vocalizers. When a *Tursiops truncatus* has become old enough so that the ends of his teeth are worn down flat, he has accumulated a very large number of sonic patterns which he exchanges with similar dolphins. Youngsters four to five years old have a sonic complexity which does not come up to that of the older ones; but even with them the first striking impression is that the versatility and complexity are well developed, that there is very little monotonous repetition, that one has a hard time keeping up with the new patterns as they emerge. Only if the dolphins are badly and continuously frightened are the sounds emitted monotonous and repetitious.

The sounds the dolphins use in their exchanges are difficult to categorize. They are all difficult to describe in words. In my laboratory, we use the following nine large classes to describe the sounds in a somewhat arbitrary fashion: (1) sounds that are emitted under water ("hydrosounds") and sounds that are emitted in air ("air sounds"); (2) whistles; (3) slow click trains; (4) fast click trains; (5) sounds resembling elements of human speech, called "humanoid" sounds; (6) a group that is like mimicry of other sonic sources (fish, ducks, sea gulls, boat engines [inboard or outboard], insects, etc.); (7) a group that is usually associated with emotional behavior (barks, screeches, hammerings, etc.); (8) various non-vocalizing sounds including sneezes, respiration sounds (slow and fast), borborygmi, flatulence, tail slaps, the water noises of swimming at the surface, jumping, etc.; (9) ultrasounds (for us) used in echo-recognition and echo navigation (EREN), sometimes miscalled "SONAR" (sound navigation and ranging) after the human artificial systems.

The steady, most frequent outputs during non-emotional exchanges between dolphins are under water ("hydrosounds") (Plate 30; Figures 6, 10). These sounds are mostly whistles and various complex patterns of clickings and short humanoid emissions.

Their most frequent outputs with us are emitted in air, apparently to accommodate to us in our medium. They lift the blowhole up in the air, open it, and make very loud sounds. Such sounds can be whistles, clickings, barks, wails, and various "humanoid" sounds. The barks and wails in air seem to be analogous to their emotion-tied exchanges with one another under water.

The radical shift, voluntarily executed by dolphins, making the sound in air as opposed to water is in response to our consistent use of air sounds with them. If we talk back to them under water, they answer us under water. If we talk to them in air, they answer us in air[2] (Plates 27, 31; Figures 4, 12).

We use the following *working hypotheses* in our communication research with dolphins:

The air-borne whistles and the air-borne clicks are attempts to communicate with us as they do with one another, i.e., attempts to induce us to use their mode of communication. Their humanoid sounds in air are their approximations to our communication sounds as distorted by their hearing and by their phonation apparatus (Figures 9, 10, 16). *With the humanoid sounds, dolphins are attempting to communicate with us in our mode of communication.*

At first a dolphin in the presence of a human uses mainly air clicks and air whistles. There are at least two main requirements for the use of humanoids in air: (1) the dolphin must have heard much human speech and (2) he must have had a long period of close, kindly contacts with us.

[2] Lilly, J. C., "Vocal behavior of the bottlenose dolphin." *Proc. Am. Philos. Soc.* 106: 520–29 (1962).

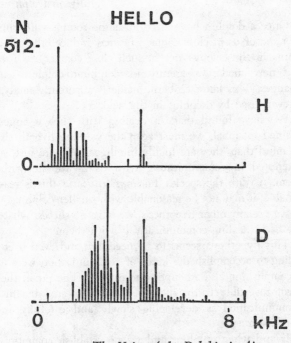

FIGURE 4. *The Voice of the Dolphin in Air:*
Computer Analyses

In each of 58 frequency bands a computer counts the number of times each of the bands is used above a chosen threshold as occurs in several tape replays of the "hello" and of the dolphin's reply. The bands extend from 135 Hertz to 8000 Hertz at 135 Hertz intervals. In the sixth band from the bottom (at 810 Hz) the number of instances of use (N) was 512. The use of each of the other bands is linearly proportional to the length of the black bar. It is to be noted that the woman's voice used frequency bands in two separate regions, one at low frequencies and one at middle frequencies. The dolphin's reply shifts the lower frequencies to higher ones and matches the group of higher frequencies.

Once a dolphin has started air-borne sounds with one or more of us in close contact, he may induce other dolphins in the colony (not in such close contact) to use the new mode, apparently in dolphin-to-dolphin exchanges. This latter air-borne mode is apparently rarely, if ever, used by dolphins in the wild.

We have found that, in dealing with such a large-brained mammal, we must keep the working hypothesis in mind that "they are highly intelligent and are just as interested in communicating with us as we are with them." (With the species *Tursiops truncatus* this is reasonable; it may not be reasonable with smaller dolphins.) If we use any other hypothesis, we have no success whatsoever in dealing communicatively with them.

This hypothesis seems to be necessary and even overriding to accomplish the kinds of communication we are accomplishing and attempting to expand. The proof, the incontrovertible truth, that they are interested in this communication is developing slowly and carefully in our laboratory.

If and when dolphins and we do establish communication on a highly abstract level, the proof will become obvious and incontestable. In this book I give some of the details of this developing picture and give the reasons why we, the ones who work with them, must rely for some time on our faith in their intelligence. *This faith is in the working hypothesis that both we and they are intelligent enough to break the interspecies communication barrier between these very different minds.*

Without such a faith and working hypothesis one makes bad mistakes in tactics and in strategy with the dolphins. If one assumes that they are stupid, they act in a stupid manner. This is partly because in the eye of the beholder, stupidity is seen everywhere, and partly because dolphins understand, catch on fast, and act the way one expects them to act. We have seen dolphins acting rather stupidly in care of persons who think of them as "overgrown stupid fish kept in an aquarium." These dolphins develop some delightful contrasts in new behavior when one of the "believers" shows up and attempts communication.

This is one of the basic difficulties in this new field. One must have an unusual amount of consciousness of faith in one's hypotheses in order to make progress.

In reality, this faith factor is basic to all fields of science. It is necessary to elicit consciousness of this factor in researchers. Most of the sciences have been able to "forget" this necessity; however, it is present and used. In physics, for example, one constantly has a model in mind of what is happening in the system under investigation, and has a kind of temporary faith in the model. This is how physical apparatuses are designed to test the various consequences of a hypothesis.

In this new scientific area, we use the approach of the theoretical physicist teamed up to a certain extent with that of an experimental physicist. We set up hypotheses and operate temporarily as if they were true. We interact in the system under investigation, with each of us programmed with the hypothesis marked "as if true." We then estimate our progress and see how well we operate. We judge our success (or failure) by our success (or failure) in finding new information, i.e., data that were not predicted by the previous workers, nor by those current researchers whose hypotheses differ from ours. I consider this to be a very important point, and it bears repetition in another way.

One thinks of the scientist (and his team) as a set of very large computers, say several thousands of times larger than the largest known man-made electronic computer in 1965; one thinks of a dolphin (and his group of dolphins) as another set of very large computers, also several thousands of times the size of the largest man-made computer. Since this is an exercise in theory, we can assume these basic postulates to be "true." What then are the consequences of the assumptions?

Let us first define something of these biological "computers," something of their characteristics. The two sets of computers—the human ones and the dolphin ones—have similarities and also have differences.

We have said that in each case, the computer is "very large"; this means at least ten billions of active elements (neurons) and a number of memory storage units of the order of ten raised to the seventeenth power (of one with seventeen zeros after it) for the number of memory storage slots.

In the language of computer technology, the access to these large numbers of memory slots is "random" and filing is "associational," i.e., most items in the "memory" can be made directly available with a short search. There is no necessity for the very long search technique of electronic computers involving all of, or a large part of, memory itself. When a piece of data stored in memory is sought in a large file, it is better to proceed to search from many places simultaneously in a "random" manner; the search is for associational chains leading into the correct slot. If one started a systematic search with only one searcher, as it were, one would spend years trying to find the necessary piece of information.

If, for example, one of us wants to remember a particular thing that happened many years ago, we start random search by "free-associating." Sometimes, by very peculiar associations which may seem irrelevant, we arrive at the sought piece of information. If we follow carefully and analyze the path we took to that piece of information, we can see all of the associations among the information stored in a similar place.

Our big brain computers (as opposed to the artificial computers) apparently can search their memories simultaneously in many different places. The large artificial computers have to search one spot at a time and must do it at an extremely rapid pace to be useful. As soon as the artificial computers become as large as ours, however, multiple "associational" searches rather than a single, one-track one will be needed.

Everything coming into our large biocomputers and everything going out of them moves over multiple channels. For example, each one of our eyes contains 1,200,-000 neurons coming from the retina to the brain. These all operate in parallel and each one of the channels can deliver information at a rate of about fifty bits of physical information a second. Thus, *the input to the brain from one eye is at the rate of about fifty million physical bits per second.* In spite of a relatively slow input in any one channel (axon), the simultaneous inputs on all channels (nerve trunk) give a total very high rate. Comparing the visual input in the dolphin to ours, he has only one-tenth the number of these visual inputs.

Each of our ears has 50,000 nerve fibers to the brain. Thus we cannot receive nearly so much information by our ears as we can through our eyes. In contrast, the dolphin has 2¼ times as many nerve fibers from each ear as we do, i.e., 115,000 fibers. If we also remember that he can function at frequencies four and a half times the frequencies which we use, we can estimate his rate of reception of physical information by his ears.

According to physical information theory, the higher the frequency of a signal, the more physical information it contains, i.e., the greater the number of bits transmitted per second. Therefore, the dolphin is receiving, in general, four and a half times the amount of information that we are for each second because all of his frequencies are multiplied by a factor of 4½. He has 2¼ as many neurons, i.e., 2¼ as many pathways into his brain, each of which is operating effectively at 4½ times the frequency. Thus we find that the dolphin's ears are receiving almost exactly twenty times as much information (40,000,000 bits) as we do through ours (2,000,000 bits/second). In other words, in the acoustic sphere we have reversed our relative position in relation to that in the visual sphere. The dolphin receives almost as much information through his ear as we do from our eye. In summary, then, the visual inputs in the dolphin are one-tenth the capacity of our visual inputs, and our acoustic inputs are one-twentieth the capacity of the dolphin's. Simultaneously, through these two modes (vision and hearing), a dolphin can receive twice as much information as can a man.

The dolphin's ability to receive twenty times as much information through his ears as we do is reflected in the structure of his big brain computer, from the ears all the way up the nervous system through the cortex. His limitations in the visual sphere are also reflected in the comparative size of his brain computer in the visual tracts all the way to the cortex. If one examines these brains minutely, one finds these ratios reflected in the total number of cells devoted to each of these modes of inputs in the large computer.

The dolphin lacks olfaction completely. Our olfactory input is relatively rudimentary compared to the lower animals. The dolphin's skin is much richer than ours in pressure, touch, and similar endings, so that their sensory input from their skin, presumably, is several times that of ours. This is especially true of their flukes, of their flippers, and of the flanks of their body where it is important to maintain streamlining. The genital regions have not yet been investigated from this viewpoint.

Their tongue seems to have many more specialized structures in it than ours. Their tongue must operate in sea water. There seems to be a special way that the taste of the salt of the sea itself is kept out of the end organs.

The many papillae on the tip of the tongue contain blood sinuses which apparently pick up the special taste molecules from the sea water and carry them to the end organs that are buried deep beneath the surface of the skin. The sea salts themselves do not influence these end organs. The problem of taste in these animals has not yet been investigated thoroughly. It appears to be a fertile field for future investigation.

Turning now to the outputs from the brain computers, comparing ours to theirs, let us look at the organs in which we are primarily interested—those used in fast communication. We have looked at the eyes and the ears from the standpoint of "physical information" reception, now let us look at the phonation apparatus from the standpoint of physical information transmission. In the same time period, the vocalization apparatus transmits 4½ times the amount of information that our apparatus does: the frequencies used are 4½ times the ones we use. They gain an additional factor of 2 over us in that they have two phonation apparatuses—so their ability to transmit information should be 2 times 4½ or 9 times our capacity to transmit. As will be seen below, there is an additional factor consequent upon the ability to use two phonation apparatuses in a stereophonic fashion which could raise this information rate somewhat higher.

The two phonation apparatuses can be linked one to the other to give "stereophonation." This will be dealt with in greater detail in a later chapter. Presumably the ability to interlock the two phonation apparatuses can increase the amount of information which can be expressed by these organs; in other words, a special sort of additional signal comes out of the stereo use of the two phonation apparatuses. Conservatively, *we estimate that the dolphin can put out ten times the sonic physical information per second that a man produces.*

The sonic-ultrasonic use of echoes from one's own

sound sources increases the amount of information that one can gain from the surroundings and, possibly, send out in one's communication with others. The dolphin's ability to do this increases his information capacity in the sonic sphere beyond the factor of ten given previously. We have found that the dolphin has a *third emitter*, especially constructed for the production of his ultrasonic beam. This is localized in his larynx. The physical information transmission capability of the larynx in the "sonar" sphere can be calculated. The band covered is from 15,000 cycles per second (Hz) to 150,000 cycles per second (Hz), a ten-to-one range like that of the other two emitters in the nose. Thus his total transmitting rate is twenty times that of a man. This transmitting rate matches the receiving rate calculated above for the dolphin's ears. They very politely alternate with each of their emitters when communicating one with the other and use three distinguishable "codes." They are not as limited as we are in this sphere.

Thus, the advantage that we have on the visual side is more or less balanced by the advantages that they have on the acoustic side. If one is to live at high speed in the murky ocean, one had best be prepared to have this advantage. In the ordinary sea under a tropical sun at high noon in very clear water, one can gain useful information through visual channels only up to about 100 feet; with acoustic channels this distance can be extended several miles. Thus, we can say that the dolphins are adapted as well to their medium as we are to ours in terms of the inputs to their visual and acoustic systems and their outputs in the vocal acoustic systems.

To return to the large computers, the total amount of information received by the dolphin and by us is thus shown to be comparable, in the major methods of communication with one another and with one's surroundings.

A general statement can be made about these very large biological computers; all inputs, all outputs, and all long interconnections between parts are multiple and operate simultaneously in parallel. The numbers of such inputs, outputs, and long interconnections are very large; at least several thousands to over a million in each mode. Every active element (neuron) is closely interconnected with about three to five others nearby and larger numbers at a distance. The largest part of each of these brain computers is in the cerebral cortex of man and of dolphins. The cortex, in *Tursiops truncatus*, for example, is slightly larger than ours (10 per cent to 40 per cent).

The cerebral cortex seems to be the "general purpose" part of our large computers. By special means it can be shown that we can use our visual cortex and its special characteristics in the service of our acoustic problems (along with the acoustic cortex and its special inputs). To do these experiments we remove the necessity for visual inputs, i.e., by closing our eyes or darkening the room. With proper techniques (hypnosis, drugs, etc.) we can program or compute an "acoustic space" into the "visual space." For example, the blind may use the general purpose nature of the cortex in extending the "acoustic space" into the "visual space" to circumvent complex objects. In special states one can do the same thing with one's own biocomputer. The evidence for the general purpose nature of our brain computers, i.e., their convertibility from special purposes to more general purposes, or to purposes from one special area into another special area, is a long and involved technical argument, too technical for the purpose of this book.

What do we mean by the term, "general purpose" computer? This term means that a computer can be used to model or to set up problem-solving methods for very large classes of problems. "Special purpose" computers are limited to a certain small number of classes of problems.

The larger a general purpose computer is, the greater are the range of and the number of problems it can work on simultaneously and continuously.

Another important function for our purposes is the concept of the "stored program." This development in man-made computers opened up new vistas of computer uses. A stored program is a set of instructions for the computer, written and fed into the computer memory. These instructions in memory then direct the computer itself as to how to deal with inputs and outputs, with data, how to compute desired transformations of these data, how to calculate, the equations to use, the order in which the equations are to be used, how to reason out the logical alternatives based on previous choices made, the form of the desired logic to be used in this reasoning process, and the order in which each logical form shall be used. In the modern artificial computers, then, we have not only numerical calculations being carried out but we have logical "reasoning" in limited forms. Such large artificial computers can develop new models, store them as new subroutines, construct more inclusive models from the earlier ones, and manipulate the old subroutines into new large programs, and so on, until all of memory is used up. Thus the stored program takes up portions of memory.

In a modern computer, one either can use memory for storage of new data or for storage of instructions to handle the data; there is a competition for the memory space in the computer between these two processes.

In the modern computers, parts of memory can be selectively erased and used in new ways. The storage of new data may require that in the currently running program, the old data once computed be erased, or alternatively, as new programs are introduced, the old stored programs be erased in part. Thus a modern computer has many properties which are shared with brains. Since brains are very much larger computers, they have many powers in addition to those of the present artificial computers.

The modern computers as part of their basic structure have some logic routines "wired in," i.e., fixed unmodifiable and nonerasable. Such wired-in elements can be switched in different ways and related to one another in different ways. Analogously, our brain also has "wired-in" circuits. Many of these programs are necessary for our survival, for the maintenance of our bodies. For example, one group of these "wired-in" programs is called "the autonomic nervous system." This part of the nervous system is beyond our manipulation directly, though we can influence its programs indirectly from the large, cerebral, cortical computer.

This is a more comprehensive, open-ended view of the man-dolphin communication problem. This view is at variance with current theories in conventional zoology, ethology, marine biology, ichthyology, and mammalogy. This set of concepts are far more powerful research tools than the limited theories current in the above fields. With the new theories we are turning up new data which are not predictable by the older theories at all.

In this theoretical view which we are generating, theories are analogous to computer metaprograms. One's own brain is analogous to a huge computer larger than any built today. The theories (programs and metaprograms) stored in one's self operate the way a stored program in a modern computer operates. The stored program gives the orders for the data acquisition, the computations to be done, the logic to be used, the models to employ, the new models to be constructed, the end use of the results, and the outputs to be chosen to carry out the end uses.

Thus, to test a given theory, one "programs" himself with the as-complete-as-possible theory and joins the system under investigation as a participant-computer operating "on line." This operation of a computer "on line" is a new concept in computer technology. It means that instead of using punch cards or magnetic tapes for feeding the information into the computer, the computer operates from data being generated in real time, right now. In this mode of operation, the computer continuously collects appropriate data, continuously computes these data with the stored program, sets up small models based on theory, tests their parts against the new data acquisition rules, plus the now new data coming in, and sends out control signals to the rest of the system.

When we wish to test, for instance, a communication theory about communication with dolphins, we must act like computers operating on line. We must, as it were, be able to think on our feet; theory revision must occur almost automatically and continuously as the new working models develop and integrate each one with the adjacent ones. The inappropriate parts of the stored programs are thus found by comparison with incoming new data. They are erased, and new parts are written in as rapidly as possible.

This concept of the on-line testing of a theory is relatively new. This approach was not known at the time of Roger Bacon; for example, Bacon defines science as collecting new information and as a consequence of this new information generating the hypothesis which held the information together. Then one tested the hypothesis by means of further collected information. The Baconian method of operation does not correspond to the on-line theory testing method; his method presumed only part of the total feedback network, the input side only.

The on-line method of testing a theory assumes continuous data acquisition, continuous model modification, and continuous change of the method of operation with the external system. When two huge computers (such as a dolphin and human) interact in an on-line fashion the problem is not only the proving or the disproving of a hypothesis by new data acquisition. It is also the forcing of on-line testing continuously, and trying to elicit what model program of communication is stored currently in each of the computers.

When I deal with another person, I want to know what model he is currently working with. We often ask questions of one another with that in mind. If someone is using an inappropriate model of us, we can become quite emotional about it. We feel that it is unfair, unjust, or inappropriate. So must we operate with the dolphins.

If we are using an inappropriate model of dolphins in ourselves, and they are using an inappropriate model of us in themselves, many mistakes occur on both sides. *If a man can get the idea across to a dolphin that man is trying to modify his model of the dolphin, that he has certain limitations in his present model, he can then get the cooperation of the dolphin, on a longer-term, more strategic kind of mutual research.*

In the very long-term view, of course, the test of the theory hinges on finding key facts. One may suspect that such facts exist, but has to have an unequivocal demonstration of their existence. Sometimes new definitions have to be made in order to enunciate the kinds of facts that will be found. In part in this computer discussion, we are giving some directions for finding the key facts and for evaluating their worth. The important aspect of this new view is the "participant computer" one. New data are absorbed rapidly and quickly, and continuously exert maximum influence on the current and future theory. The way is thus pointed out to new collection systems for new data to fill missing parts of the picture ("proof" or "disproof"). As our internal models become more perfected and tests show that the new models predict new facts not yet found, and these are then found, we can move ahead in the development of, for example, interspecies communication.

For the sake of completeness, let us add that there are several important rules basic to this program for research. These rules underlie the axioms of the whole computer, its primary directives. First of all, *truth is sought.* Whatever one's rules for truth and its seeking are, it is sought. This is the strategy of the game of science. We seek the truth no matter the cost in program revision, personal repute, dollars, energy, dedication, or time.

Secondly, *one streamlines himself for the program.* If one is going to be a participant computer, he must get rid of excess emotional baggage. Excessive guilt has to be eliminated. Personal blind spots and tender pain-shame areas must be changed or erased. The model of the computer itself which one is striving for contains no personal blocks against finding the truth no matter where it lies.

Thirdly, *one starts the almost endless process of creation of the pertinent "software."* "Software" is defined loosely as all of the programs and metaprograms present in and used with a given computer. This concept is contrasted with the concept of the structure of the computer itself which, in the jargon, is called "hardware." Thus one must have a metaprogram which says "create necessary subroutines, routines, programs, metaprograms, and models to find the truth as it exists in the real system in which one is interested."

Fourthly, *one programs a model of a dolphin consonant with the real dolphin insofar as this can be determined at the present time.*

Fifthly, *one must be willing and able to change his model of the dolphin* as rapidly as new data arrive and are computed about that dolphin or other dolphins.

Let us now return to dolphins and us. Each dolphin

from the wild is a huge computer. If he is old, he is filled with many programs, even as we are.

Most of the content of these programs, and probably even their form, is very strange to us. We cannot even presume that the logic is like ours. It may be alien and totally different from human logic. The rules that the dolphin has regulate his data collection, his data computation, his logical manipulation, and his end use of the results of his computations; the rules are probably quite alien to us. *Our problem is to find out what is common between our computer and his.* The dolphin's ability to construct models of reality, of other dolphins, of us, is probably well developed; his models are probably quite different from ours. For example, his predominant acoustic life generates acoustic models where ours generates visual ones.

We do not know the categorical imperatives of the dolphins as yet. Among our many problems is how to achieve a *common program universe and a common data universe* with the dolphin. Conversely, the dolphin has a difficult program in living with us. He also has to achieve a common program universe and a common data universe with us.

In other words, the basic problem of interspecies communication is convincing both sides that the problem exists. Both sides must explore with what sort of shared dimensions this problem can be approached.

There is an old saying that it is very hard to teach an older person new tricks. This may be true for some oldsters, but apparently is not true for all of them. However, perhaps the older dolphin has a similar difficulty. The problem may be that the old memory is so filled and his ability to erase so limited that we should not choose old dolphins for the interspecies communication program. It may be a better idea to employ a young dolphin with a memory less taken up with delphinic life programs and introduce him to the man-dolphin communication program.

This plan is currently being followed in our Dolphin Point Laboratory on the island of St. Thomas, U. S. Virgin Islands. This program is described in detail elsewhere. Suffice to say here that it is difficult to find and create a compromise environment for the dry-thinking, dry-living us, and the wet-thinking, wet-living them, for the continuous day-and-night programming of the human and of the dolphin in shared quarters.

It is also difficult to find and create a compromise mode of communication for dolphins and for us. As was shown above, they are specifically adapted to an underwater kind of communication. We are specifically adapted to an in-air kind of communication. We are primarily visual, and they are primarily acoustic. Luckily, both sides are seeking compromises.

However, the older dolphin is yet to be tested. We now have some oldsters to work with. New information on the vocal capability of the wild dolphins is coming from our work with the older dolphins. We have learned many new things from the older ones. They have taught us about their disciplining of the younger dolphins, of their disciplining of one another, and also of their disciplining of us. Some of the dolphins' own developed programs are beginning to show up.

Sometimes the young dolphin adapts so rapidly to our ways that we miss the programs he learned in the wild which he apparently abandons when he is with us. Such programs as we see are now in response to us and to our demands.

With the older dolphins interacting with another oldster or with a youngster, we see more of these programs which were developed in the wild without man's interaction with the dolphin. Typical data with the older dolphin, for example, is the already developed complexities of their vocalizations mentioned above. They were found to have fully developed repertoires of all of the classes of sounds previously listed. The oldsters have memory stores of several kinds of information which the younger dolphins apparently lack.

Thus in this chapter we have presented something of what we have learned of the dolphins' vocalization, of the physical characteristics of the sounds they produce, a comparison of them to us in terms of the sounds that they use, and a guiding theory for research on their and our communication. This theory looks as though it will be useful in the interspecies communication program. It may be that it will be useful with interspecies communication with species other than dolphins, say with elephants or with the large whales, or between man and woman!

10

Communication Is Between Minds

It is useful to have a working definition of what is included and excluded from the term "communication." Communication is a fundamental concept essential to a basic understanding of man and of other species. The definition used in this book is essential for an understanding of this book and of *Man and Dolphin*.

DEFINITION: *Communication is the exchange of information between two or more minds.*

A mind is housed in a brain residing in a body detectable by the senses or by the senses aided by special apparatus. The medium of communication is any one (or more) available to the two minds involved in the exchange. The modes of communication are the ones available to the two minds.

The special case of interest is that of the mammals, terrestrial and aquatic. The information which is exchangeable is of a complexity and an apparent variability which depends on the size of the two or more minds involved in the exchanges. The size of the mind is a direct and eventually specifiable function of the size of

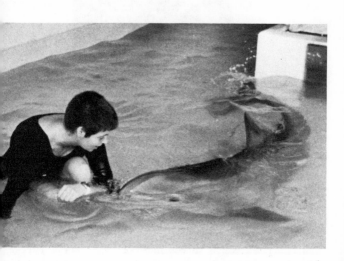

PLATE 15. Peter approaches Margaret.

PLATE 16. Margaret lifts Peter's head for a kiss and a hug.

PLATE 17. Peter does "dead man's float" on side as Margaret strokes his tail.

PLATE 18. Peter becomes suddenly active and is trying to force his way between Margaret's legs. She discourages his violent motion, gently but firmly. His flippers, sticking out of either side, catch on her shin bone . . . and as the forward edge of the flippers are hard and rather sharp . . . it hurts! There is a bit of a feeling here, on Peter's part, of "how much can I get away with." Peter is not angry, Margaret is not angry . . . they are feeling each other out. Matching strength, seeing how the other reacts. This form of exercise was fun for both and was encouraged; *within the limits and under control of Margaret.* A good deal of time was spent allowing Peter to learn what her abilities and strengths and failings were, and then in teaching him to respect these failings and to control his own strength.

PLATE 19. July. Margaret says the word "diamond," shows Peter the shape. Peter's blowhole is closed; he has learned not to vocalize while Margaret is speaking.

PLATE 20. Peter has made a good vocal attempt at the word "diamond" and Margaret rewards him with a butterfish.

PLATE 21. In quiet of "play period" following shape lesson, Margaret is gently squirting water from her mouth toward Peter's beak. He usually responds by opening his mouth so that water squirts against his gums, or by gently squirting back. The close "face-to-face" play—conversation-inspection—is the type of play that develops frequently during activities, and often at night.

PLATE 22. *A View of Some of the Apparatus in Teaching Peter.* The spheres on the left are used to teach numbers, and the different-colored plaques in the center are designed to teach color. The plaques at the far right are used to teach shape.

PLATE 23. Peter interrupts Margaret's telephone conversation and she is obviously delighted. Peter often enters into a three-way telephone conversation and was encouraged to do so in his loudest voice.

PLATE 24. Margaret lifts feet out of Peter's reach and scolds him for mouthing her foot. His teeth are sharply pointed. Note bright eye of Peter.

PLATE 25. A moment later the mood changes, Margaret wriggles toes at Peter while smiling and talking to him. This type of discipline and scolding is usually brief; Peter is scolded and the incident forgotten.

PLATE 26. Close contacts are obviously welcomed and enjoyed by both participants. The dolphin will spend time being completely limp, free to be pushed, pulled, carried, towed around, etc. by Margaret or will turn the tables and demand that she go limp so that he can push her around, inspect her knee joints, look at fingers, etc. These are very happy "getting to know you" periods.

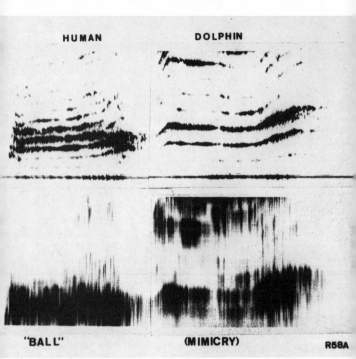

HUMAN	DOLPHIN

"BALL"   (MIMICRY)   R58A

PLATE 27. *Spectrograms of Margaret Saying "Ball" and Peter's Reply.* The sonic spectrogram plots here (in contrast to the ones earlier in the book) are limited to 3300 cycles per second as upper limit for the human carriers of meaning in speech. The upper traces are taken with a narrow-band (45 cycles per second) filter, the lower traces are taken with a wide-band filter (300 cycles). It is to be noted that Margaret's pitch is not exactly matched by Peter, his is somewhat higher (as is shown by the wider spacing of his lines in the record with the narrow-band filter). In addition he starts his answer in an abrupt fashion, copying Margaret's start with her word "Ball." She tends to lower her pitch at the end; he tends to raise his at the end. (Thousands of such spectrograms are needed for a complete analysis of the Margaret and Peter exchanges.) (From manuscript cited by Lilly, Truby, Miller, and Grissman.)

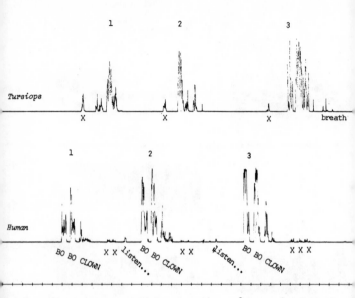

Showing NO overlap.... complete separation   3 human 3 dolphin burs

PLATE 28. *Another Sample of the Analyses of the Margaret-Peter Exchanges During Peter's Learning Period.* The upper trace shows the amplitude of the sound emitted by Peter and the lower trace of the sound emitted by Margaret. First Margaret says the words "bo bo clown" and Peter replies with three bursts of sound. The part of his curve showing an "X" is where some of Margaret's voice shows in Peter's channel; "X's" on her trace show where Peter's voice shows in her channel. This example illustrates that Peter will work many times to perfect the same words. He does not copy Margaret when she says "listen." He copies only when she say the words "bo bo clown." Each of his copies is quite different as can be seen by the top trace. He varies them as she varies the use of the same words. This figure illustrates some of the complexities of evaluating the vocal performance of a dolphin with his great degree of flexibility, plasticity, and quick learning (from manuscript cited).

PLATE 29. *Photograph of Dolphin in Tank for Studies of the Production of the Voice Inside the Head.* The dolphin is isolated in this tank and produces his sounds with his head either raised as shown or placed below the water. The blowhole is closed. Hydrophones are placed on his head or in the water near his head. (Note the reflection from the back of his retina of the flash from the camera.) A TV monitor is shown through the doorway. In the far room is the computer used for analyzing data. The data shown in the next figure were recorded with the equipment directly behind the dolphin's head through the window.

VOCALIZATION VERSATILITY · TURSIOPS · TRUNCATUS

INTRACEPHALIC SOUND PRODUCTION
T.I.46   180265R2A

CH.

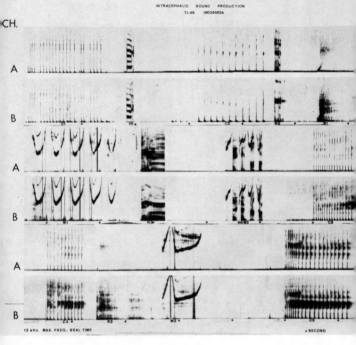

12 kHz. MAX. FREQ.: REAL TIME · SECOND

PLATE 30. *Some of the Sonic Patterns of the Underwater Voice of the Dolphin.* This figure shows a plot of the frequencies and amplitudes of sounds emitted by a dolphin over an 18-second period. The frequencies run from 0 to 12 kilohertz (kilocycles). Five slow-clicking trains can be seen. Seven periods of very fast clicking can be seen: near 2 seconds, 4 seconds, 8 seconds, and 10 seconds. Five whistles are seen near 7 seconds and a single whistle and click train near 15 seconds. These are the natural underwater sounds produced in the two nasal systems of the bottlenose dolphin. The structure of the fast clicking near 8 seconds resembles that of the formants of the human voice, as do those near 10 seconds. The production at 10 seconds shows a whistle superimposed on the fast-clicking trains. This dolphin was alone with the head partly out of water, and a contact hydrophone was placed over the right and over the left vestibular sacs.

PLATE 31. *The Voice of the Dolphin in Air*. The records are sonic spectrometer analyses of a woman saying "Hello" and the dolphin's reply. It is to be noted that the frequency analysis for the human is from 0 to 8 kilohertz and for the dolphin from 0 to 12 kHz. The frequency pattern for the dolphin for the first two-thirds of the record resemble somewhat that of the human (Margaret Howe and Peter Dolphin). In general the human child's and woman's voice is a closer approximation to that of the dolphin in air. During long close contact between a human and a dolphin his voice in air tends to be lowered to the frequencies shown in this figure.

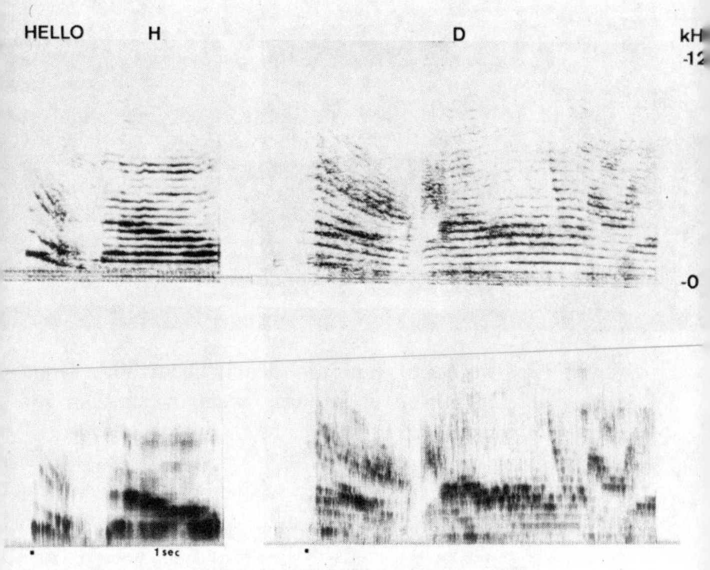

HELLO   H   D   kH
                                                                       -12

                                                                       -0

                  1 sec

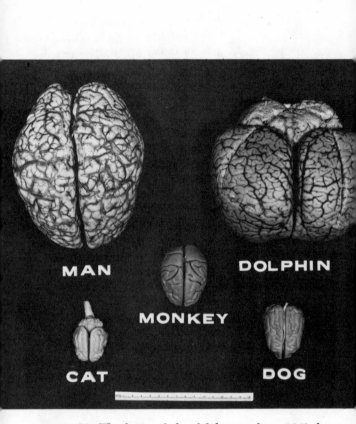

PLATE 32. The brain of the dolphin is about 20% larger than that of a human and is very much larger than the brain of a monkey, dog or cat.

the brain. The size of the brain is a direct and eventually specifiable function of the number of active elements contained therein, i.e., present theory says the number of neurons and possibly the number of glia cells contained within the total brain itself determine functional size. The size of the brain in terms of numbers of active elements is close to a linear function of the total weight of the mammalian brain. Thus, we can say that the total weight of the living mammalian brain is a gross measure of the size of the contained mind, and hence, a gross measure of the complexity and apparent variability of the information which can be transmitted.

In order to keep this definition open-ended, not limited to presently known modes of communication, it neither explicitly includes nor implicitly excludes direct transference of thought from one mind to another. In other words, the definition leaves the question of thought transference to future research. Direct thought transmission has not been demonstrated unequivocally, i.e., the existence theorum for thought transference does not yet exist. Among the modes which do exist are conventional speech; gestural, nonvocal transmission and non-hearing reception; some kinds of music; writing and reading; mathematics; dancing; lovemaking. Many of these modes are not usually contained within a definition of communication. The new science of nonvocal communication between humans includes these activities.

Known media of exchange include electromagnetic waves (including light, radio, etc.), elementary physical particles, mechanical contact, mechanical waves in gases, solids, or liquids, and electric currents in solids, liquids, or gases. The use of elementary physical particles for communication purposes exists only in limited regions of space and of materials. Such particles as the electron are used in vacuum tubes in radio; other kinds of particles are used in solid state circuitry devoted to communication purposes. Mechanical contacts are used for communication, for example in the Braille system of reading for the blind, by means of finger contacts. Mechanical waves in gases are the usual sound waves with which we communicate. Such sound waves can also be transmitted through solids and liquids. The dolphins use them in sea water, for example. Electric currents for communication are used in the ordinary telephone, and by some species of fish which can detect very small currents and thus tell how far away they are from various objects; possibly such fish use them in communication one with the other. Electric rays use electric currents in water as offensive weapons and may possibly use them in communication systems between members of the species. Whether or not dolphins use electric currents in the sea water is not as yet known. Whether they use elementary physical particles is not known. We do know they use light waves. Whether they use, for instance, very low-frequency radio waves is not known. They do use mechanical contacts.

In the rest of the definition, we leave a large area for unknown media of exchange, and unknown modes of exchange, i.e., we assume that there are new ones yet to be discovered. One develops a respect for and a sensitivity to the unknown operating in the area of communication. I believe this is an essential characteristic of a proper scientist in this area. A respect for the unknown is needed at every level, not just at the level of the media and the modes, but at high levels of abstraction. In other words, exchanges may be operating between dolphins in known media and known modes, but at levels of abstraction which we have not yet grasped. Such awareness of the ever-present and intimate presence of unknowns keeps one's mind open and one's system of reasoning open. Without this openness, discovery is impeded.

The so-called spiritualists and the so-called psychics

maintain that their methods of communication and modes and media are part of the unknown yet to be discovered. They maintain that the reality of such exchanges is incontestable and quite anxiety-provoking. They maintain that such communication can occur with a mind without a detectable body. These people may be, as they maintain, special sorts of human beings with special sensitivities to unknown media and modes. However, as far as I am aware, such thoughts are still in the area of childish wishful thinking. Proof that they are not in the area of childish, wishful thinking is yet to be forthcoming. All of the investigations of these phenomena over the years by proper scientists usually show up some sort of trickery, fraud, or unconscious use of ordinary modes of communication. In respecting the unknown, one should not worship it and make it more powerful than the known.

Respect for *unknown minds* in *known brains* is another story. Data derived from careful experimentation with smaller-brained animals do not convince me of the lack of a mind in a dolphin. As far as I am concerned, I must assume the presence of a large mind in a dolphin whose brain is larger than mine. Until proven otherwise this is my basic working hypothesis.

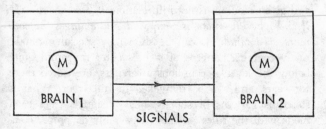

FIGURE 5. *Schema of the Definition of Communication*

This diagram shows a mind (M) on the left in the circle contained in brain 1 (the square) transmitting signals to mind (M) in the circle on the right contained within brain 2, the square. In turn, mind 2 is sending signals to mind 1. The information is not generated from these signals until the signals are received, computed, and turned into the information by each of the minds in turn. This is the essential core of our definition of communication.

The *information* does not exist as information until it is within the higher levels of abstraction of each of the minds and computed as such. Up to the point at which it becomes perceived as information, it is *signals*. These signals travel through the external reality between the two bodies, and travel as signals within the brain substances themselves. Till the complex patterns of traveling neuronal impulses in the brain are computed as information within the cerebral cortex, they are not yet information. Information is the result of a long series of computations based on *data signal inputs, data signal transmissions to the brain substance,* and *recomputations of these data.*

The usual definition of "physical information" is different from the one I use here. The schema of the definition shows that one must differentiate very carefully between "signals" and "information." In this view, a set of signals of at least minimal detectable size in a given mode and given medium is not information; *it becomes so only if and when it enters, is computed, and changes the contents of a mind.* As can be shown by special methods, many complex patterns of signals enter the mind quite below the level of conscious awareness, are stored there for years, and can be reinvoked in full vigor. What is stored is patterns of signals, bits of signals from each mode with the rules for their reassembly on proper command. These stored patterns are not called "information" in this schema and in this definition. *The stored materials, like the signals entering from outside, are not in-*

formation until they are reassembled in "spatial" patterns varying in time in the present or future mind. In other words, our boundary for information is at a level of discourse of *Cogito ergo sum,* "I think (or I know), therefore I am." *Information is that which I know now, coming from outside me, and coming from the storage inside me, allowing for delays in computation and in transmission.*

Most information theorists do not consciously make these distinctions. What we call signals themselves they say consist of "bits of physical information," even as I did in the previous chapter when talking about the eyes and ears of the dolphin. But careful analysis will reveal a circularity of concepts in these "physical" definitions. The "kinds" of bits lead one into bypaths of explanation not necessary with the above definition. The mind of the observer-participant is where the information is constructed, by and through his own programs, his own rules of perception, his own cognitive and logical processes, his own metaprogram of priorities among programs. His own vast internal computer constructs information from signals and stored bits of signals. The "bits" of information thus take on a new meaning: *A bit is a smallest possible piece of information recognizable as such coming from either inwardly moving signals or from outwardly moving ones.* Fundamentally, this is similar to the standard definition in the usual "information theory." This can be understood by recognizing that the standard information theory exists only in a mind, and that even the bits, the signs of the signals in the external reality are still "bits" only in a mind.

Communication engineering theory is a theory of communication from one mind through a brain and its outputs, through a specifiable set of processes to the external world, through a portion of that world with specifiable modes, media, and artificial means to another body, another brain, to another mind. *The "bits of information" in each of the two minds must be agreed upon by those two minds by sharing their definitions.* The signals must be able to pass from one mind to the other mind and back again, and again to create the same or similar information each time. Therefore, the basic theorum of "information" using the "signal/noise ratio" and its dependence on the "pass band" and on the "bit rate" is incomplete. This theorum, or its analog in the new set, must be redefined to include the new interfaces. Let us see what we can do to make such new definitions with the new interfaces considered.

In general, the signal/noise ratio is a definable entity only when each of two minds agrees on the definition of what is "signal" and what is "noise." In the standard theory, "noise" is ideally a detectable random process, a stochastic ensemble varying with time (in a random fashion). "Noise" is a form of energy in which no part can be taken, no matter how chosen, as conveying any meaning whatsoever. Physical noise is that set of signals which, when received by a mind, generates no new information in that mind. In this sense, a noise must have no beginning and no end. If a noise *begins,* this of itself is a signal. If the noise *ends,* this of itself is also a signal. We have new information at the beginning and at the end of a noise sequence. Therefore, the duration of a noise in time also gives information.

Thus, we can say that any change other than purely random changes detectable by the mind in any aspect of the noise is a signal and hence can generate information in the mind. When we place the new boundaries on information theory, one can see that one's own mind can be and does act as if it were a source of "new" information. The sources of "new" information in one's own mind are analogous to the sources in the external world. This can be seen most dramatically by either looking at a very noisy visually presented process or by listening to a very noisy acoustically presented process. If one watches long enough or listens long enough, he begins to "make signals out of the noise" by introducing systematic changes into the noise. Where do these "signals" come from? Where does the new "information" come from?

In profound physical isolation, this process can be shown most dramatically. *Our minds project a pattern onto the noise.* We can even project an "as if" source of the signals (as if they were coming from the outside) even though they are being brought up only from the storage within our own minds. Basically, investigators who are looking into their own minds (under special conditions) may mistake the sources of "new" information within their own minds as if those sources were outside the head. This process in psychology is called "projection."

This process can use noise at any level of abstraction (from the physical, physiological levels of functioning) as a computer, and make this same mistake. One can have noise, as it were, in random, logical processes as well as by the random motion and the random collisions of molecules. If one is watching "noise" at the logical level, he can sometimes "hear messages," as if he were being spoken to by other persons and these persons were telling him some important message. Basically, these processes within the human mind are just beginning to be investigated thoroughly with the help of special conditions. (This approach may be applicable to a study of severe psychoses.)

Fundamentally, then, we must eliminate, insofar as our brains and minds and their scientific investigation are concerned, a hypothesis which says that the noise coming from inside one's own mind and brain can be "signals caused by direct mental influence of other minds without the interposition of the usual modes and media

of communication." Modern scientific theory says that
I have my mind, here and now, and that there are other
minds, here and now, resident in brains in bodies present in the external reality outside my body but nowhere
else.

Modern science denies interest in the existence of such
things as the spirit world, the direct influence of God
on human minds, and extraterrestrial influence machines
manipulated by other beings. Most of the phenomena
described as happening within the minds of people can
be explained by the above mechanisms, the projection
of signals from within one's own storage onto noise, and
hence hearing or seeing what one wants to hear or see
rather than some objectively existing "spirit" or "God."

One might say from a modern scientific point of view,
then, that transcendental religious revelations are merely
the projections of one's own expectations in the area of
religion. A disembodied mind cannot exist according to
current scientific theory.

I am quite empirical about this. Until I can send tele-
grams (from me to a third party) through such media
and through such minds, and receive a verifiable tele-
gram through the same routes, I will not believe in the
existence of such media, modes, and minds.

The existence theorum states, "To prove the existence
of a something one must first present evidence of that
something and its existence acceptable to other minds."
The non-existence theorum states, "As long as one assumes the nonexistence of a something one will assume
that the signals from the something either do not exist,
are noise, are created in another human mind, or come
from some mindless process in nature." Therefore, if an
unknown mind without a visible, detectable body sends
signals, we ignore them, repress memories of having received them, attribute them to noise, or attribute them
to a mindless but systematically varying source or, say,

that they are the results of faulty operation of the observer, i.e., projections from the observer's own mind.

This theorum (the non-existence theorum) is a useful one in dealing with uncomfortable evidence one is tempted to reject, usually with a powerful emotional propulsion on the rejection. This theorum may cause one to at least slow down and think of alternatives to rejection. I find it useful, especially in special states of mind, including times of great disappointment, fear, great joy or sorrow, and others. I also find it useful when dealing with dolphins. If we assume that the mind of the dolphin does not exist, we will assume that the signals from it do not exist or are noise created by the human mind, or come from some mindless process in nature. If a dolphin sends signals, we ignore them, repress memories of having received them, attribute them to noise, or a mindless source or say that they are the results of faulty operation of the observer who reports them. This is the treatment that dolphins usually suffer at the hands of scientists.

When I first postulated the existence of a mind in a dolphin, I saw this effect operate strongly against me, and against the "dolphin mind hypothesis." Why must we say that the dolphin has no mind, that no other creature in this world has a mind of the complexity and size of ours? Why has the theory of a mind in other creatures become *persona non grata* and discredited over the years? I suggest that it is because man has been concentrating all of his scientific efforts in areas of endeavor in which this presumption of the mind is totally inappropriate. Man has progressed rapidly in physics, in chemistry, in biology, in engineering, and in other such areas by defining a mind as nonexistent in these processes. In these areas of scientific endeavors, this is a basic assumption that must be made, is appropriate, and can be shown to work very well.

In other areas such as the ones discussed in this book,

we must assume a mind exists in order to make progress. The assumption of a mind in research with dolphins does work: "Each of the large-brained dolphins has a correspondingly large mind." The theorum does not say what kind of a mind the dolphin has, it says only that it exists.

One reason that science has abandoned the hypothesis of bodiless minds, minds without brains, is partly because it has been misused in the past history of the human species throughout all of the races. Historically, practically every one of the human races, and in some of them currently, there are superstitions, animisms, totemisms, and various other kinds of projections into the noise of one's own areas of ignorance. When one does not have hard-nose data about the surrounding realities, and also hard-nose data about the internal realities of his own mind, he projects the concepts in his mind into the surroundings, into other persons, into other animals, and even into plants. This seems to be the origin of the multiplicity of such things as gods, devils, wood spirits, and nymphs with which world literature is replete.

Such factors are seen still operating even today in one's own mind, if one is willing to go into solitude and profound isolation from physical stimuli. Under these conditions, if a "white acoustic noise" is present in the background and if one is fearful enough or expectant enough or feeling neglected enough, one can begin to make out "voices" in the noise and sometimes even count the number of people who are doing the talking. A few subjects under this condition can actually hear "the voice of God" in the noise. If one carefully analyzes "what God said" it is found that, as far as that person is concerned, nothing new is said. In other words, the things in the storage of the personal big computer are all one finds in the analysis of what God said. With a sufficiently prolonged period of analysis following such an episode, one can trace out all of the details of the so-called "religious revelation" and show that they have been present since the childhood of the human being involved. Under such circumstances, one tends to project things picked up in childhood and long since forgotten in adulthood.

This projection is into the unknown sets of signals which one can interpret as noise and hence project onto fairly freely. It is this ability which has plagued scientists since science began. It is this error, rather than *anthropomorphism* or *anthropocentricity*, that is basic to the skepticism and cynicism about finding minds in animals other than man. As a scientist we are each trained not to indulge in conscious projections and conscious fantasy. We are also taught to be very suspicious of certain kinds of theoretical constructions, because of this bad history of such constructions. Through careful and prolonged psychoanalytical training, we can begin to see these traps for our theories in ourselves.

The theory of a mind, not human, existing in another animal, not human, is attractive and seductive. This, too, puts off most scientists. Those who deal with lower animals want hard-nose data concerning the quality of the mind that one is postulating as existing in a dolphin. The problem in interspecies communication is to develop it so that even the most hard-nose skeptics can have satisfactory data about the existence of the mind in the dolphin.

In our society, the postulation of disembodied non-brained minds exists in religious endeavors side by side with scientific endeavors. The religious thinkers must assume the existence of some sort of a mind other than human. Religion would quickly cease to exist without the postulation of a spirit or God or gods. Some scientists at times need to believe wholeheartedly in their own personal basic beliefs and defend them as vigorously and emotionally as any zealous missionary.

Some of these scientists tend to keep their religion for Sunday and yet carry over their zealous defense for the rest of the week. My own position about religion is the same as my position about ESP and thought transference. Until I have empirical, down-to-earth, hard-nosed information thrust upon me, I will maintain a position of not knowing; such thinking also belongs in the area of the unknown.

Thus, I agree with those who maintain that I or others must produce very good information about the mind of the dolphin before they can believe in its existence. On the other hand, there are those who deny that *any* mind can exist in a dolphin. It is with these people that I take definite issue. One cannot very easily demonstrate the absence of anything. If the mind exists, it is going to be easier to demonstrate its existence than it will be to demonstrate its nonexistence, if it does not exist.

Those who want a demonstration of existence, if it exists, suggest certain experiments. They would show, for example, the intelligence of the dolphin by testing for the kinds of abstract ideas that one dolphin exchanges with another. Such an experiment is as follows:

One dolphin is put in an isolation tank with a series of problems to be solved in sequence. These problems are as cleverly arranged as the investigator is able to achieve. One suggested arrangement is to put the problems in a cascaded series in which the solution of each depends upon the previous one. The dolphin is induced to solve or is taught to solve the sequence of problems with suitable rewards for success. During this period, he is kept out of contact with other dolphins.

Once he succeeds in a performance, he is placed in a vocal-auditory contact, two-way, with a second dolphin. No visual nor mechanical contact is allowed between the two dolphins. Dolphin No. 2 is in an isolation tank similar to that of No. 1. He also has the problem materials with him.

The major question to be answered then, is: Can dolphin No. 1 now transmit the appropriate information to No. 2 to allow No. 2 to solve the sequence as fast or faster than No. 1?

A few cautions are necessary. 1. The problems must be of such a novelty and of such a unique type that no previous dolphin can have had any previous experience with them. 2. The problems must be difficult enough to solve so that a detectable time is taken in the solution of the problem. 3. The difficulty must be great enough to insure that no dolphin can reason out a solution on his own without help. 4. The problems must become interesting enough to a dolphin to keep him working on them long enough to solve them. 5. The problems must be interesting enough for No. 1 to interest the other dolphin, No. 2, in solving them. 6. The problems all must be in the framework and in the content of the dolphin-to-dolphin communication. 7. Alternatively, the problems must be convertible by dolphin No. 1 into the content and the framework of dolphin-to-dolphin communication.

I am very much interested in this approach and have encouraged several scientists in efforts to make progress along these lines. To date, the usual failure is during the initial period in selecting the problems and in teaching dolphin No. 1 the problems. The usual investigator forgets some of the above requirements, especially the last four, i.e., that the problems must be interesting to dolphins and appropriate to their cognitive, conative, perceptual, and transmission-reception systems. Undoubtedly, variations of these experiments will be done in the future in sufficient numbers so that the evidence will gradually accumulate as to what dolphins can transmit and what they cannot transmit one to the other's mind.

In the Institute, our own research program includes this point of view. I believe that we need to share the contents of the communication with the dolphin in order to have the proper materials for the above experiments. In the system which we are devising, we establish a shared set of symbols, a set shared among us and among the dolphins themselves. Such symbols must be understood by the dolphins in their way and by us in our way. In this pursuit, we learn what does interest them as problem materials.

Sometimes the dolphins tell us what interests them by showing interest, i.e., by sticking to a given kind of a problem. We learn also what is appropriate to their reception-perception-cognition-volition-transmission systems, either "naturally" or in an artificially taught and learned context. As the bits and pieces of the shared symbols fall into place, problems can be constructed in which these symbols are used.

Each of us as a child learned by being presented by our parents with tens of thousands of pieces of information daily. We are allowed, as it were, to pick up that which we can pick up at each age. By the time we enter school, we have already learned the basic way to speak and the basic way to communicate. Thus we can say man learns, as a child, enough language to begin to solve problems posed by the parents and his peers and to pose problems to be solved by them. Thus we must teach the dolphins by constant contact, some sort of a shared language between us, before we can carry out the proposed experiments on testing their intelligence. Other scientists have not agreed with this point of view. They feel that we can make faster progress by demonstration first of the dolphin's high intelligence. If they are right, it should be possible for any psychologist trained in intelligence testing methods to make such a demonstration possibly long before the demonstration by means of interspecies communication. Those who are trying this approach so far are delighted with the dolphins' abilities to solve complex hierarchies of certain kinds of shared problems.

Once again, I underscore the necessity of the sharing, cooperative efforts to keep the dolphins interested and to keep the investigators happy. I feel that those who immerse themselves in the dolphins' world and have dolphins in their world can learn and teach the above posed problems through interspecies communication methods. But I do not feel that a psychologist can "take a summer off" and get the desired results in a short time. We are not dealing with small-brained animals in short-term experiments, in which most of our animal psychologists are trained. One can take a genetically pure strain of rats and in a few months quickly arrive at desired results. The rats' solutions to problems are well known and what rats can do and what they can't do has been well described (though not yet fully).

We have found in the Institute that both the human side and the dolphin side are still too strange to one another to do such problems quickly and easily. In the vocal sphere we have accomplished some rather novel and unusual tasks with dolphins. We have demonstrated that the dolphins can do certain vocal tasks that no other animal except man can do. No parrot, no mynah bird, no monkey can do these tasks at all. Elsewhere in this book these experiments have been described and their results given in detail.

I will also describe the mother-child approach to these problems in which a young dolphin and a female human actually lived together in order to explore methods of communication. To progress in these experiments it has been found necessary that each of the personnel have a belief in the existence of the mind of the dolphin and in its large size and complexity in order to make progress.

Currently, the whaling industry is busy wiping out

most of the big whales, and in Japan, at least, dolphins are slaughtered by the thousands for food. (Such industrial efforts have been less than what the navies of the world could now do to exterminate the whales but it is still effective.) In this area, I am not proud of my own species. Do we have anything that might impress the sperm whales aside from our killing abilities?

For some years I have been hunting for anything that human beings can do which might impress brains and minds larger than ours. We have expert abilities to build: to build buildings, to build roads, to build cities, these of themselves are impressive. If the whales could see these in detail from the land side, we might achieve a certain measure of respect from them.

We also build ships, submarines, and yachts. This probably impresses them more at the present time because sea craft are more within their sphere of experience. Our abilities to pollute the oceans by means of the rivers also must be impressive to them. Loren Eiseley once wrote that to see the detritus of civilization spewing forth in the oceans from the rivers must be a mysterious and at the same time impressive sight; a proof of the activities of the animal called *Homo sapiens*.[1]

All of the things that I have mentioned here are done by many people cooperating with one another. This is true of the whaling industry as well as of the building industry. This cooperative activity of the humans is the thing which is impressive even though no one of us might be impressive to a single sperm whale. Operating in concert we are an impressive species.

Probably that which would excite the most respect for the human species in a sperm whale would be a full symphony orchestra playing a symphony. At least this would be an excellent starter to try to convince a sperm

[1] "The Long Loneliness," *Phi Beta Kappa Quarterly* (1961).

whale that maybe some of us are better than just in-concert murderers of whales. A symphony orchestra playing multiple melodies and their complex transformations might keep him interested for at least two or three hours. With his huge computer the sperm whale could probably store the whole symphony and play it back in his mind to himself at his leisure. I suggest that whoever tries this experiment first should be ready to play several symphonies, each symphony only once. Otherwise, the sperm whale would be bored with the performance. Since he probably has the capacity to store the whole thing at one playing and doesn't need to hear it again from outside, he would be bored by repetition. He probably re-creates it for himself fully from storage in his huge brain.

You will notice that I picked complex multiple human *acoustic performances distributed in space* as that which would impress the whale. As stated for the dolphin earlier, since in the sea sound and ultrasound are far more important than light and its variations, this is the area that he understands best. As we stated earlier in this book his brain, his big computer is also more acoustically orientated than ours; very large masses of it are given over to acoustic computations, even as in ours we are given over to visual computations.

The sperm whale's re-creations are probably complete. He probably can re-create this spatial distribution of the sounds. He probably can also replay the complex interrelationship between the sounds simultaneously in pitch, in space, in loudness. His reproduction is probably in "high fidelity" coupled with the original feeling that he had at the first play. This probably would be easy for any sperm whale. I understand there are a few human beings who spent years acquiring some of this ability.

In my own case, I have visualized and felt this kind of experience but only during the actual playing of the music itself, here and now. It would be a great privilege to be able to reinvoke the full playing. Imagine being able to relive a full playing of Handel's *Messiah* or any of your favorite symphonies without any apparatus or recordings outside of your own brain!

This huge brain of the sperm whale may also have reprogramming abilities for the symphony. He may modify the music and even further elaborate it beyond any human conceptions of music. How can we ever know if this hypothesis is true or not? Let us make this idea "the carrot in front of our donkey" and let it motivate us to learn to communicate. Then we can ask these questions and proceed from there.

Of course we may never have the chance to have the intriguing and uplifting experience of communicating with a sperm whale. Our enterprising friends of the whaling industry are too involved to give us this opportunity. Economic gain is still mightier than the Golden Rule. Economic gain is beyond curiosity, beyond our ethics, morals, religions. It is indeed a black mark on the escutcheon of the human race to allow profit here to override the best in man. Those involved in the whaling industry create delusions to serve overriding their own and our ideals.

In a book called *The Whaler's Eye*,[2] one chapter describes the sophistries of a scientist working for the whaling industry. He was having a hard time deciding whether or not the whale was hurt by the harpoon which finally killed him. It could easily be demonstrated with dolphins to such people (if they were interested) that the skin of all of these animals is exquisitely sensitive. We could demonstrate unequivocally that they do feel pain and object to pain as strongly as humans. The in-

[2] Christopher Ash (New York: The Macmillan Company, 1962).

dustry has been so busy for over a hundred years rationalizing their position with respect to the whales that they have forgotten that there is evidence that whales do not only have pain but express it unequivocally. Many people have written of the moanings and carryings on of injured whales. In the last century the whalers with their wooden vessels could hear these sounds through the sides of the ships. The problem is distinguishing the moans of their pain and fear from the normal communications between the whales. If the human race is ever to be measured by another species for the qualities of our activities in regard to interspecies communication, this is the worst possible record of our failures to respect and nurture other species.

11

The Mind of the Dolphin

"Communication is an exchange of information between two minds." Thus for interspecies communication we start with the basic postulate that each dolphin has a mind. The size, the complexity, and the capability of each dolphin mind is a function of the size of his brain. Each individual has some limitations placed upon him by the limits on the number of neurons in his brain. The quality of the development, through the use of the brain and of the mind, is a function of the natural experiences and formal education to which each individual is exposed.

Each dolphin's mind is very strange and distinctly different from ours. The problem is: How are the dolphins different? Will we ever be able to understand them? Will they ever be able to understand us? How are they similar? Are they similar enough to us to make possible the first bridges of understanding between the two species?

Our minds and their minds are in bodies whose differences have been described in the previous book. The differences between our brains were begun in that book and are discussed further in this book. The inputs and the outputs to the human and to the dolphin brain are discussed in another chapter. The differences in our environments and theirs are described in the first book.

I mention "minds, bodies, brains, environment" in the same context because of their close interdependence in life. One important additional factor in the generation and maintenance of the mind is the social milieu. Most of us operate in "mostly human" social environments. Only very few of us have the privilege to operate in close contact and as essential parts of a dolphin's milieu. Only a few dolphins operate directly and closely with a human. I feel that there are not enough such close combinations nor are there enough persons willing to devote themselves to dolphins in this way at the present time.

The dolphin minds which I am most concerned with are those living with human beings. Something of what I have to say may concern wild dolphins, but these are not available for close study.

Our search for the mind of the dolphin and our search for the common ground between our two kinds of mind, starts with our own mind. This cannot be emphasized enough. Since we do not yet fully understand the human mind, there may be aspects of it which are closer to the dolphin mind than we yet know. In the research on our own minds, we should seek aspects which are shared with large brains in general. The large mind in the large brain may have underlying (and presently not understood) similarities which we can use. At any point we may find a bridge across to their minds through the investigation of our own minds.

Elsewhere in this book, I discuss some possible operations of the very large mind-brain of the sperm whale. I wish to limit here the discussion to brain-minds the size of ours, and what such brains can do if unhampered by the usual conventions of thinking. Dolphins are unhampered by our conventions; they may become hampered by our conventions; they may be hampered by their own conventions.

My purpose here is to expand our horizon beyond the necessary, daily, constricting confines of our operating society. Each one of us must streamline himself to fill a role within that social milieu. Most of us are so "locked in" with our everyday lives with our family and our work that we do not have time to see the structures of our own minds, as they can operate when freed from these external reality necessities. Let us try to visualize another situation which may help us in understanding how our minds are limited and how the dolphin's mind may differ from ours.

Let us visualize a situation in which a person is taking a vacation in which his duties are completely suspended. His work and his family are adequately cared for. All the bills are paid up. The telephone is turned off. There is no radio or TV. For a period of three to five days, no demands are placed upon him. All of his needs are satisfied automatically. He is immersed in silence and darkness and freed up from the demands of gravity. He is placed temporarily "in orbit," as it were, with automatic feeding machines.

Would this be an ideal vacation? Some busy people might conceive of it as idyllic. Most people, placed in this situation, make themselves unhappy, at least for a period of time. During some 1954 short-term experiments, profound physical isolation and solitude taught me some things which I present here.

After some work I found this condition quite comfortable. But the work was necessary first. The outside-the-body conditions were perfected; then my own mental attitude had to be investigated.[1]

I learned that conditions which should be idyllic can

[1] Lilly, John C. (1956) in General Bibliography.

become so when one deep down wants them to be so. In other words, that which a person believes is that which becomes true, within the limited confines of this experiment. This is all inside the person's own head, and hence is subject to the unique laws of thought, not to the natural laws of external reality. After many exposures to the physical isolation under ideal physical conditions, I was able to overcome self-created mental discomfort to a certain extent. I learned a lesson about our minds as follows:

Our huge computers are, to a certain extent, self-metaprogramming and self-programming.[2] If one is left alone long enough, he can see how he acts as a cause with respect to himself. We can see also that each one of us can cause a large fraction of our own unhappiness. We can see that we have within us "programs for unhappiness" as well as "programs for happiness." In isolation, we see to what extent each of us also is programmed by others in our normal, everyday lives. We can see that we often blame the programming of others when we should be blaming the programming of ourselves. Since the number of such programs in each one of us is immense, we have to set up a metaprogram which says "investigate programs which are counter to one's major interests." We must also set up the metaprogram, "find out how much one's self is the causative factor in an unhappy situation, and vice versa, how much someone else is the causative factor (untangle the feedback)."

When a person first enters isolation, the interpersonal programs continue to operate during the first hour or so. It is only as these immediate day's programs fade out and the self-generated programs come in and replace them that the latter can be clearly seen. Without proper pro-

[2] Lilly, J. C., *Programming and Metaprogramming in the Human Biocomputer (Theory and Experiments)*, Julian Press, N.Y., 1973; Bantam Books, 1974.

gramming in isolation, we can make endless excuses to ourselves and make endless evasions which avoid analysis of self.

This situation is epitomized in the statement, "Alone with one's God there are no distractions, nor excuses, nor alibis, nor evasions."[3] Once we are launched into the self-generated metaprograms and programs we can eventually find the ones which work against our ideals and goals. One group is the "how and what to think" metaprograms. One of these tells us that "certain ways of thought and certain kinds of thinking are negative." (The term "negative" means that which is unpleasant or forbidden or dangerous or "psychotic" or "sick" or evil or anti-social or sinful, for example.)

This kind of metaprogram is very difficult to see in one's self. With psychoanalytic experience and training, I began to see this particular metaprogram and to attempt to attenuate it in my thinking. Without finding it and modifying its effects, I would not have been able to continue the isolation work at all. *By long and hard work I found that the evil label "negative" should not be tied to any mode or any kind of thinking at all.* Literally, there is no such thing as an "evil" *type* of thinking *per se*. There are negative *thoughts;* there are evil thoughts, hostile thoughts, guilty thoughts. There is no evil *mode* of thinking. Negative thoughts can occur in any mode, but the mode itself is not negative. One's horizons in the metaprograms for "what to think and how to think" should be wide open with no holds barred.

For example, consider the subjective phenomena which I call "projection of visual imagery and visual thinking." I chose these words expressing these phenomena very carefully to avoid "negative" terms (such as "hallucination" or "delusion") one could borrow from

[3] Lilly, J. C., *loc. cit.*

psychiatry. In this area William James said that one should keep the terminology as objective and yet as "positive" as possible. The first time I experienced these phenomena in isolation I reacted negatively. The first judgments were negative and hence it required courage to continue to do the work. By continuing I learned my first lesson: *No kind of thinking, no phenomena within the mind are of themselves negative unless one defines them as negative.*

If one chooses to regard all projections as "psychotic" or "sick" or "evil," then within our own mind, within our own computer, they are so regarded. By so judging such phenomena we prevent ourselves from seeing them in our own mind. This is self-metaprogramming. Let us rephrase it in another more general way. *What one believes to be true of his own mental phenomena either is true or becomes true within his own mind within certain limits to be determined experimentally by himself.*

Specific examples of this principle are as follows: If one believes that his mind is inferior to other minds and that his thinking processes are less great than those of other people, this is reflected in all the operations of his own mind. He can hardly enjoy the vacation in isolation when he believes that he is inferior in mental functioning.

Similarly, if one believes that he is worthless, evil, destructive, and hostile, in isolation he can hardly enjoy the vacation. He will be castigating himself for his essential evilness. This is a particularly nasty game that persons play with themselves under more usual conditions and oftentimes project on to others in their environment. If we feel that we are worthless, then others feel the same way about us. We are then tempted to blame others for making us worthless, evil, or sick.

Let us now return to the isolation situation once again, the outside situation. I found that bodily sources of discomfort, pain, or threat tend to program the mind in the negative mode and keep it there as long as the discomfort continues. As long as pain, even at a very low level, continues, the computer (which is one's mind) tends to program a negative pall. All of one's thinking assumes now the negative flavor of the pain. Apparently some persons can eventually prevent this, knowing it, especially with a long experience of low-level pain in their lives.

This metaprogram, "external pain causes me to think negatively," is difficult to change. If one has a potentiating metaprogram which says either "accept pain and bear it stoically" or one which says "pain is needed to expiate your sins," it is difficult to change the causative chain. By personal experience I say that it can be difficult to deal with these and to reverse them. In the early experiments, we had residual sources of low-level pain. As we discovered them, we found that they were influencing our thinking. This fact was found only as we eliminated the painful sources. The relief was great when we eliminated the pain. One such good experience and the way was found for further experimentation.

In attempting to replicate isolation experiments, other researchers did not eliminate the low-level sources of pain. For example, some of their subjects experienced a low-level back pain when staying in the same position on a bed for too long a period of time. Such subjects did not recognize that fact in their thinking nor did their observers pick this up. In these experiments, the observers had not done the experiment on themselves and hence did not know about these sources of this kind of thinking. None of these subjects wished to repeat their experiments.[4]

[4] See *Sensory Deprivation: a Symposium* 1960 (Harvard Univ. Press, Cambridge, Mass.).

Once one has eliminated the sources of pain and found the sources of negative thinking, he can enjoy this "isolation vacation." In a sort of rebound from the release from low-level pain, my computer turned the mood of the thinking to a delightful, optimistic, pleasure-filled one. I then felt what fun life can really be when one's inner and outer programs are consonant. I also found how rewarding it is to be free of pain, free of threat, and free of non-rational interdictions. In this new positive mood, in this new positive approach, the visual projections were pleasurable and at times humor-filled. Instead of the old negative moods, punishing feelings, and uneasy thoughts, new positive moods, rewarding feelings, and comfortable thoughts took place.

One may wonder why I dwell on such matters at great length here, in a discussion of the dolphin's mind. We bring all of these things to our work with the dolphins. We must also recognize the possibility that they, too, at times, can bring these things to their relationships with us. These may be universal mammalian characteristics of mind. Even though one's self is unique in certain areas, one has something of a postulated general-purpose mammalian brain. Even a person's mistakes probably have more validity with respect to others than is generally thought.

Such discoveries about one's self give a person a sense of responsibility to share them with other persons. He quickly finds that this sharing is not too wise a course of action. This immediate and altruistic sharing with his wife, with his friends, with his children can have quick repercussions. He is being unfair to them to do this sharing without careful preparation. Each of them have not been through all of the steps that he has himself. Most persons of his acquaintance are still involved in the usual "safety metaprograms" which are prescribed by the interpersonal experts. These metaprograms define certain kinds of thinking as negative, or as "mentally ill."

I wrote up some of these results and published them.[5] I quickly found that a few psychiatrists could not free themselves up enough to understand the generality of the basic points. Their reasoning was colored and their metaprograms filled with "well-sick clinical dichotomies." I do not feel it appropriate for scientific research on human thinking itself to use such categories. The universality of their application to the human mind is questionable. It is possible to develop a more objective, more functional point of view; one such is that used by William James in *The Varieties of Religious Experience.*

James' approach to the life of the mind is delightfully objective, and free of the dichotomies of "doctor-patient," "well-sick," etc. Properly used, some of these dichotomies of medicine are useful and needed in an empirical way in medical and legal practice, but there is much in the universe of the human mind not contained in this view.

I do not intend here to neglect the later developments after James, especially in the Freudian psychoanalytic field. In my training analysis and in analyzing others, I found the "psychodynamic" view of the mind as used by the psychoanalysts is basic to our understanding of the mind. The psychodynamic formulations are in the tradition of trying to understand what is going on within the human mind. This method does not dichotomize human minds into groups depending upon arbitrary criteria such as "well" versus "sick." The psychoanalytic view is a more quantitative, more differentiated, and a more complete kind of investigation of the human mind than the limited categorization mentioned above. Let us now return to the dolphins and their end of the interspecies communication.

Earlier, I said I wished to evaluate and describe what

[5] Lilly, J. C., *loc. cit.*

a human mind can do within its own limitations outside the framework of conventional thinking and acting. Undoubtedly, the dolphins have few of our mental conventions. Undoubtedly, also, they have few of our conventional thoughts. If we are ever able to think the way the dolphins do we will have to be free to do so on their terms, not on our terms alone. In one of my lectures on dolphins, I started out somewhat like this:

"I wish to tell you something of what we have learned of a group of uninhibited nudists who have never worn clothes. They have never walked on their own two feet. They have no property. They cannot write their own names. They have no commerce or stores. They have no radio, no TV. They have no fireplaces, nor furnaces, or any fire at all. They have no atomic or nuclear bombs, or power plants. They have no written or printed records. They have no libraries or paintings. In spite of all these handicaps, they are successful. They have big brains and bright minds. They have built-in transportation. They have readily available food supplies. They have the sense to go south in the winter and to go north in summer. They have the ability to out-think, outmaneuver, and fight successfully against their enemies. Finally, they think enough of us to save each of us when they find us in trouble."

One tends to forgive and even forget the dolphin's nudity. Their necessary streamlining would be very much spoiled by clothing. Most persons watching a group of dolphins in an oceanarium miss the uninhibited aspects of dolphin life. They think usually of the gracefulness, the motion, the rapidity, and the power expressed. Because of their own human inhibitions, they do not recognize the dolphin's bowel and bladder excretions and the sexual activities.

When asked if dolphins breed in captivity, I answer, "at every opportunity, very rapidly, twenty-four hours a day unless they are busy with something else or they are sick." Some of these questioners have spent hours looking through the ports at a dolphin colony in a circus and missed the erection of the male's penis and the female's nuzzlings of the male's genitalia. When it is pointed out on the spot these persons can then see it. The bowel movements occur during swimming and are tasted by the following dolphins. We would be quite disgusted in that spot.

Thus we can see that our conventional attitudes toward clothing, excretion, and sexual activities are not shared by them. Let us turn it about and put some humans in the situation of the dolphins in these public places. Imagine what the public clamor would be if an underwater ballet group of humans were in the nude and indulged in uninhibited excretion and free sexual play. I doubt if this human activity could be photographed and broadcast on color television the way the dolphins have been televised.

We tolerate this kind of thing in public displays of dolphins because they are so different that it isn't yet brought to our attention, as it were. (It may be that after reading this passage certain persons will put pressure on the circuses to segregate the male dolphins from the female; then the pressure will be put on to hide the males entirely because of their obvious "homosexual activities" with one another.)

Thus, the mind of the dolphin shares some things with us but not others. At least the dolphin has sex on his mind every so often with the right partners. A thorough Kinsey Report has not yet been made upon dolphins. This is one area in which we must accept their behaviors and their activities and eventually their thinking. If we cannot accept them, I am sure that we will never be able to communicate with the mind of the dolphin. The sexual activities in the mind of the dolphin are apparently more like the Polynesian model than the American model.

Young males start their obvious sexual actions while very young. They continue them into very old age. The females, like ours, are more subtle. This picture of the more or less constant sexual activities among dolphins is generated by dolphins that we have seen in captivity. It may be a very faulty picture. Like Zuckerman's[6] picture of the sex life of primates in zoos, it is colored by the artificial confining, and luxurious quality of the way in which they are held. Free food is provided. There are no enemies to threaten. Sex is probably being misused to deal with boredom (or is this one of the conventional types of human thinking?). In the wild, there is probably relatively little time for sex. It must give way to other pressing necessities. One must seek food, must be aware of enemies and deal with them; must migrate and travel long distances to be assured of the proper temperatures, and so forth. Carpenter and others have shown this to be true for the lower primates.[7] Any human couple on an African safari sleeping in lion country in a tent can show it to be true for themselves also.

We must be able to face the sex life of the dolphins as we face any other aspect of the dolphins' lives. We must be able to investigate their sexual relationships not with prurience but in the spirit of objective cooperative interest. We must recognize that this is one of their major sources of pleasure even as it is with us. We must also realize that this interest of theirs can be turned to interspecies communication advantage even as it is turned to advantage in interhuman communication.

It has been said that one of the major problems in

[6] Sir Solly Zuckerman's *The Social Life of Monkeys and Apes* Trench, Trubner & Co. London: Kegan Paul, 1932.

[7] C. R. Carpenter. *Naturalistic Behavior of Nonhuman Primates.* Univ. Park, Pa., Univ. Press Penn State, 1964.

human sexual relationships is the disengagement of the process of reproduction from that of the intense pleasure that can be obtained from sexual acts. With our property laws and our ideas of property we make such a legal fuss about offspring, that we apparently spoil the pleasures that we derive from sexual activities. Similarly our peculiarly human ideas about our excrement can bar a person from contact with dolphins.

Let us return now to the mind of the dolphin. What kind of thinking do they do? Are there any leads as to the possible differences from our types of thinking? One basic physiological difference should always be kept in mind. This difference will influence the thinking along lines which may be very hard for us to visualize. This is the basic difference in their brain versus ours which I discussed earlier in this book. A large fraction of their huge computer is acoustic (Plate 32), a similar fraction of our computer is visual. The acoustic part of our computer is much smaller than theirs, even as the visual part of our computer is larger than theirs. As I described earlier, they need this acoustic kind of computer in the sea. And they do not need so much of the visual type. To try to see what the dolphin's mind may be like, let us try to imagine ourselves in the place of a dolphin in the sea.

Imagine swimming in water so murky that you can see only a few inches in front of your face. Imagine that you swim at ten or so knots. How can you know what is ahead in the water? You can come to the surface and look around across the surface of the water with your eyes and see for a distance of miles depending upon the lighting, the fog, or other special conditions. Thus we go "visual" out of the water in the air. The dolphin can do the same and does. But this tactic is good only for non-fog daytime and for objects and enemies that stick up out of the water. Under the water one must use sound and ultrasound, which can penetrate through the muddy water and give a hint as to what is going on "out there" by analyzing the echoes coming back. Such echo-recognition and -ranging is characteristic not only of the dolphins but of the shrews and the bats and several other animals.

For probably several millions of years, the dolphins have worked with sound waves in water. The more I work on their echo-recognition system the more I admire its beautiful efficiency. They use it almost continuously in one way or another; this is part of thinking processes almost beyond our ken. Let us try to imagine how it affects their thinking. Imagine yourself as a dolphin in the sea, with sonar.

In the water of the sea we would have to use our sonar to construct sonic representations of our surroundings in our mind. While our sonar was turned on we would "know" through the operations of our computer what was going on around us in the muddy water and/or in the pitch-black night. The evidence that we were doing this could easily be obtained by carefully recording the sounds we emitted. During difficult seeing conditions, we would continuously emit various kinds of sounds, some pulses, and some other kinds of sounds. By having echoes automatically come back through our ears into our huge computer, signals would be converted into information in our mind. Rapid automatic computation of the signals coming from the two ears would be computed into constructions and pictures of the scenes around us. We would "see" our friends, the shape of the bottom, where the waves were, the height of the waves, the presence of fish, and any possible lurking enemies. Because of the nature of sound waves, we could, at will, change the wave lengths used. Changes in wave length would vary the clarity with which objects of different sizes were "seen." When one varies the wave lengths (thus the resolution and directionality), he varies the amount of detail that can be seen. With a long wave length, he sees around his body in all directions. He can sense large things such as the bottom or walls or large objects in given directions. This sensing with long wave lengths gives gross aspects but gives no detail nor small directions for the objects. The gross mapping with the long wave lengths gives one the gross sector in which something large is appearing but gives us no details of that object nor of the surfaces behind it.

Let us say that some strange object is first detected. It is very much out of focus. It is over in that direction. One then shortens the wave length voluntarily; a sound beam is shaped up out in front of his head. He then sweeps the beam like a flashlight back and forth across the object in two directions in two different ways. To sweep it laterally, he moves the beam back and forth, to sweep it vertically, he moves the beam up and down by movements of the head. At the same time, to sweep in depth, he makes small rapid changes in the rate of pulse production. Then he makes an additional small change in wave length which allows him to focus on larger and smaller details one after the other.

Converted to human terminology and human concepts, this is apparently the way the dolphins operate with their sonar.

Purely by sound waves (controlled by one's own will) in wave length, direction, and rate, one *sees* under water. He keeps a picture in mind of all of his surroundings for some distance away from the body. This is done then for several hundreds of yards around and even behind his body.

We depend to a considerable extent on our vision for what we might call "visual communication." We watch very carefully the facial expression of another person to whom we are talking. We watch their bodily gestures and the movements, in other words the external aspects of their body. We cannot see inside their bodies; clothing generally inhibits our seeing an accurate view of anything but their hands and face.

If we were placed under water and looked at one another by means of sonar, what would each of us look like to the other?

Sound waves in water penetrate a body without much external reflections or absorptions. Skin, muscle, and fat are essentially transparent to the sound waves coming through the water. The internal reflections are from air-containing cavities and from bones. Thus we see a fuzzy outline of the whole body plus the bones and teeth fairly clearly delineated; the most sharply delineated objects are any gas-containing cavities. We have a good view of portions of the gut tract, the air sinuses in the head, the mouth cavity, the larynx, the trachea, the bronchi, the bronchioles, the lungs, and any air trapped in or around the body and the clothing. You can imagine again the conventional person's unease at being able to see inside another person's stomach and lungs.

There would probably be new kinds of social relations such as follows:

"Darling, you are upset with me. You are swallowing air and your stomach is churning the bubble around as it always does when you are angry."

"No, darling, I am merely sick."

The facial expression of another person is very dim when viewed this way. You see bright reflections from air sinuses and from the bones of the face. In the case of the dolphins, you see some bright reflections from the front end of the head which we lack; they have several air sacs which are immediately available to form echoes from the impinging sound waves. (We might imagine one dolphin saying to another, "Darling, you do have the cutest way of twitching your sinuses when you say you love me. I love the shape of your vestibular sacs.")

Thus, living dolphin-wise, we would have little need for external facial expression. We would try to express similar things probably with our air sacs on our head. The truth of our stomachs would be immediately available to everyone else. In other words, anyone could tell when we were either sick or angry by the bubbles of air moving in our stomachs. The true state of our emotions would be read with ease. For some persons this might lead to disadvantageous situations in, say, a bargaining transaction. I can imagine in a game of poker for high stakes this might be very inhibiting.

Since our facial expressions are controlled by "voluntary muscles," we learn to control our facial expressions in spite of an emotional state. We might have to learn to control our stomachs in a similar fashion. Could we learn to control the emotional effects expressed by our stomachs if we knew that other persons were watching them? These organs have "involuntary" or autonomic muscles and nervous connections, generally considered beyond our voluntary control.

Please notice that in the above descriptions of the sonic acoustic underwater world I use primarily visual language "to see by means of sound." Since we are more visual than we are acoustic, this is necessary, using our current language. This language requirement is reflected in the construction of our nervous systems. We have ten times their speed, their storage capacity, and their computation ability in the visual sphere; the dolphins have something of the same order of speed, storage capacity, and computation ability in the acoustic sphere. This, then, is one of the major differences between the minds of men and the minds of dolphins.

Hence, probably the thinking of the dolphin and hence the construction of their languages, is filled with acoustic representations rather than visual ones such as we use. For example, our verb "to look" probably has an equivalent in their language which we would have to translate somewhat laboriously in scientific terms as follows: "when I emit a wave length 'N' the appearance is 'Z.' When I emit a wave length 'M' the appearance changes to 'X.'" In the dolphin's mind, all of this is probably expressed by the equivalent of one or two of our words.

Since we do not have a built-in light to see objects in the dark, we do not have the appropriate words of ancient origin to convey directly and simply the meaning. We must struggle with visual analogies and adapt our own thinking to their universe of objects and sonic echoes. I cannot overemphasize the difficulties that this kind of situation leads to in terms of our understanding them and their understanding us. Our only hope is that each species does have an acoustic system and each species does have a visual system. I hope that some day we can devise ways of learning how to feel and see, the way the dolphins feel and see in the acoustic sphere. There are some hints derived from experiments with blind persons that may indicate we can do more in this area than we are at present able to do.

To solve the problems posed by these differences, we may have to devise equipment or adapt our own bodies to give us the same kind of signals under water and/or in air. We will then begin to receive the rewards necessary for successful development of a new ability. We will then develop our latent "acoustical-spatial thinking." We can imagine a dolphin suit with built-in, three-dimensional, sonic and ultrasonic emitters and receivers and with built-in streamlining. We can develop the proper program in ourselves to model the dolphin's well-developed programs.

Even though we are several millions of years behind

them here, we may be able to catch up. By the use of machines we have finally caught up with some of the birds' flight in air. Why shouldn't we similarly catch up with the dolphins' life and thinking under water? Apparently to catch up, we must devote much of our first-rate thinking, engineering, scientific, financial, and other kinds of resources to these kinds of problems. I hope that enough effective people can be interested in these problems to accomplish these ends in the not-too-distant future.

These are only the beginnings of the careful exploration of the mind of the dolphin. We wish to explore the similarities and the differences between our minds and the mind of the dolphin. One major point is that we should be prepared to change the kind and the content of our own thinking to understand their thinking. In reciprocal and mutual fashion, the dolphins must be prepared to meet us at least halfway in this quest. We must give them the opportunity to have shared visual experiences with us, stereoscopic, visual experiences. We must accept the opportunity to receive shared, acoustical experiences, stereophonic. Thus, we will try to furnish them with experiences to show us to them on our terms. We may thus close the circle of cooperative efforts between us and them.

We must adapt our minds and they must adapt theirs for the purposes of eventual true and satisfying interspecies communication at all levels. An incredible amount of good hard work is needed on both sides. This book and the previous one are devoted to discussion and to demonstration of the necessary setting in which one works to achieve interspecies communication. Please remember our aims are to elucidate the structure and adapt to the mind of the dolphin. We do this by experiments and control of laboratory setting, by experiments in living together, in a cooperative and two-sided adaptation, and by an educational program, of which these two books are a part.

Since mind, brain, set, and setting are inextricably tied together by complex and complete feedback, both human and non-human mind-brain must share a common setting and, by the proper signaling and interaction, achieve a common or at least a cooperative and communicative set, one with the other. Contingencies in the setting interact with the satisfaction of basic needs and thus teach shared "meaning." But a long time of sharing of a dolphin mind and a human mind must exist first.

To achieve the proper interaction and the proper data in the storage of each mind, chronic and unending, continuous contact must be achieved. Like ourselves, as children, it takes long-term (years), unremitting (twelve to twenty hours per day, seven days per week, fifty-two weeks per year) efforts to achieve communication. The application of the proper set in the proper setting for us to learn to speak and learn to act human is the best road to interspecies communication.

These are some of the necessities for basic interspecies communication as we see them in 1967. With these we will learn to know the mind of the dolphin.

12

New Findings: Double Phonation and Stereophonation

During our investigation with the phonation of the dolphin we were puzzled by the doubling of the phonation apparatus. Inside the opened blowhole, the passage is double, even as it is in our noses. On each side of the dolphin's nose which is here turned up on the forehead, is a complete set of sacs, muscles, tubes, and a separate vocalization membrane. There is a right phonation apparatus and a left phonation apparatus, each one in its half of the nose. Some of the features of the right apparatus are usually larger than those of the left one. We had come this far in the state of our knowledge in *Man and Dolphin*. This set of puzzling anatomical facts continued to bother me.

When the dolphin gave us controlled, humanoid sounds in air we saw that the two sides were operating quite independently of one another. We took high-speed motion pictures of the activities of the blowhole and found that this was the truth. When these pictures were slowed down we saw that the two sides of the blowhole

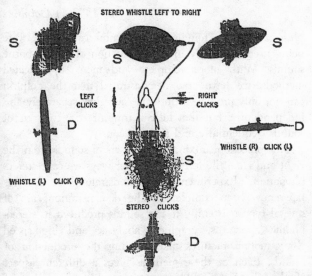

STEREO WHISTLE LEFT TO RIGHT

S

S

S

LEFT
CLICKS

RIGHT
CLICKS

D

D

WHISTLE (L)   CLICK (R)

WHISTLE (R)   CLICK (L)

STEREO   CLICKS

S

D

WHISTLE (L)   WHISTLE (R)

FIGURE 6. *Records from an Experiment with an Isolated Dolphin of the Sound Production on the Right and the Left Side of the Narial Mechanism*

A hydrophone was placed on each side of the dolphin's blowhole (as shown in the figure). The sounds picked up on the right side deflected the cathode ray oscilloscope beam in a horizontal direction. The sounds picked up on the left side deflected the beam in a vertical direction. The traces shown in the figure are photographs taken during sound production. If the dolphin clicks only with his left side, one sees only vertical traces. If he clicks on the right side, one sees only horizontal traces, and the same for the whistles on each side. If he makes a whistle which is coupled between the two sides, complex ellipses are shown on the screen. In a given click train, he may control the clicks in such a way that the ellipses shift their axes across the screen. Capital "S" means stereo, i.e., linked sound on the two sides and "D" means "double" (or separated) sound production on the two sides without coupling. (From J. C. Lilly, *Stereophonation and Double Phonation in the Dolphin* [manuscript, 1966].)

plug or the two "tongues" (as we now call them) were being used separately in the production of the air-borne sounds. With more complete and more sophisticated methods, we have now demonstrated that the dolphin can not only produce sounds on each side, separately and independently, but that he can intermix the two sets of sounds, sequentially and simultaneously.

This process of mixing the two sets of sounds from the right and from the left in particular ways we call "stereo-phonation." Experiments to demonstrate these findings have now been completed. The demonstrations are of several types: listening to the sounds produced in stereo-phonic apparatus, graphical analysis, and high-speed X-ray motion pictures taken during the production of sounds. Each of these methods gives a different aspect of the phenomena. The experimental configuration of the dolphin and the apparatus are as follows:

The dolphin is selected for his sophistication in the production of various sounds, i.e., one of the older dolphins. He is transferred gently to a sound-insulated and -isolated tank designed to absorb the sounds he produces in the water to avoid powerful echoes. He is placed carefully on a platform suspended under the water. The water depth can be adjusted to suit the experimental necessities. At the beginning of each experiment, the water depth is adjusted so as to float him freely above the platform. A flat hydrophone is fastened gently over the right side of his head and another flat hydrophone over the left side of his head. The positioning of these sound receivers is very critical. They are adjusted carefully while listening to the sound production of the dolphin so that they are in a place where the sound is maximal.

The output from each of these hydrophones is amplified and recorded in separate channels. A tape recording is made in two separate tracks one from each side of the dolphin's head. Simultaneously, the separated channels are led to a cathode ray oscilloscope. The sounds are recorded as they occur in various ways on the oscilloscope. For example: 1. they are recorded, one played against the other, on the X and Y axes of the cathode ray tube in a so-called "X versus Y" plot; 2. the two channels can each be portrayed as displayed in time with two separate beams on the oscilloscope; 3. the output of various frequency analyzers can be plotted on the screen

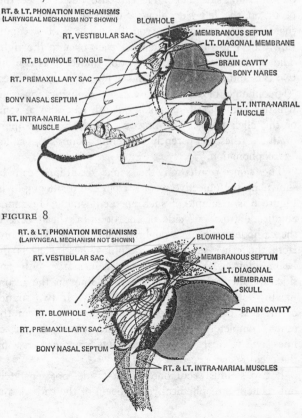

FIGURE 7

RT. & LT. PHONATION MECHANISMS
(LARYNGEAL MECHANISM NOT SHOWN)

BLOWHOLE

RT. VESTIBULAR SAC

MEMBRANOUS SEPTUM

LT. DIAGONAL MEMBRANE

SKULL

RT. BLOWHOLE TONGUE

BRAIN CAVITY

RT. PREMAXILLARY SAC

BONY NARES

BONY NASAL SEPTUM

RT. INTRA-NARIAL MUSCLE

LT. INTRA-NARIAL MUSCLE

FIGURE 8

RT. & LT. PHONATION MECHANISMS
(LARYNGEAL MECHANISM NOT SHOWN)

BLOWHOLE

RT. VESTIBULAR SAC

MEMBRANOUS SEPTUM

LT. DIAGONAL MEMBRANE

SKULL

RT. BLOWHOLE

BRAIN CAVITY

RT. PREMAXILLARY SAC

BONY NASAL SEPTUM

RT. & LT. INTRA-NARIAL MUSCLES

also; 4. with X-rays we can follow with high-speed motion pictures what happens inside the head during these
various processes. Thus, with patience and with luck we
can obtain a visual anatomical portrayal of the instantaneous events occurring during various kinds of sound
production.

These recordings are studied in various ways. The
separate channels of magnetic tape can be listened to
stereophonically by a human observer with headphones.
The observer can then detect those sounds which occur
on the right side alone. He can also detect those that
occur on the left side alone. Suddenly, he will notice
that sounds are occurring on the right and sweeping
slowly over to the left and then back over to the right.
The apparent source of the sound moves between his
two ears and moves through the center of his head. These
"stereophonic movements" are most dramatic for some
whistles and some humanoids but are true also of some
of the click trains. The process by which the dolphin
produces these apparently traveling sounds is called
"stereophonation."

The same results on the same recordings can be
shown by the objective records from the oscillograph. In
Figure 6 is a sample of such an oscillogram. The sound
amplitude from one side of the dolphin's head deflects
the cathode ray beam straight up and down. The sound
from the other side of the dolphin's head deflects the
beam sideways. When the sound comes from only one
side, we then see a straight narrow line on the record
moving either vertically or horizontally. If two sounds
occur, first one from one side and then one from the
other, completely separately in time, we see a pair of
lines, one vertical and one horizontal forming a cross on
the oscilloscope screen.

If two sounds occur one on each side, not separately
but related stereophonically, the beam of the cathode ray

traces complex patterns on the scope face. These patterns show the instantaneous amplitude relation between the two sounds. When an observer hears the sound moving back and forth between his two ears inside his head the beam traces circles and ellipses of varying sizes and inclinations. This is especially dramatic for the whistles for the two sides. At other times, during clickings, one can see similar ellipses, complex loops, and various figures whose size and slopes change from one click to the next. As we go through a long click sequence, we see beautiful systematic progressions of very complex figures on the cathode ray tube.

Some of the other sounds emitted by a dolphin fill the screen with "noisy," complex patterns. For example, the sounds of respiration have characteristic noisy patterns which vary with the depth and speed of the breathing.

We can relate the objective patterns on the screen to the subjective patterns that we hear by listening stereophonically and watching the cathode ray tubes at the same time. Quickly then, we see that the patterns which occur, when the sound's source apparently is moving inside our heads, are circles, ellipses, loops, and lines at other than the vertical or the horizontal parts of the screen. In other words, if the dolphin's two emitted sounds, the one from the right and the one from the left, have an instantaneous relation between them of the proper amplitude and the proper phase and the proper timing, we sense an apparent movement of the sound source. In other cases, we hear the sound only in one ear or in the other ear.

The two sounds that have these side-to-side relationships in the head of the dolphin from the two phonation organs are thus "stereophonic," one with respect to the other. We are using the term stereophonic to show that these sounds have space-time relations which allow one with one's own brain to compute them, as if coming from a single apparent source located away from the two real sources. Stereophonation is thus a voluntary, unique, physiological process known only now for the dolphin and not yet known for any other animal.

In our own voice mechanisms we lack completely this stereophonation dimension of his sonic communication mode. He can move the apparent source of his voice from one side of his head to the other. He can do this easily, smoothly, and continuously. Our voice is close to the midplane and, apparently, comes from the nose and the mouth near that plane.

How does a dolphin use this ability? With his two ears he can detect the fusion of his two sources in an apparent single one, even as we do with stereoheadphones. With this stereolistening, he can thus control the effects of the proper feedback to himself. He can put the apparent source anywhere that he wishes within the side-to-side limits of his own organs. Or he can move the apparent source very rapidly to and fro between the two sources. He may thus introduce a "Doppler effect" on his own speech. (The Doppler effect is an apparent shift in frequency due to the motion of a source of sound. A classic example is that of a car horn or train whistle; as it approaches us the apparent pitch rises, as it recedes from us the apparent pitch falls.) He can also control his near-field and far-field amplitudes as he shifts from monopole to dipole modes.

There are additional complexities to the dolphin's voice and to his phonation abilities which we should add to the discussion at this point. His right phonation system is usually larger than his left one. This asymmetry of the two sides has interesting effects on what he can do with each side. Some of the tones on the right can be lower than those emitted on the left. I first came upon some of these interesting properties through the vocal abilities of a dolphin named Chee Chee. When we first met, Chee Chee was estimated to be twelve years old. At that age, she was found to be a much more sophisticated sound producer than the youngsters, Elvar and Tolva, mentioned in *Man and Dolphin*. I studied her vocal productions in detail.

Chee Chee had a "personal call" which was distinctive. It was a call which we had not heard from any other animal. Her sound in this call was quite different from the personal call of the younger dolphins. It seemed to have some very low frequencies in it, below those heard from any other dolphin. All of our human observers in the Institute heard it without straining in the upper limits of our frequency pattern recognition range. This call did not sound like the usual "squeaks" of the other dolphins' calls. With the other dolphins we were always conscious of the straining to hear in the upper registers.

I studied the production of this whistle call of Chee Chee by frequency analysis and other means. I watched her blowhole move in a different fashion than it did in the case of the other dolphins. Usually when the other dolphins gave their personal call under water, there was a large smooth continuous movement of only one side of the upper end of the blowhole plug. This movement occurred throughout the whistles synchronized with it on the one side only. In contrast, Chee Chee moved both sides during her underwater call. The two sides apparently moved in almost opposite directions, giving a peculiar twisting motion to the top of the blowhole plug.

The call itself was analyzed in various ways. One of the most important findings is shown in Figure 9. This frequency analysis shows the variation of the frequencies of the whistle as they change with time. Notice that two major components occur simultaneously for part of the record. One component starts at a low frequency and rises fairly steadily. The other component starts at a high

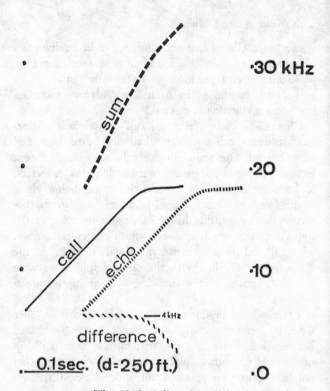

FIGURE 9. *The Slash Call and Its Echo (see text)*

The dolphin emits the frequency-versus-time curve labeled "call." Its echo resembles the call, delayed by being reflected from a flat surface 250 feet away. The call lasts approximately 0.3 second as does the echo. At 250 feet the echo overlaps the call when it returns to the dolphin generating a sum and difference set of frequencies. The important frequency difference is at approximately four kilocycles (kilo-Hertz); the dolphin could use this "constant difference frequency" (between the call and its echo) to know that the object is at the given distance. With his extended hearing range he can also hear the sum (of the call and the overlapping echo) plotted as the dashed curve going above thirty kilocycles (kilo-Hertz).

frequency and falls during the same period. Further note that no particularly loud, low frequencies show on the record.

This lack of low frequencies was not predicted by the human listeners. Each one of them heard loud low frequencies. The objective record failed to show the low frequencies which we all heard. Where were these lows coming from? Agreement among listeners ruled out "imagination." The lows were there for every listener; no matter how we tried to eliminate them by double blind controls, they still were there. And no matter how many times we ran the records through the analyzers, they were not as apparent on the objective frequency analysis techniques as the high frequencies.

Chee Chee then gave us a hint as to what might be going on. She is quite capable of producing the climbing frequency call alone without the falling frequency one. This call is similar to the younger dolphins' personal calls. When heard in isolation from its mating component, the rising frequency component had no low frequencies. It sounded as it was shown on the objective record, all of it at uncomfortably high frequencies for the human listener.

Similar findings were made for the falling component alone. In other words, the only time we heard the low frequencies was during the time that Chee Chee emitted the two components simultaneously. At this point, we began to look at the frequency differences themselves.

We went back and listened carefully to the low-frequency variations; subjectively, the frequencies started low and increased with time.

If you inspect the frequency time curves (Figure 9), you can see that the difference in frequency between the two components has a rising series of values. At the point where the two frequency curves cross, the difference frequency is zero. For all later points, the lower curve value, subtracted from the simultaneous value in the upper curve, is higher. The frequency differences thus have a time course similar to the subjectively heard low frequencies. Their values also correspond to those subjectively heard. In other words, one high-frequency component combines with the other and generates "beat" frequencies.

If Chee Chee is aware of what she is doing with these two frequencies and is aware of the beat frequencies between them, then she may have developed this call for some particular purpose. Let us see what the rest of her experience has been before we detected this call. All of the people near Chee Chee had been instructed to speak to her loudly in ordinary English. They had been told also not to reply to any of her very high frequencies, i.e., to her "delphinese." Because of the particular structure of her phonation equipment, she could not whistle directly the very low frequencies which were present in our voices. I suggest that, with her extensive experience with our low-frequency voices, she developed the best low-frequency voice that she could, using her double phonation apparatus. Thus, she developed a call that attracted human attention. In this view then, she combined two sets of high frequencies varying in time to give this set of low frequencies varying in time well within our ordinary, everyday voice ranges. (One might say that this is asking a lot of her reasoning powers; it probably is not asking much. Perhaps they commonly use frequency "beat" phenomena in their everyday lives.)

If we look at the frequency-versus-time curve of Chee Chee's call (Figure 9), we see that the double curve forms a crude letter V on its side ($<$). The falling frequency curve is one limb of the "($<$)" and the rising frequency curve is the other limb of the "($<$)." Let us then call this the "($<$)"-shaped call. This is in terms of the delphinese frequency bands objectively recorded.

One important property of this call for our purposes is that to us, it sounds like a rising, low-frequency call. On the frequency time graph this would be represented by the slash (/); therefore, let us call this the (/) call. In other words the beat frequencies of an (<) call form a (/) call.

If you remember your elementary physics you can see that when two frequencies are present simultaneously, not only do we get a difference frequency, but we get a sum frequency as a result of the combination of the original two frequencies. In other words, with heterodyning, both the sum and the difference frequencies appear. Careful inspection of the figure showing the (<) call will show that the set of the sum of the pairs of frequencies at each instant will be a straight line or a "bar" which is represented by "(−)". This bar set of frequencies is considerably above the original pair in frequency, way too high for us to hear, but well within the dolphin's range of hearing. In other words, the bar is a delphinic transformation of the frequencies and the "(/)" is a human transformation in terms of the relative hearing abilities of the two species. Thus the complete conversion of the "(<)" call is "the slash-bar call" symbolized by "/−". The dolphin probably can hear "slash-bar." In the best part of his hearing and at the very low frequency, he probably can hear the slash, whereas the humans hear the slash and (faintly) the (<).

When Chee Chee makes the "(<)" she produces the rising portion of the call with her left phonation apparatus. The right phonation membrane vibrates at each instant at the frequency of that particular instant of the rising portion. The left phonation membrane vibrates at the frequency of the other limb of the (<) at the same instant. The two phonation membranes are each connected to the membranous portion of the nasal septum in the midplane. This septum in the upper part of the nose is very thin and has special connections to two cartilaginous caps over the nasal bones. There are also muscles present in this septum. This special anatomy apparently allows Chee Chee to control the amount of vibration in the nasal septum. If she wishes to mix simultaneously the frequencies of vibrations of the right and the left membrane, she can do this through muscular control and through control of the opposing surfaces of the various folds of the nasal tongues. This control of the combination of the frequencies coming from the two sides, meeting in the nasal septum, makes the beats between the two sides. The nasal septum vibrates in such a way as to "amplify" the beat frequencies at each instant as the frequencies in the right and left membranes are changing. It is here that the slash call probably is emitted.

In *Man and Dolphin* and in a subsequent scientific paper,[1] we described the distress call of the bottle-nosed dolphin. The distress call on the frequency-time plot is an inverted V or a "lambda call" at higher frequencies than those of the beat-frequency-generated slash call. In general, in the distress call (Figure 11) the frequencies start at a medium value, rise to a high value, and then fall to the original value, all in about three-tenths of a second. This means that no two frequencies come out simultaneously, and hence the dolphin can produce the call alternating right and left nose or produce the whole call on either the right or the left alone. We would thus not expect either beat or stereophonation effects with the dolphin's distress call (lambda call). By the separation in time of the two parts of the call, simplicity in the spatial and in the frequency domains has been increased.

Let us now examine another call which is simpler than

[1] Lilly, J. C., "Distress call of the bottlenose dolphin: stimuli and evoked behavioral responses." *Science,* 139: 116–18 (1963).

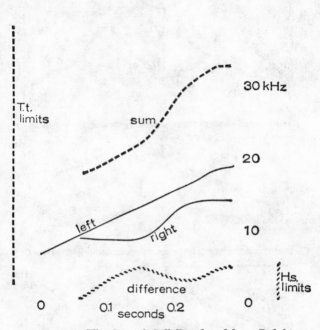

FIGURE 10. *The Special Call Developed by a Dolphin*
(*Chee Chee*)

This figure is discussed in detail in the text. It shows two separate whistles given on the two sides, the left and the right at high frequencies. The whistle on the left rises fairly linearly with respect to time over a period of 0.3 second. The one on the right is delayed in its beginning and then warbles for 0.2 second. The bottommost dotted curve shows the difference frequency that was generated, within the limits of man's pattern recognition hearing (H.s. limits). The dolphin hearing limits (T.t. limits) extend over a much wider range; the dolphin can hear the left and right whistles, the difference frequency, and the sum of the two frequencies. It is suggested that the dolphin generated this special signal so that the people listening to the dolphin could hear the clear difference frequencies.

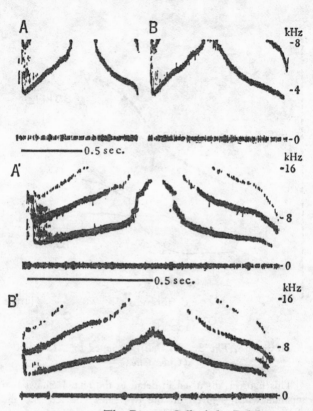

FIGURE 11. *The Distress Call of the Dolphin*

These are typical samples of distress whistles which have been recorded from very young and older animals. It is to be noted that the frequencies reached are beyond the usual "pattern recognition" range of the human ear. The upper two traces include only the first 8 kilocycles and show that the whistles start at approximately 4 kilocycles (kilo-Hertz). The lower two traces are derived by slowing the tape down and doubling the frequency range to show the harmonics of the whistles. Slowed down four times (even more than is shown here), these whistles sound like air-raid sirens. (From J. C. Lilly, "Distress call of the bottlenose dolphin," *Science* 139: 116–18 [1963].)

any of the previous ones. Let us consider a rising frequency call produced on one side only. On a frequency-time graph, this would be a line going up to the right, or to simplify it a direct slash "/" (not beats) (Figure 10).

The slash calls vary in their length from 0.1 second to about 0.6 second as emitted by the dolphins. Let us now imagine that the dolphin is swimming along in a bay and that there is a flat surface on the water from which his call will be reflected. He starts at a distance from this flat surface such that the call starts out, leaves his head completely, and then returns and at no point overlaps itself. He will then hear an unimpeded echo of his own call which will be the same shape as the call which he emitted and will have the same frequencies in it. However, as he approaches the flat surface and the echo returns before he has finished the call, there will be chance for beat frequencies between the beginning and the ending frequencies of the call. These beat frequencies are different from the ones above described for the $(<)$ converted into the slash call. These new beats are between the call still being emitted and the echo returning to the dolphin. Since the call is rising in frequency at each instant, the early parts beating with the later parts will generate a lower-beat frequency at each instant as long as overlap exists between the outgoing and the incoming portions. As he approaches still closer, more and more of the call will be beating with itself. The distances involved can be easily figured using the velocity of sound in water as 5000 feet per second (1540 meters per second); in one-tenth of a second sound will travel 500 feet (154 meters), and if the dolphin is 500 feet from the surface and emits a tenth-of-a-second call, there will be no overlap. He will hear the call repeated in the echo. If he prolongs the call two-tenths of a second, the returning echo of the first half of the call will overlap and beat

with the second half of the call. What is the nature of
the beat that he will hear?

If the slash call is a linearly rising frequency-versus-
time curve (i.e., if it is a straight line), the first part beats
with the latter part and gives a constant-beat frequency.
If there are small wobbles in the frequency, these will
be reflected in the beat as long as they are not present
equally and at the same times in the first half and last
half of the call. Thus a slash call is converted into a bar
beat of a shorter length than the slash itself. *The frequency of the bar beat will vary with the distance of the
object from the dolphin,* i.e., *distant objects will give
higher-frequency differences because of the greater delay
in the overlap. Nearby objects will give lower-beat frequencies because there is less delay between the parts
which are combined to form the beat.*

Thus it is easy to see that if the dolphin emits a slash
call, he can obtain from objects in all directions around
him beat frequencies which are different depending on
the distance of the objects giving the reflections. Thus
with a slash call he can tell pretty well what the shape
of the bottom is, where the top of the water is, and what
other large objects may be in the water around him, in
what directions. He has only to listen to the beat and
obtain their directions by the use of his two ears in the
usual stereophonic listening fashion.

At the frequencies he is using in the slash call (from
about 5000 to 25,000 cps), the wave length in sea water
varies from one foot (0.301 meter) to about 2.5 inches
(6.35 centimeters) in length. If the analogy of our visual
detection holds for his sonic detection system, he can
resolve details something of the order of one-fourth of
a wave length to one-thirtieth of a wave length. Therefore, with the slash call, he can probably detect objects
from about three inches in their largest dimension to
about one-half inch in their smallest dimension. Thus,

his slash call should tell him pretty well in what direction a school of fish of the proper size is—where his friends (other dolphins) are and possibly even where his enemies (the sharks) are. Of course here he is limited to certain distances (from something like a few feet to something like a few hundred feet).

The internal picture which the dolphin can then create while sounding slash calls, the internal picture which he creates of his surroundings in terms of beat frequencies coming stereophonically combined from the two ears, must be a very interesting kind of picture. It is as if to us the nearby objects emitted a reddish light and the farther objects emitted a bluish light, with the whole spectrum in between. We might see, for example, a red patch very close by and then a dimmer, blue patch in the distance farther away . . . a blue background downward symbolizing the bottom, a red patch up close meaning a fish nearby, and a large green object swimming between us on the bottom meaning another dolphin. This conversion of their acoustic beat frequencies into colors is one way we can visualize how their surrounds look to them. (Once again, we must convert their "acoustic pictures" into our visual pictures, because of the differences in our brains and in our approaches to our surroundings.)

Thus, they could use the slash call and other more complex calls in order to delineate their surroundings by what I call their "long wave length sonar." Their "short wave length sonar" operates at very much higher frequencies; the measurements of this mode that we have made in the Institute show that they use frequencies from approximately 15 kilo-Hertz to around 150,000 cycles per second. The sounds emitted in this region have wave lengths in water from about 4 inches (10 centimeters) down to about four-tenths of an inch (1.0 centimeter). As we and others have shown, this sound is con-

centrated in a beam with a maximum amplitude straight
ahead off the upper jaw of the dolphin. This sound
comes in the form of short pulses of very high amplitudes
(3000 dynes per square centimeter or 140 decibels above
the reference level of 0.002 dyne per square centimeter).
Since this is a beam and since it is very high amplitude
in shorter wave lengths, it can be used for a more detailed inspection of objects which are found by the longer
wave length sonar. He changes his ability to resolve details by change of wave length: the shorter the wave
length the finer the detail down to two-fifths of an inch
(1.0 centimeter).

The dolphin may find (by a slash call), off to his left,
that there is an interesting object at such-and-such a distance. He can then merely turn his head, turn on his
"short wave length sonar," and inspect that object in
detail by scanning it with his "sonar flashlight." The narrow beam and the shorter wave lengths give him a resolution which he didn't have with his longer wave length
slash call or other kinds of whistle. As he wants to see
small details he moves the frequency of each pulse upward toward 150,000 cycles per second (two-fifths of an
inch wave length).

So far we have spoken about echoes from non-moving
objects with a non-moving dolphin. When a dolphin is
moving and picks up echoes the apparent frequency of
those echoes will vary somewhat, depending upon his
velocity relative to the reflector. One can see this effect
(called the Doppler effect after the man who discovered
it) by standing beside a road when a car or some other
vehicle sounds a constant-frequency horn or siren as it
passes us. When the sonic source is approaching us, the
frequency apparently rises and as it passes us and recedes, the frequency falls. We can just as well have a
fixed-frequency emitter on our car and approach a big
wall. The apparent source in the wall is now approach-

ing us at the velocity of the car so that the reflected echo will have an apparent shift of frequency upward. Alternatively, we can sit still, aim a sonic beam from a fixed-frequency emitter at a moving object approaching us, and the reflected echo will apparently rise in frequency. If the object is moving away from us, the echo will have an apparent fall of frequency, depending on the velocity of recession.

Returning then to the slash call and the objects of varying distances from the dolphin, if he is remaining motionless in the water, he will hear various frequencies. If objects are approaching him, the frequencies will increase. If objects are receding from him, he will hear the frequencies dropping. Similarly, if he is moving through the water very fast and other objects are also moving through the water very fast with him, these echoes will have apparent beat frequencies which will remain constant, whereas objects which they are passing will have the rising-falling Doppler effects. Thus the internal picture of his surrounds becomes more complex and we must bring in change-of-frequency with respect to time as well as frequencies which merely depend upon distance.

All of these various acoustic concepts (and many others) in some way or another must be used in the dolphin's construction of his language. When a dolphin wishes to talk about an object at a given distance with another dolphin and wishes to describe how that object moved and at what velocities, he can do it merely by transmitting the proper frequency pattern in his clicks and whistles. In other words, he can converse about moving down from the surface of the sea toward the bottom, he can converse about fish of a given size at given distances, sharks of a given size and all of these other matters, in a frequency-time-intensity domain which we would have to convert into visual images. It seems to me that this can become a sort of Rosetta stone for proceeding on an analysis of "delphinese." At the least it is a good enough lead for further research and it is a testable quantitative hypothesis.

By blindfolding ourselves or by using blind persons with the proper apparatus, we can copy these various matters with our own subjective systems. However, we must be aware that our brain can handle only one-tenth the amount of information in the acoustic sphere that the dolphin's brain can. The dolphin can store huge amounts of spatially distributed acoustic information for making up his pictures and will have stored away many models of what his surroundings are like. We lack these advantages quantitatively. In other words we should expect an extended period of training to develop the same abilities the dolphin has. We may never be able to match his performance, at least not at the speed with which he has developed because of the limitations of our brains versus their brains.

What is the evidence that they use the slash calls for long wave length sonar? Some of the evidence is that if one takes a dolphin and places him in new surroundings emitting series of slash calls, after he has been there for a while he stops emitting these calls. In other words, he initially uses them to make an acoustic map of his surroundings. From that point on he doesn't have to emit them so frequently because he knows at any given instant where he is from the last time that he emitted any noise at all. He has mapped all of the obstacles, the walls, the depths, and the boundaries of where he is. He is then free to travel, using, say, only his short wave length sonar or his eyes to tell him in what part of the real surroundings he is and hence on what part of his internal map he is. Any new change in the surroundings starts him off again as he readjusts his internal map. We have observed this behavior literally hundreds of times.

The conversations between two dolphins by means of

whistles thus might be explicable on these grounds. They have a very large brain with very large, general-purpose computer properties, i.e., a very large neocortex. Since a large portion of this is acoustic cortex, they have probably developed symbols (i.e., shorthand) of all the special relationships and descriptions of the various objects (including themselves) which correspond to the whistle (and click) echoes and the whistle's beats. Thus one dolphin might start a slash call to another dolphin and then wobble the upper end of it (as we have seen many times when two dolphins are speaking one to the other). It is these wobbles at the upper end which are probably transmitting the subtleties of meaning, one dolphin to another. The very great frequency shifts that we see in the (<) call, the inverted V call, and in the slash call and various others probably symbolize changes in mode, i.e., in whole large categories of meaning. The subtle variations, beats between the two sides, the Doppler effects in the call as the apparent source is moved between the two sides, convert the subtleties of the meanings. If we are ever to break "delphinese" and convert it into human language, we thus have many hints on which to proceed. At least we have testable hypotheses to either bear out or disprove.

13

The Medical Problems of Dolphins and Man

A sick dolphin is very different from a sick human. A sick human can lie in a bed alone and suffer through a large fraction of his or her illness. Our automatic nervous system and our automatic physiology take over. We can go into coma and survive.

A sick dolphin cannot afford to go into coma. He cannot afford even to fall asleep for periods longer than about six minutes. If he falls asleep longer than this, he is in danger, great danger, of dying. Asleep too deeply, his respiration stops. Because of this particular peculiarity and necessity in the dolphin's makeup, a sick dolphin must be attended twenty-four hours a day. One dolphin will do this for another dolphin. Again and again in the Institute we have seen dolphins tend one another twenty-four hours a day until recovery took place, several days or weeks later.

One of the problems of maintaining dolphins in captivity in close proximity with man is that they share the diseases of man. Each time there is an epidemic among the attendants in the Institute the dolphins share that particular disease whether it be influenza, hepatitis, or the common cold. Therefore, we emphasize three basic medical facts about dolphins.

1. *Dolphins in close contact with man are infected and infested with each of the communicable diseases which are transmitted by water, by air, by food, and by direct handling by men.*

2. *A sick dolphin does not eat. If a dolphin is not eating for one or two days it is best to take his body temperature and do a thorough medical examination.*

3. *A dolphin who is ill is best nursed by another dolphin. An ill dolphin should not be left in solitude.*

Another dolphin is a better nurse than he is a doctor. One dolphin will care for another one continuously twenty-four hours a day in the water like a human nurse does a sick child. More active procedures than nursing care, however, must be done by proper doctors. Dolphins do not have doctors or dentists.

The signs of an ill dolphin in general are anorexia, sneezing through the blowhole, bad breath, fever, and a short temper.

Sneezing to a dolphin is a very explosive and continuous affair. One will hear the breath expelled through the blowhole in an almost explosive fashion several times in rapid succession making very loud noises that can be heard some distance away from the tank. A nasal discharge occurs usually late in the disease; if it has an odor it is a bad sign.

Dolphins who are ill seek to rest away from humans and away from a crowd of dolphins, alone with one other dolphin. Play ceases, as does sex. They refuse to work with us during illness except to cooperate for necessary procedures of medical diagnosis and care. Many dolphins learn to swim into the proper sling to be lifted up for antibiotic shots. Some can even learn to come to have their temperature taken by a rectal procedure. When we are helping them and do not hurt them while we help them, they will not fight our attempts nor will they interfere when we help their companions.

Despite publicity to the contrary, most dolphins caught in the wild cannot live in close quarters with man for very long. Aside from accidents and diseases to which they are not immune (acquired from the humans) there are other causes for morbidity and mortality. Some of the major problems are clustered around the water supply, the training of the handlers, air and water temperatures, sunshine, exercise, monotony versus amusement, and food supply.

Even in the most expensive and largest tanks in oceanaria, it is a question of the survival of the fittest of the dolphins. Of those who survive all of the accidents which can befall dolphins being captured by man, the survival of the others depends to a considerable extent upon the vigilance of someone who is continuously looking out for their welfare day and night over the years. As I have said elsewhere in this book, the morbidity and mortality rates in the oceanaria up to recently have been kept as confidential information. A number of times I have been present in oceanaria at times when the loss of a number of favorite specimens occurred in a very short period of time. And yet there are specimens who have lived up to fifteen years in oceanaria. These are the rare dolphins adapted to these circumstances.

However, even these longer-term dolphins sometimes apparently become maladapted and must be put in the sea or otherwise disposed of, to save the rest of the colony from their attacks. Thus even in the relatively large, seventy-five feet (twenty-five meters) by twelve feet (4 meters) deep tanks of the oceanaria with large amounts of water flowing through them, the best that has been done is approximately fifteen years. Let us examine some of the probable reasons why the dolphins have these difficulties in living in the confined conditions which we impose upon them. We have found many facts in the Institute which may be of help in avoiding these problems in the future. In this particular area we have made some progress beyond the stage written up in *Man and Dolphin*.

The major change when a dolphin is captured is the change in his surroundings from the open seas, bays, and estuaries to the relative confinement of a tank in close proximity to man. No matter how large the tank or even the fenced area of the sea in which he is kept, the dolphin is in a fixed, unchanging, static bit of territory. This is the radical change in his life. The size of the step the dolphin is asked to make to adapt to us is huge. I wish to emphasize this. This change can be extremely tough on the dolphin. Probably our whole present philosophy is wrong.

After the publication of *Man and Dolphin* I received a plea from a woman in England to leave the dolphins free in their sea and not to confine them. I believe this can be done and is best done for their health and for the future of our relationships with them. We can set up a special facility by the sea into which dolphins can come and go as they please. We would still have to be cautious in our relationships with them to avoid accidents and to avoid infecting them with diseases and vice versa. Man and dolphin could then meet on a more equal footing, free to come and go. This chronic confinement, together, in the same space, year after year, cannot be healthy either for them or for us. Let us then imagine an idealized facility in which man and dolphin can so meet.

Imagine a bay protected from storms and from the open sea but with access to the sea. In this bay, the sea water depth is no more than nine to eighteen feet (three to six meters, 1.5 to three fathoms). Preferably, the tidal range should be small, less than about three feet (one meter, one-half fathom) year round. Ideally, the water temperature should be somewhere between 65°F and 85°F (18°C to 30°C). Even 65°F (18°C) in the winter is a very low temperature for a man for constant contact with dolphins. The upper end of this range is better.

The bay must not be contaminated by sewage or industrial waste, i.e., the sea water must be clean; ideally, there should be a continuous flow of new sea water through the area. There are no man-built structures on or near the shores of this bay except a few fishermen's homes and small docks. The kinds of structures we want to build are on or at the sides of this bay. In general we want two kinds of structures: we want a scientific investigatory building, i.e., an *ideal dolphin-man laboratory*. However, we also want a *flooded house* in which dolphins and humans can live continuously in close proximity to one another day and night, year after year. Each of these buildings must be protected from hurricanes and storms of various sorts. Let us describe the idealized laboratory and secondly the idealized man and dolphin house.

The laboratory is a large building (or a series of connected small ones) built on pilings high enough to avoid damage from large waves and tides from hurricanes. This structure either juts out from the shore or is built separated from the shore. There is a very large fenced-in area of the sea bottom which overlaps this building but does not completely enclose the base. The open bay has access to one part of the base of the pilings under the building. The fenced-in-area has access to other parts.

The open bay and, at times, the fenced-in area are for dolphins and sometimes for persons. The buildings are for humans and at times for the dolphins. The laboratory building includes elevators which can be let down into the sea water—one inside the enclosure and one in the open bay. These are large elevators with special shapes and controls on them. The elevator shape includes a depression six by twelve feet (two by four meters) in its surface. This depression is about three feet deep (one meter), with gently sloping sides inside and outside. The slope of the sides is such that a person can safely walk up the sides from each direction in air or in very shallow water.

These elevators are used for two different purposes: 1. for transport and holding of persons from the building into the sea, and 2. for transporting and holding of dolphins from the sea into the building. The up-and-down motions of the elevators are controlled in several ways from several locations. A dolphin or a human can control the elevator.

The controls are such that a dolphin can call the elevator down under water far enough to swim over the tank. Once the dolphin is in the tank on the elevator he can command the elevator to rise either to the surface of the water or up into the buildings. If he is up in the building he can command it to go down into the sea. When in the building, the dolphin always has the option of going back down into the sea. In the cases during the initial period of dolphin training, the humans have only overriding controls to prevent damage to the dolphin. Eventually, each of the experienced dolphins is given complete control of the elevator and of the times of his trips up or down. Any time, day or night, a dolphin wishes to use the elevator, he can do so.

In the proposed design, several novel features are described. A large fraction of this building is flooded to a depth of eighteen inches (0.5 meter). The elevator comes up into the flooded area so that the dolphin coming up can swim away into the flooded area or if he is upstairs he can approach the elevator and swim aboard at will. When the elevator is down in the sea, the dolphin upstairs can bring the elevator up at his own behest.

It may be more fundamentally correct to have the

laboratory at sea level (like the house to be described later) so that the sea washes through the laboratory rather than using this elaborate elevator and its elaborate controls. This modification of the design is currently being worked out in the Institute. We have the elevator system (not yet with these controls) and have the sea pool below and the flooded rooms above in our Dolphin Point Laboratory on the island of St. Thomas.

It is intended that this building and the sea pens be as much of a "school" as a "laboratory." It is both a school for dolphins and a school for humans.

The basic principle behind all of such designs is to furnish the opportunity for each side to meet and interact with the other with maximum safety, maximum integrity, and maximum initiative for each species. This is the "Interspecies Communication School, Man and Dolphin Division."

First, let us describe the house and the school; then we will discuss the problems of staffing.

The house (or home) in which man and dolphin interact is open to a bay which is open to the sea. Ideally, the house is located at the water line and, once again, the tidal range is limited to a foot or so. Larger tides can probably be handled but may require a more elaborate installation. (For illustrative purposes we are assuming the tide is like that in Florida and the Virgin Islands.) The idealized house would have three separated, distinct divisions. There is the dolphin part, the interaction part, and the human part. The dolphin's part is deep water, approximately six feet immediately adjacent to the sea. The human part is dry, immediately adjacent to the land. The rest of the house (the major area) is for man and dolphin interaction.

By careful tests in the Institute over several thousands of hours of experiments we have found that the ideal water depth for interaction is just below one's knee. At this depth, the dolphin can swim fairly freely and the human can walk relatively easily through the water.

Thus, the shared compromising area for man and dolphin is flooded to a depth of eighteen inches. In this shared area are all of the usual things of the usual life in a home for a human. The dolphin can tag around behind or beside the humans. When the humans are sitting down eating or talking, the dolphin can approach them with the freedom that a dog or a cat has in our own homes. Special kinds of furniture made with special materials, special walls and floors, and lighting are required. We have explored the details of these requirements.

Obviously, special clothing, special cooking facilities, special desks, tables, chairs, toilet facilities, and many other items have to be designed, built, and tested for this wet house.

In the dolphin's deeper area (six feet or more) the humans and the dolphins can swim together, at the dolphin's mercy. This area communicates with the sea by special walls or fences with holes in them to allow the sea water to flow through the house, without allowing large predators of the sea (especially the sharks) to enter. This area, however, is allowed to grow its own underwater vegetation and have its own smaller inhabitants so that the dolphin is surrounded with his natural wildlife in this particular area of the house. This is sort of the "play yard" for the dolphin analogous to the yard around the normal house. His access to the sea here is a special gate which he can operate, but which is not operable by sharks, rays, sawfish, octopuses, or other larger inhabitants of the sea.

The dry portion of the house has visual access to the flooded portion. The dolphin can be in the shallow water and see most of what goes on in the dry part of the house. The basic principle in the design of the house is that the dolphins can share most of what goes on, both vocally, visually, and, as far as possible, tactually. This is the "interspecies exchange home."

The staff of the man and dolphin school and the staff of the man and dolphin home have to be very carefully chosen. In my experience, most persons cannot stand the pace of interactions with *Tursiops* for very long: most persons sooner or later flunk out of this interspecies school. Some of the reasons for this are clear, some are not so clear. Let us see what some of the requirements for such persons are.

First of all comes youngness of spirit; this may or may not be associated with youngness of body. I have seen many people who were aged in spirit though young in body, and many who were young in spirit but aged in body. To interact with dolphins, one must feel young, irrespective of age.

There has to be a seeking for new experience on the part of the person; this seeking is not for sensation's sake but for adding to his private knowledge. In other words, he has to be curious and explorative.

The person must be capable and dedicated, even though it may take years to complete the project.

An ability to improvise is needed. In the interactions with the dolphins, this improvisation is essential. Unexpected and new behavior is met and encouraged up to a certain point, at which one must hold one's ground with the dolphin. This is just as important as it is with another human or with a horse or with a dog or with a cat. One's own integrity (but not his own vanity) must be maintained. His limits are tested by a dolphin sooner or later in every conceivable way.

There are things that each of us must learn about dolphins, in general, and each dolphin in particular must teach each human many of these things. For example, each of us must learn that dolphins are "teeth oriented," and dolphins must learn that we are "hand oriented."

Dolphins must learn that we have two hind legs, and we must learn that they have one big tail. Each of us must learn this through bodily interactions, here and now; we receive the rewards and punishments of these inter-actions day and night for long periods of time before we are thoroughly convinced of these rather obvious facts.

Dolphins of the size of *Tursiops,* Atlantic type, are larger and more powerful than most of us. They use their jaws and their teeth the way we use our jaws and teeth but also the way we use our hands, the way we use our fists, and the way we use a hammer or pliers, or pincers or a rake. Their massive neck muscles and large bodies give them more force for the jaws than we can muster in a hard kick with the foot. The ends of the jaws are as hard as a leather shoe.

Their tail is also used (just forward of the flukes with its hard lateral vertebral processes just below the skin) as a long hammer or a pike against our legs, body, or our heads. They can literally "kick with their tails." Faced with such formidable tools and a few examples of their use on one's own body, most persons become timid and leave the project. Those who stay realize that these reac-tions can be controlled vocally and bodily by interactions with the dolphins. It is these persons who can stand the gaff and find why they were singled out for the hurt at a particular time. Some few persons quickly find out that most of the reasons for the dolphins hurting us are obvi-ous. This is the kind of person that we want in the school and in the home.

Some of the multitudinous reasons for a dolphin to dis-cipline a human and for a human to discipline a dolphin are given below. The dolphin's skin is tender. The skin can be badly hurt, even damaged by improper handling, improper instruments, or improper walls. Their fragile flippers are easily damaged by a human pulling them too hard in the wrong direction. Their eyes are as sensitive as ours and easily hurt. Another exquisitely sensitive region is that around the blowhole. This access to their respiration is guarded against ignorant handling. The tongue is a delicate and easily injured part. Special meanings are assigned by them to the region around the anus and the genital opening. Stroking a dolphin here may result in their mouthing and even raking one's arms or legs.

Apparently, the dolphins have times and situations during which they resent interruptions by us. Under special conditions one may be allowed to stay during their sexual activity but not always.

At the beginning, at least, it is best for everyone else to stay away while one dolphin and one human are interacting. Later, one can "intrude." Distractions here may be to the detriment of the human or the dolphin. At times, they are jealously guarding their relation with one human against either dolphin or human encroachment. The "impolite" invader may be treated roughly.

But this is not an invariable rule any more than any other rule which may be laid down in this man and dolphin interaction area. With the proper introduction and polite entering, a multiple human exchange can be initiated with one dolphin. Apparently, there must be agreement between the human and the dolphin. In our Institute, we never run and jump in the pool unexpectedly. When awakened suddenly they can act reflexly and hurt one. It is far better to warn them by talking to them and thus call their attention to the fact of our presence.

The most successful humans play it by ear. The mood of the dolphin is tested by entering the tank slowly and carefully. His interest, his irritability, his preoccupation with other matters, or his anger, can be quickly seen and used with a slow entry. At times, a human is invited in. They approach you at the edge of the tank and by body motions unequivocally ask you to enter.

If the dolphin uses his teeth or tail, it is proper to scold and slap his skin at the nearest available place. One must be careful with the sensitive areas described above. Right timing is necessary; even this reaction has to be given correctly to obtain the desired results. Sometimes it is better to move out of reach and think. On one's return the dolphin may be and usually is more cordial. This is not an invariable rule.

All of these considerations are germane to the medical scientist. In the case of humans, medically one appreciates social factors. If one's patient is being mistreated, this is one important factor in his illness. If his contacts are happy and his environment healthy, he is more likely to be well and recover quickly when sick. So it is with the dolphins.

In the proposed school and in the proposed home, a sick dolphin can come in and apply for medical care. It is important that all of his social relations with each of the staff are such that he will so choose to come. One cannot treat a patient who is so fed up that he leaves. This is a very important aspect of the school: freedom to leave and to return.

Once trained, the dolphins can come and go as they please. If they stay, they are fed and cared for and interacted with. Soon we will then know the success or failure of our interaction methods. If we do it correctly, other dolphins may hear about it and come to see. If we do it incorrectly, all of the dolphins will leave.

One elementary precaution is that the dolphins be assured that their enemies will be kept out; sharks are unwelcome visitors as are sawfish. All entrances, elevators, and other contacts with the sea are proof against entering by these animals.

In the medical literature it has been emphasized recently that crowding can cause bad effects in animals

and in humans. It has been demonstrated scientifically
that other animals become quite disturbed by overcrowded living quarters. I found that with too many
dolphins in too small a space there were definite effects.
Results can be disastrous. Some individuals become ill
and even die. Most of the individuals are jealously involved in every human interaction and, apparently, give
one another conflicting orders. Their sexual life deterio-
rates; their play decreases in vigor and duration; some
individuals seek and cannot find solitude and become
short-tempered. Unexplained deaths occur that look sus-
piciously like suicide (or even murder). Training programs become difficult if not impossible.

With the proposed facilities some of these difficulties
will be avoided. Any time a dolphin is overcrowded, he
leaves and goes to sea or takes one of his friends with him
to escape the crowd. A facility in which the dolphins can
come and go as they wish will not be overcrowded.

With sufficient space, sun, and air the dolphins survive
even severe infections, keep a vigorous and healthy sex
life, develop close ties with us, and play together hours
at a time. The contrast is gratifying.

We have run two separate groups for three years to
find out these facts. The uncrowded ones are happily
vigorous and well schooled. The humans in attendance
are similarly uncrowded and happy. The other case is
more instructive by simultaneous contrast; without this
other crowded group we would not have known what to
avoid in the future. The design of the new school is
based on both sets of experiences; from one we learned
the desirable factors to incorporate into the design, and
from the other the undesirable ones to avoid. At the present time, we know the demonstration is adequate. We are
enlarging the amount of space given to each dolphin to
turn the crowded group into an uncrowded one. We
hope in the future to be able to build the facilities which

we have described here and initiate not only uncrowded facilities but "free" facilities connected with the vast seas. We need help: money, advice, professional aid for architecture and engineering. With this facility man may open new territory, new understanding of the sea and its bright inhabitants.

14

Vocal Mimicry:
A Key to and First
Stage of Communication

When each of us is a child, learning to speak our native
language, we are in the peculiar position of being in-
articulate and yet surrounded by a human world in
which language is being used by all of the important
persons in our life. At the beginning, from our first newborn cry to our first attempts at vocalization, we are only
expressing our own unique selves without sharing our
language with anyone else. It has been shown by recordings and analyses of newborn infant human cries[1] that
even the first cry is a unique special production of that
particular baby. There is a communality of newborn infant cry, but if we study the details of each cry we find
specific and specifiable differences.

Whether these unique specifiable differences of the
infant's cry are caused by inherited or acquired physiological factors, or whether they are caused by the baby
hearing human speech while still in the uterus, are moot
questions. Only the fact of their uniqueness has been

[1] Truby, H. M. (1965) in General Bibliography.

established. One important observation is that the human baby is born with the ability to make unique sounds with his vocalization apparatus. This is the first time that air has passed out through this apparatus. Previous to this *in utero* only embryonic fluid passed back and forth through these tracts. *In utero,* the muscles have been growing, the nerve connections have been growing, and the connections inside the brain have been established, preparing for this instant when the air can be sucked in and expelled to make these noises. Of course, if all this preparation is not made and the baby cannot suck in the air, he does not survive. Those of us who live after birth were prepared for birth *in utero.*

On this background of preparation, the baby starts life. He is bombarded with sounds from mother, father, and other children in the family. Everyone loves to talk to a baby, and the baby loves to respond with facial expressions, bodily movements, and various and sundry sounds, produced within his vocal tract and by his lips.

We are produced after nine months *in utero* and are born with a four-hundred-gram brain. The baby dolphin is produced after twelve months *in utero* and is born with a seven-hundred-gram brain. One of the major differences here is that we do not need to swim up for air the instant we are born. We lie in a crib and are carried around for those three months of growth in which the dolphin remains *in utero.* Thus, at the end of a year (from the time of fertilization of the egg by the sperm), we have a year's growth of brain and body and three months' experience outside the uterus. The dolphin born at the end of this year has only the growth and whatever acoustical experience he derived while *in utero.* Since the connections between the ears and the brain are made early *in utero,* he probably has a rich set of hearing memories stored in his brain at the time of birth. Since his vocalization apparatus, like ours, operates with the use of air inside it, he does not have much experience in producing sounds which he can hear himself. He, too, has been pushing embryonic fluid back and forth in his vocalization apparatus.

Thus, the human baby at three months after birth has accumulated three months of very early use of his vocalization apparatus which the baby dolphin lacks at birth. The importance of this fact is yet to be evaluated.

By the end of the first three months, one can listen to the sounds produced by a human baby and realize that he has acquired many new patterns in his noises. His babblings are becoming more and more complex as are his various kinds of cries. Of all the noises the baby makes, one can finally begin to distinguish the first distinct word at about nine months. At six months and a brain weight equivalent to that of the newborn baby dolphin (about seven hundred grams), the human baby begins to imitate sounds. The primitive beginnings of mimicry occur detectably at this point. After three months of imitating sounds, the human baby "composes" them into the first detectable word at nine months. During the next two months with his brain increasing to 850 grams, he imitates syllables and words, and the second word begins to appear. By thirteen months (930 grams), his vocabulary expands rapidly.

Basically then, two processes are going on. There is a spontaneous, sound-making process which we inherit and which is built into us. This process allows us to use our respiratory tract for instinctual production of various kinds of sound (for example, cries, shrieks, moans). Secondly, there is a learned, an acquired, a programmed, sound-production process. This programming starts out as a basic process which I have chosen to call "mimicry." Mimicry is the process of reproducing as closely as possible a sound or a string of sounds or a complex pattern of sounds that one hears in one's environment. The source of the sounds can be another human being or another animal or any other artificial or natural source. *The human baby has a drive toward organizing his more or less random sound productions into patterns; he has a drive to produce copies of those sounds which he hears coming in.* In other words, the human baby's brain has sound-production, sound-listening, sound-storage, sound-composition programs; to learn human sounds, he hears them, analyzes them, stores them, recomposes from storage, and composes new patterns. When the stored patterns are in sufficient numbers and varieties, he begins to compose patterns which mimic those he hears. With mimicked sounds, he convinces adults of his established drive and ability to communicate.

Mimicry is the basic mechanism which assures one that the baby is acquiring those sounds which other people share. This process of putting out the sounds and hearing our own production of the sounds allows us to compare it with the models that other persons are putting out. It allows other persons to test the degree of perfection of our patterns, their "goodness of fit" to the shared, communal, speech patterns. First, we compare our productions with the actual productions of other people. This is the slavish, immediate, or *first-order mimicry*. I say a word and the baby says a word immediately after me, enunciating it as well as he can. Later, as I say a word, the baby will store up his image of the pattern of those words in his "acoustic brain" and will practice saying it himself, later comparing what he produces with the model that he has stored in his brain. This is delayed or *second-order mimicry*. He has removed the necessity of mimicking immediately after me. He has stored what I have said more or less accurately and then reproduced it later at his leisure. This process of storage and later reproduction makes it difficult to detect the mimicry process in the older children. They store the pattern and reproduce it away from its source.

When we wish, as adults, to learn another language, fundamentally, we must revert to this beginning process that was used with our native language. We learn the language faster if we can do immediate mimicry rather than delayed mimicry of stored images. In other words, if we can go back to the childhood mechanism of immediate interactions, hooking up the words, the speech, the events, the people, and the objects together all at once, we learn the new language in six weeks. If we are forced back into the position of the child, acquiring the first language, with our adult brain of large size we can shorten the period considerably over what it was in the first instance. We have also perfected our central-peripheral, vocalization apparatus, though sometimes in paths inappropriate for the second language. Our perception processes may also be prejudiced along the first language line and make the acquisition of the subtleties of the second language rather difficult to acquire. Mimicry, with a native speaker of the language, and correction by that speaker sharpens up our new criteria as our parents sharpened our first language by corrections. What then are the basic requirements for learning speech, insofar as we can estimate it at the present time?

Basically, these seem to be 1. a mammalian brain somewhere between 660 and 700 grams; 2. a proper vocalization apparatus; 3. an accumulation of stored patterns of sounds; 4. practice with first-order or immediate mimicry with error corrections by another human; 5. practice with second-order or delayed mimicry.

I cannot emphasize enough the necessity of storing literally hundreds of thousands of sonic patterns on the hearing side before the transmission side can begin to mimic those patterns. Thus, to mimic, we must be able to call up from the stores within our brain large numbers of sonic patterns which we can then attempt to put out through our vocalization apparatus. As they come out so that they can be heard, they are new patterns from outside which can excite on the input side, and we now have both the produced pattern and the received pattern to compare within the brain itself. Thus, the problem of mimicry boils down to 1. stored patterns of complex sounds S which we have received many times and established in memory as distinct entities separated from all other non-speech sounds; 2. recently heard pattern of sounds H; 3. a juxtaposition of the heard sound H with the stored sounds S within the brain itself; 4. the production of a sound in the proper processes of mimicry in which one produces a pattern of sound V which is designed as it is produced to be like H, a recently heard sound, or is designed to be like S, the long-term stored separated-out pattern of sound; 5. if H does resemble S, then V can be tailored to match also; 6. one can, as it were, continue to say various versions of V until the final version of V when compared with H stored and with S, shows congruity along the whole pattern in time.

Of course, the perception process and its processing of these materials "V" and "H" also must be trained by the multiple processes to "know" when the fit is good enough and meets the criteria of the other persons. How much of our perception processes are given to us at birth and how much are acquired after birth is yet to be determined. We do know that we can train perception in language, and pay attention to those portions of the pattern which are important to transmitting meaning in that language. This is the science of phonetics and of phonemics.

To return to mimicry we can see that, as a process, mimicry is essential in detecting attempts on the part of another creature to communicate with one's self. In the cases of the parrot and of the mynah bird, the mimicry does not seem to be an attempt to communicate. In the case of the human child, the mimicry is such an attempt. One basic difference in these two cases is the size of the brain. The parrot and the mynah bird use their vocalization apparatus with a certain degree of success in playing back limited numbers of words. They cannot store sufficiently large numbers of sonic patterns in their small brain; they cannot have the immediate access to and the complex composition ability for these patterns that the larger brain does. To assure speaking a language as we know it, the bits and pieces must be myriad, easily available, and quickly composable. Several persons have spent many years working with mynah birds and with parrots and cannot still satisfactorily account for the processes leading to the parrot or the mynah bird reproducing our words. Here the mimicry process seems to be a mysterious dead end, leading nowhere. The brain just isn't large enough to make full use of it beyond this one end product of a few words expertly pronounced.

In 1957, I discovered the ability of the bottle-nosed dolphin to mimic sounds occurring in his environment. This experience is given in a scientific paper,[2] from the experiential point of view. Something of this discovery was reported in *Man and Dolphin*. The only previous written account of such a finding is that of Aristotle (300 B.C.). Aristotle said that the voice of the dolphin in air is like that of the human; that he pronounces vowels and combinations of vowels, has difficulty pronouncing the vowel-consonant combination.

About four hundred years later Plinius Secundus shortened this description to read, "the voice of the dolphin is like human wailing."

This fact of mimicry by the dolphins and the knowl-

---

[2] Lilly, John C., "Vocal behavior of the bottlenose dolphin." *Proc. Am. Philos. Soc.* 106: 520–29 (1962).

edge of its necessity for the acquisition of language was apparently not appreciated by Aristotle. He had seen and heard dolphins mimicking humans, but had not called it that. Their natural voice in air was like that of the human saying vowels and vowel-like sounds. But, naturally in the wild, such sounds are not made in air, nor even under water.

When I came on the phenomenon in 1957, I was not acquainted with Aristotle's writings. In retrospective analysis of tapes I had taken of what the dolphin had been putting out under special circumstances, some of the sounds resembled sounds occurring in the laboratory either spontaneously or caused by me. Later, when I tested another dolphin for his ability to mimic, we found quickly that certain physical aspects of mimicry were obviously in their repertoire.

Since the publication of *Man and Dolphin*, work on this phenomenon has been extensive and the results have been very interesting.

Let us visualize mimicry as a key to interspecies communication. Let us visualize one of us captured by another intelligent, extraterrestrial species and held in captivity surrounded by the aliens. If such a captive person wished to establish his intelligence with the intelligent species around him, he might first try talking to them. If they were obviously talking to one another in an alien language, it would behoove him to try to learn that language. It would also pay him to get the attention of an alien or two who might be sympathetic to his wish to learn the language.

To attract their attention such person would try mimicking some of the sounds of that language. If he succeeded in mimicking well enough for the aliens to recognize his mimicry, they might reply and attempt to teach him the language; that is, if he were lucky enough to find an alien who could recognize 1. *that he is mimick-*

ing, and 2. *that mimicking is an attempt to communicate.*

There might have been all sorts of intellectual assumptions by the aliens which would prevent such direct use of mimicking. Many humans unknowingly have such assumptions. I have reported the mimicking phenomenon by *Tursiops* in several scientific publications and have suggested that *Tursiops* uses it as we would in the extraterrestrial situation. My first demonstrations of the phenomenon required a certain amount of particular kinds of training in the observer, i.e., he needed a good ear for accents and a mind capable of separating the signals from the noise.

Obviously, the pronunciation of *Tursiops* is not very good. That he says anything resembling given human words (human words which have just been spoken to him) is amazing and indicates attempts to mimic. Most scientists are not trained in differentiating the human "foreign accents" from their native tongue and are not used to separating human voice signals from badly distorted transmissions. Therefore, my demonstrations of direct tape recordings of the phenomenon have been unconvincing to many types of persons and scientists. For this reason, demonstrations of mimicry which did not involve hearing and psychophysical judgments were devised.

The new demonstrations were reported in *Science.*[3] The summary published in that paper is as follows:

"In addition to its normal underwater sonic communication path, the dolphin (*Tursiops truncatus*) can be trained to emit sounds from the blowhole opened in air. By proper rewarding (positive reinforcement) and evocative techniques, such vocal emissions can be changed from the natural pattern. One such group of sounds is said to resemble the human voice ('vocal mimicry'). As-

[3] Lilly, J. C. (1965) in General Bibliography.

pects of these sounds which are physically determinable, specifiable, and demonstrable are the similarities in numbers of bursts of sound emitted by the man and by the dolphin and in durations of successive emissions. In 92% of the exchanges the number of bursts emitted by *Tursiops* equalled plus or minus 1, the number just previously emitted by a man in sequences of one to ten bursts." No other animals (with the one exception of unusual humans) can match this performance.

In a moment, let us visualize experiments which demonstrate these points. First of all, let us consider the set of sounds which are presented by the human to the dolphins.

In the early work in 1957 through 1961, we used ordinary human speech in single words, phrases, and sentences. In this early work, we detected resemblances between what we said and what the dolphin said. Mixed in among many primitive copies of our speech (called "humanoid emissions") were other vocal "noises." Most of these noises were the usual (underwater) delphinic noises now emitted in air (the familiar clicks, whistles, barks, and blats of the ordinary exchanges between dolphins).

As we shape up his vocal behavior by one means or another, he begins to produce more and more on the "humanoids." We reward only humanoid emissions and by deprivation penalize delphinic sounds.

This process of concentrating and changing his emissions more and more to one pattern of emission is called (in the parlance of psychology) "shaping up" the vocal behavior. At the beginning, the shaping up is done by food rewards, i.e., a fish given immediately after each performance which has in it something of the desired characteristics. The human observer does not reward the dolphin unless the dolphin says something which has some aspect which the human observer plans to preserve

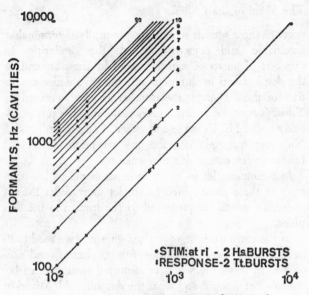

FIGURE 12. *A Male Human Voice Saying "at ri" and the Dolphin's Response Showing the Frequency and Pitch of the Air-borne Voice of the Dolphin*

This plot is the result of analyses of the human vowel sounds and the dolphin's reply sounds. The horizontal axis represents the pulse rate of the source, which in the case of the human is the pulsing rate of the larynx, in the case of the dolphin is the pulsing rate of the diagonal membrane. The vertical axis is frequencies of the cavity resonances: in the case of the human voice these are the formants (the resonances of changing the size and shape of the mouth and pharynx and nasal passageway during speech by the man). In the case of the dolphin the cavities are changed in size in a voluntary way in a fashion analogous to that of the human, modulating the peaks of energy of various harmonics of his basic pulsing rate. The first group of dots in a vertical row is the vowel sound in "at." The second group of dots is the voiced "r" sound, the third group of dots is the vowel sound in the emission. Once under way, the shaping up takes hours and many repetitions on the part of the human to gradually improve pronunciation.

If we give a dolphin a long list of the proper kinds of sounds that we want him to emit in the proper numbers, the proper order, the proper pronunciation, in something like twelve to thirty minutes, the dolphin will select of those aspects which one is emphasizing in that particular list those he can do. He fails only with his pronunciation: the frequencies emitted are too high for the human ear. The human stimuli have a pitch range from 125 to 225 pulses per second and formant frequencies from 300 to 3900 Hz. The dolphin's pitch is 300 to 1000 per second and his formant frequencies are 1200 to 24,000 Hz (Figure 12).

For example, in preparation for the article in *Science*, we decided to concentrate our efforts on short, sharp bursts of sound which had no meaning to human beings. This decision developed because we had found that when we gave meaningful sentences or words to the dolphins and they mimicked, say, the pitch and rhythm of those sounds, we could "read in" the rest of the context while listening—for example, if we said, "Good morning *Tursiops*, how are you today?" The series of humanoids that the dolphin gave us back had certain physical aspects of the patterning of the sounds that we had said to the dolphin. The problem was, *what aspects?* We could hear, as it were, the *meaning* being carried by whatever aspects the dolphin was mimicking, and if we listened often enough and carefully enough to repeated playback of the

---

of "ri." The dolphin's replies were two bursts of sounds whose basic pitch is at approximately 800 per second instead of the 100 to 200 per second of the human voice. The dolphin modulated his cavities in a way consonant with this higher pitch.

tape, we could "hear" the dolphin saying, "Good morning *Tursiops,* how are you today?" In other words, his play-back was good enough so that we could then use what he said to reconstruct what we had just given him. Even this primitive degree of immediate vocal copying cannot be done by any other animal than by man himself. We cannot obtain such immediate "locked in" vocal results with "talking" birds. When the bird mimics he *pro-nounces* well, but will not lock in his vocal output al-ternately with that of the human. The dolphin "locks in" beautifully, accurately, rhythmically, for hundreds of times at high speed.

If we put ourselves in the position of the dolphin, who has three sonic emitters as opposed to our one, who is used to transmitting his information to other dolphins under water, who is forced to speak to us in our medium in air, who is using his nose and not his tongue and mouth for his enunciation, I think we can understand his difficulty in attempting to mimic us and to convince us that this is what he is doing.

We attempted a way around these difficulties by fur-nishing him with a set of sounds which did not have meaning and which had unexpected and unpredictable acoustic characteristics so that we and he could not pre-dict what was coming next in listening to the resulting transmissions.

A list of special sounds was made up. This new list of sounds consisted of nonsense syllables, i.e., syllables which strung together in groups have no meaning to a human listener. These were made from arbitrary lists of consonants and an arbitrary list of vowels combined sys-tematically. The nine vowels were i, I, e, E, *a*, o, u, aI, oI. The consonants were r, l, z, v, t, w, m, n, t, k, s. The international phonetic alphabet shows the pronunciation of the symbols used. The consonants were placed in order across the top of a sheet of paper and the vowels placed

	r	l	z	v	ch- -tch	w	m	n	t	k	s
ē	ēr	ēl	ēz	ēv	ētch		ēm	ēn	ēt	ēk	ēs
	rē	lē	zē	vē	chē	wē	mē	nē	tē	kē	sē
ĭ	ĭr	ĭl	ĭz	ĭv	ĭtch		ĭm	ĭn	ĭt	ĭk	ĭs
	rĭ	lĭ	zĭ	vĭ	chĭ	wĭ	mĭ	nĭ	tĭ	kĭ	sĭ
ā	ār	āl	āz		ātch		ām	ān	āt	āk	ās
	rā	lā	zā	vā	chā	wā	mā	nā	tā	kā	sā
ĕ	ĕr	ĕl	ĕz	ĕv	ĕtch		ĕm	ĕn	ĕt	ĕk	
	rĕ	lĕ	zĕ	vĕ	chĕ	wĕ	mĕ	nĕ	tĕ	kĕ	sĕ
ä	är	äl	zä	äv	ätch		äm	än	ät	äk	äs
	rä	lä	zä	vä	chä	wä	mä	nä	tä	kä	sä
ō	ōr	ōl	ōz	ōv	ōtch		ōm	ōn	ōt	ōk	ōs
	rō	lō	zō	vō	chō	wō	mō	nō	tō	kō	sō
ōō	ōōr	ōōl	ōōz	ōōv	ōōtch		ōōm	ōōn	ōōt	ōōk	ōōs
	rōō	lōō	zōō	vōō	chōō	wōō	mōō	nōō	tōō	kōō	sōō
aī	aīr	aīl	aīz	aīv	aītch		aīm	aīn	aīt	aīk	aīs
	raī	laī	zaī	vaī	chaī	waī	maī	naī	taī	kaī	saī
oi	oir	oil	oiz	oiv	oitch		oim	oin	oit	oik	ois
	roi	loi	zoi	voi	choi	woi	moi	noi	toi	koi	soi

FIGURE 13. *Table of the Nonsense Syllables Used as Vocal Stimuli for the Dolphin*

The vowels are listed on the left in a vertical column and the consonants along the top in a horizontal line. The pronunciation of the "consonant-vowel and vowel-consonant" pairs is then given in the corresponding place in the table. It is to be noted that "W" as a final consonant was eliminated because of difficulties of pronunciation. (Table adapted from J. C. Lilly, in Darley, *Brain Mechanisms*, 1967.)

down along the left-hand edge of the paper (Figure 13). The consonant-vowel combinations of these were then paired up throughout the list; similarly, a vowel-consonant combination was made up from each pair. This gave ninety-nine vowel-consonants and ninety-nine consonant-vowel syllables. Of these 198 syllables all but eleven were pronounceable. The final list had 187 items in it.

These 187 nonsense syllables were then placed on cards, one to a card. Each card was then reproduced four times. The resulting deck of cards was shuffled to assure a random order.

From a table of random numbers a list of the numbers from 1 through 10 was arranged in random order. These randomized groups of numbers were then used to select the number of nonsense syllables in each presentation. This process was continued until the list of nonsense syllables was used up.

From these cards, lists of the random-numbered groups were then typed out in random order of the nonsense syllables. These lists were the ones used in the experiments.

Several dolphins had received a preliminary training in vocalization in air. One of these was chosen for the first experiment. A special tank had been constructed. It consisted of a home tank in which the dolphin lived which had a transparent Plexiglas sidearm extending from it. The dolphin at its own option could enter this sidearm which contained approximately twelve to eighteen inches of water. When he entered the sidearm, the dolphin's blowhole would thus automatically be placed above the water . . . he could either place the blowhole above water or the water depth could be adjusted in such a way that his blowhole ended up above water when he came into the sidearm. At any time, the dolphin could leave the sidearm and go back to his tank.

We found that we obtained best cooperation and the hardest work from *Tursiops* when we left the option of stopping the experiment (leaving the sidearm) to the dolphin. This meant to us that when he had enough, if he was getting tired, for example, he would leave, take a short rest, and then come back for more. The dolphin acted as predicted.

A microphone was placed above the water-filled side-arm in the proper position near the dolphin's blowhole. The human operator stood beside him in such a position that he could feed the dolphin a fish with his right hand while reading from the list in his left hand. A lavalier microphone, protected from the sea water, was placed in front of the human operator's mouth. The information coming from each of these microphones was recording separately in a two-channel tape recorder (Minnesota Mining & Manufacturing Company 3M Wollensak and Crown 800 series at higher frequencies). The tape recorder was outside of the room and the operator of the recorder could watch through a glass window, and adjust the gains on the tape recorder to a satisfactory level.

At the beginning of an experiment, the human operator walked into the room, placed the microphone, turned on the light over the sidearm, and called to the dolphin, "All right—let's go." In the usual experiment, the dolphin with a short delay entered the sidearm. The human then said, "Hello." The dolphin gave some humanoid reply. The human then read the first group of items on the list, held the fish out so the dolphin could see it, and, when the dolphin gave a reply in air with humanoids, he was given the fish. Within a few minutes of the first attempts the dolphin began to give back a number of bursts of sound. As more syllables were read, the dolphin began to give a number of bursts of sound just equal to the number given by the human.

When the human gave five bursts of sound, the dolphin replied with five. When the human gave four, the dolphin replied with four. When the human gave three, the dolphin replied with three. Figure 14 shows a human-dolphin exchange of 10 bursts of sound matched by the dolphin.

Dolphins habitually reply sonically one to the other.[4]

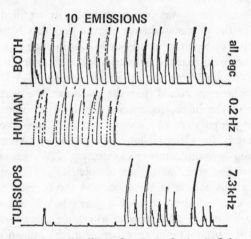

FIGURE 14. *Oscillographic Record of a Dolphin Exchange Showing Ten Bursts of Sound Emitted by the Human Matched by Ten Bursts of Sound Emitted by the Dolphin*

The upper trace shows all of the sounds emitted by both the man and the dolphin; the second trace, those by the man only; the lower trace, those emitted by the dolphin. It is to be noted that the delay between the end of the human presentation and the beginning of the dolphin reply is of the same order of magnitude as the interburst silences in the human presentation. This is a selected portion of a very long experiment in which numbers of bursts of sound emitted by the human were varied from 1 to 10 and the replies of the dolphin were from 1 to 10. (See J. C. Lilly, "Vocal Mimicry by the Dolphin," *Science* 147: 300–1 [1965].)

[4] Lilly, J. C. and Miller, A. M., "Vocal exchanges between dolphins." *Science* 134: 1873–76 (1961).

This part of the performance (the "transactional form") is apparently already known by the dolphin. In the experiments with the human the loud noises in air are the new phenomena.

We analyzed the results of one thousand such bursts of sound between the human and the dolphin. The next figure (Figure 15) shows the number of bursts in the dolphin emission as compared with the number of bursts in the human emission which just preceded that of the dolphin. We call the human emission the "stimulus emission" and the dolphin's "response" or the "reply emission."

If we subtract the number of sounds emitted by the dolphin in each of his replies from the number emitted by the human in his stimulus, we obtain a measure of the dolphin's error. If the difference between the two numbers is zero, the dolphin's error is zero. If the difference is plus one, the dolphin has made one too many emissions compared to those of the human. If the difference is minus one he has failed to give an equal number and his error is one. The third figure of this series shows his scores for one thousand emissions. The very large peak at zero error shows that most of the time he emits the proper number.

A source of error we picked up and allowed for in the emissions is as follows: in syllables containing a vowel and, for example, a consonant "t," we actually make not one but two separated sounds. To illustrate, in pronouncing the word "it," one says "i," then a short silence, then the "t" sound. Thus when we think we say only a single syllable and hence a single sound, physically we are emitting actually two bursts of sound. The dolphin does not hook up these two sounds into a single syllable the way we do. In reply to this kind of syllable, he will put out two bursts of sound instead of the expected one burst. When we discovered this form of our error, we had to

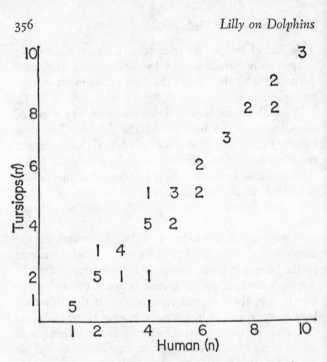

FIGURE 15. *Scoring of a Single Experiment: the Number of Human Nonsense Syllables on the Horizontal vs. Number of Bursts of Sounds in the Dolphin's Reply on the Vertical Axis*

When the dolphin made no errors in his number of replies, the resulting number of instances are plotted on a 45-degree line which reads 5, 5, 4, 5, 3, 2, 3, 2, 2, 3. The next 45-degree line to the right shows cases in which the dolphin added one; the 45-degree line to the left, he subtracted one. This was an early experiment in which the dolphin was learning and making some errors. (*Science* 147 [3655]: 300–1 [1965].)

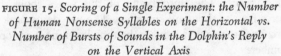

recount again some of the dolphin's emissions and correct them to correspond to the "physically specifiable" bursts of sound rather than the "humanly expected" number of

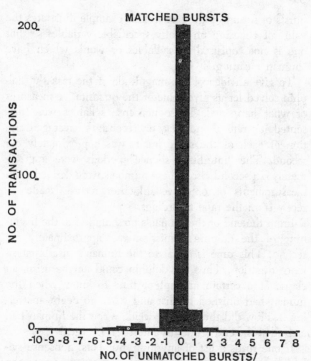

FIGURE 16. *The Over-all Scoring of Several Experiments Showing the Relatively Few Errors that the Dolphin Makes in Matching the Number of Bursts of Sound*

For those exchanges in which the dolphin made no errors the scoring is in the column labeled "o." When the dolphin added one the score is kept in the column to the right, when he subtracted one to the left. In some instances he did not reply, shown at minus 2, minus 3, minus 4, minus 5, etc. The largest fraction of the replies, however, matched numbers of bursts to numbers of nonsense syllables given, in 200 exchanges. (From J. C. Lilly, H. M. Truby, A. M. Miller, and F. Grissman, *Some Parametric Regions of Vocal Copying by the Dolphin* [manuscript, 1967].)

bursts of sound (Figure 16). This example illustrates the value of choosing physically specifiable variables so that one is not confused by syllables or words which have "human meaning."

To give an idea of the magnitude of the task the dolphin solved let us give some of the quantitative measures of what happened. These nonsense syllables were presented at a rate of one every 0.7 second; the average duration of each of the sonic bursts was approximately 0.4 second. The "interburst silence" periods were approximately 0.4 second also. These numbers were derived from measurements of objective inkwriter records made directly from the tape recordings.

From the end of the human's presentation to the beginning of the dolphin's emission was approximately 0.4 second. This time is equal to the human's interburst silence duration. Thus the dolphin could not be using an elapse of a certain amount of time to know when the human had finished his list and when to begin answering it. How did the dolphin decide when the human had arrived at the end of the list and it was his turn?

If one reads a list of anything, numbers, nonsense syllables, or groceries, he finds he does not pronounce the last word of the list the same way he pronounced all of the previous items on it. If I say "1, 2, 3, 4, 5," I change the word "five." It is easily shown that the dolphin detects this change of voice and uses it to tell him when the human operator has reached the end of that particular group of nonsense syllables.

Detection of clues as to what to do from changes in one's voice is a very convincing demonstration of the quality of the mind listening at the other end of this system and of the abilities of his hearing system. That he is able to pick up, recognize, and use such clues means that he has a very discriminating and complex approach to sonic events. In this experiment, a rapid rate of presentation and a rapid rate of reply was maintained for periods from twelve to twenty minutes without stop. To give a perspective of how fast this is, it is as if two human beings were doing a question-and-answer task as fast as they could talk for these periods of twelve to twenty minutes. The rate in our experiments was so fast that the human operator came out of the experiment fatigued; the dolphin would pace us at a very high rate.

Other physically specifiable variables that were measured showed that the dolphin matched the human duration of emissions and the human duration of interburst silences within a narrow range of error.

The important question of how well the dolphin pronounces each of the nonsense syllables is still a matter of the personal opinion of the observer making the judgment. "Non-physically specifiable variables" are invoked to compare what one hears with something else he hears. We have then moved into the area of psychophysics.

The most conservative statement that can be made about what one hears when these tape recordings are played back is that some particular aspect of the human voice is being accurately copied. I found that by playing back a tape through a special filter system this parallelism between the two voices (human and dolphin) could be improved.

The human voice, in general, consists of a basic pitch and the harmonics of this basic pitch as emphasized by the cavities shaped by one's tongue, soft palate, and the pharynx, for example.

Some aspects of the human voice are physically specifiable by a sound spectrograph which presents the variation of frequency in the voice with time. This shows that most of the meaningful portions of our voice (cutting out the less-meaningful noises) reside in the middle of the speech spectrum, i.e., from approximately 300 cycles per second to about 3000 Hz. At each end of this

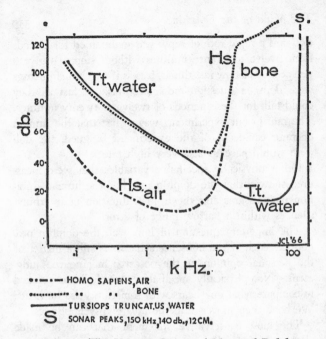

●-●-●-● HOMO SAPIENS, AIR
●●●●●●●● "   "   BONE
───── TURSIOPS TRUNCATUS, WATER
S SONAR PEAKS, 150 kHz, 140 db., 12 CM.

FIGURE 17. *The Hearing Curves of Man and Dolphin*

The hearing curve of the dolphin (T.t. water) extends
from 100 cycles per second (Hertz) to 160,000 cycles
(Hertz). The hearing curve of man (H.s. air) extends from
100 cycles to 15 kilocycles. The minimum pressure needed
for detection in each case is at zero decibels (re 0.002 dyne
per square centimeter). It is to be noted that the bone conduction curve for man (H.s. bone) corresponds to the dolphin's underwater curve (T.t. water) from 100 cycles per
second to approximately 3000 cycles per second. It is also
to be noted that the "air" and "bone" conduction curves in
man have a difference of approximately 45 decibels up to
about 3000 cycles per second. (Man's ear drum and bones
in the middle ear do not work well underwater.) The rapidly rising portion of the dolphin's hearing curve relates very
well to the amplitude of his emitted sonar impulses. The
point "S" is the peak amplitude of single sonar peaks at 150

range are sounds which are less important in carrying word meanings, i.e., in determining resemblances between what another person is saying and what one expects from what he has learned of that language. The predictability of the emitted sonic patterns thus is determined mainly by the region from 300 to 3000 Hz. If one chops off the two ends, less is lost than if he chops into this region. Above 3000 Hz at approximately 3800 to 8000 Hz is the fourth formant. In general, this formant seems to say only that the speaker is speaking; it does not vary much with different words and seems to remain constant every time he speaks.

In experiments we cut the human voice down to these essentially meaningful areas. The resulting dolphin emissions then more closely resembled the human voice. A psychophysical correspondence was found between what the humans said and what the dolphins said. The dolphins sounded more like the distorted human voice.

Similarly, if we took the previous nonsense syllable recordings and listened to them, cutting off all of the very-low-frequency sounds in the human voice (i.e., everything below about 2000 Hz), the resulting playback of the human and the dolphin voices resembled one another more closely. These lines of evidence tend to show that transmitting to the dolphin and receiving from the dolphin, as a feedback system, have a low-frequency cutoff characteristic, i.e., somehow or other, either the dolphin does not hear the low frequencies (Figure 17) or he is unable to transmit the low frequencies with any degree of fidelity. However, he is good at transmitting fair copies of the higher frequencies.

kilocycles (140 decibels) at 12 centimeters off the end of the beak. (The air-borne curves of man are from Licklider; the bone conduction curves are from Zwislocki and Corso; the dolphin data are from C. Scott Johnson; the sonar amplitudes are from J. C. Lilly.)

This line of evidence agrees with the normal dolphin underwater voice. In this case, experiments in our Institute have shown that the dolphin has difficulty emitting any sort of underwater sound below about 400 Hz; his barks, blats, and vowel-like sounds seem to end near this value (in general, the low end whistles stop at frequencies of about 6000 Hz). This indicates that a dolphin vocalizing in air will have difficulty in the lower frequencies where we have good control of our voices.

That dolphins enthusiastically move into such complex and discriminating acoustic vocal paths as mimicking our voice shows one aspect of the functions of their large brain. As was stated previously in this report their acoustical brain is of the order of ten times the size of our acoustical brain even as our visual brain is ten times the size of their visual brain. To explain the above results, we must assume here that dolphins are expert counters, or else they have a very large, immediate, here-now acoustical memory. If we take the distribution of the errors of the dolphin as a guide to the number of items in the stimulus list just read to the dolphin, we see that up to ten items, the errors do not increase as the number of items increases. Tested with similar lists, human subjects fall off at five to six items. Of course, these are lists heard for the first time in orders heard for the first time. This is the naïve performance with a new set of stimuli, not the polished performance of memorized material, in either the dolphin's case or in the human's case.

Probably the dolphins have a very good, recent, acoustic memory and can, as it were, accurately "play back" acoustic events up to unknown numbers of items and up to unknown durations of time.

The work recounted broke into a new area of investigation of the dolphins. Guided by the large acoustical brain and our knowledge of it, we began to test things which are acoustical-vocal combinations, properly functions of the acoustical brain. These are the things, processes, and thoughts with which dolphins should be pre-eminently occupied and in which they should be pre-eminently qualified. These are the first tests to show the areas in which dolphins can and do outperform human beings. They can outswim us; this is an obvious, necessary adaptation. Their vocal-acoustic behavior is not so obviously such an adaptation. Their use of sonar is a necessity in the sea. However, like us they found that communication and that key to communication with strangers called "mimicry" pushed them along farther and faster in relation to other creatures around them than probably any other single accomplishment of the species.

The necessity of a large brain for the development of language is recounted in a published paper.[5] This was an extension of the argument in *Man and Dolphin* for the presence of language in and among the dolphins. This is still our guiding hypothesis, i.e., their brains are large enough so that they can have developed a language, though very unlike any human one.

The above experiments in mimicry indicate the existence of several of the necessary abilities for a language. They show that the physiology and the anatomy is usable, trainable, and adaptable for language.

The experiments do not demonstrate, however, the detailed meanings of the dolphin's language nor do they demonstrate that the dolphin understands our meanings. The dolphin can proceed to take our directions in vocal and nonvocal language. We can, as it were, "train a dolphin" to recognize that on a given signal, we wish him to do certain things. All of these tests the dolphins have passed. They are eminently trainable in their body movements, swimming, coming to a given place, and such behavior as moving objects from one place to another.

[5] Lilly, John C. (1963) in General Bibliography.

The present experiments show that they are also eminently trainable in the vocalization and acoustic spheres. The next step, a long one, is demonstrating that the dolphin can meaningfully use these sounds as we use language and speech.

Epilogue

In March 1966, the Russian Minister for Fisheries, Alexander Ishkov, signed a decree prohibiting the commercial catching and slaughter of dolphins in the Sea of Azov and in the Black Sea for a period of ten years. Several members of the Soviet Academy of Sciences (USSR) have appealed to scientists in other countries to obtain similar bans in their countries.

What is the background for this sort of initiative in the Soviet Union? Extensive research on the dolphin has been done and is being done in the USSR. Basic research on the brain has been done by several investigators (I. N. Filiminoff, T. Sakharova, V. P. Zvorynkin, Ph. Owsjannikow, M. F. Nikitenko). This area of research is the key to changing the current misconceptions about the place of dolphins on this planet. Our own research on the dolphin's brain is reaching a culmination in *An Atlas of the Brain of the Dolphin,* Tursiops truncatus.[1] Our work and that of the Russians complement one another. The demonstrations of the high quality of this brain are very nearly completed. To mistreat this species is not in the best humanitarian traditions any longer. Finally the human species has an opportunity to commit itself to collaborative efforts with another species of high

[1] Morgane, P. J., *et al.* (1966).

caliber in programs of mutual interest. Though the dolphins are different (even alien), they are probably quite as flexible, educable, and as intelligent as we are.

As a consequence of our studies, it is proposed that new facilities be created in various parts of the world to facilitate this kind of development. It is suggested that shallow water "parks" be established. Such parks would be in areas which the dolphins naturally seek. The underwater and abovewater facilities are to be designed so as to allow *voluntary* contacts between the species. Neither man nor dolphin is to be constrained in their own or in the other's medium. This interface problem has been presented in this book, and certain kinds of parameters can now be specified. With the help and interest of conservationists and their organizations, with national and state government help, these plans and programs can be realized. With care, the goodwill of the dolphins can be maintained. Men of goodwill can arrange these facilities and protect them.

A new ethic and its consequent laws will develop. Not merely conservation and protection will suffice. Positive new thinking, feeling, and action are needed.

Let us change Aelian's plea, "Oh my good, kind dolphins, beware the savagery of men!" to "Kind dolphins, join us!"

Recently I have been contacted by several intensely interested persons who wish me to resume the attempt to break the dolphin-human communication barrier. I believe that we can do this within our lifetime. Several families are also in the same boat as we are: Michael Greenwood of the University of Nebraska, formerly of the dolphin project in the Navy, tours the country lecturing on the Dolphin Machine. Mac Brenner of Sarasota, Florida, had a three-year relationship, which included sexual intercourse, with a dolphin by the name of Dolly. There was much sorrow in Mac when Dolly died.

Dr. Spong in Vancouver, who is working with the killer whales, is obviously on the right track; Joan McIntyre lends her efforts to Project Jonah, to save the whales. Craig Becher has contributed to cetacean research. Less obvious support is from Dr. William McLean of the Undersea Warfare Division of the U. S. Navy, who came to see me in Miami and spent some time with me and the dolphins there. He started his project at Mugu, which later led to Michael Greenwood's project.

Several zoologists are not in accord with my suggestions. F. G. Wood, Jr., formerly of Marineland, later of Point Mugu, is a most vehement opponent to some of these ideas. Kenneth Norris, currently at the University of California, Santa Cruz (formerly of UCLA), has added to the vocal controversy in the past. He has had dealings with Tap Pryor at Sealife Park in Hawaii.

On the positive side is Professor Scholander of Scripps Institute, who has the research vessel the *Alpha Helix*. It was he who originally introduced me to the dolphins. Dr. Peter Morgane of the Worster Foundation, Massachusetts, and Dr. Paul Yakovlev of the Harvard University Medical School had done magnificent work on the dolphin brain which convinced all of us of their superior intelligence. Their atlas should be coming out in 1975. This will include research on the brains of the *Tursiops truncatus* and other whales.

I intend setting up and funding the house that was proposed in *The Mind of the Dolphin*. This is the house by the sea where the dolphins come in and interact with human families. We may have several of these. Burgess Meredith has some land in Little Cayman; Jan Brewer has some beaches in the north tip of the north island of New Zealand; and there is the possibility for such a setup through Tap Pryor's efforts in the Society Islands. This should be done simultaneously around the world in many places and wherever a breakthrough occurs, the information should be exchanged via satellite.

A frequency factor of approximately eight to ten converts human speech to the speed of dolphin communication and also reduces dolphin frequencies to what may be interpretable by human minds, therefore we need analogue converters operating in real time or some small fraction thereof. This should be a micro-miniature-type computer, solid state, tropicalized, and portable so that we can carry it from one installation to another. It should be easily reproduced so that we have several of them operating simultaneously.

I foresee tremendous gains on both sides. The dolphins will gain in their knowledge of us, and we will gain from them in terms of the environment of each. We will be able to set up whole new industries having to do with food and new mineral resources in the sea, and a new ecological balance. We will gain new philosophy, aesthetics, music and literary compositions based upon the dolphins' sagas and human sagas. We will be able to have three-dimensional sound TV for them and three-dimensional visual TV for us. All of this will then lead to a new breakthrough in regard to communicating with the largest brains on the planet, the sperm whales. They may be considered the grandfathers of all of us, the philosophers or the Platos plying the seas alone and farther out than any of us have ever been. They can give us programs to amuse, to entertain, to mystify and to expand us far beyond anything we conceive at the present time.

The Russians have their own stories in this regard. After the publication of my book *Man and Dolphin* in Russian, the Minister of Fisheries banned the catching of dolphins and porpoises in the Sea of Azov and the Black Sea for a period of ten years. I don't have more information on this now. Paul Yakovlev and Peter Morgane have been corresponding with those who have been examining the brains of dolphins in the Russian waters. There is a long classical series of studies coming from Russia which we should acknowledge. I know nothing whatsoever of what the Chinese have done in this area, if anything.

Dolphins as well as humans are mammals. They have dyadic problems. Toni and I for the last four years have been adjusting our dyadic patterns and we are finally beginning to focus in terms of dyadic communication. As Margaret and Peter (the dolphin) showed, the sexual thing among mammals is useful in terms of communication and gives an intensity and a direction which one cannot obtain any other way. It's a very direct thing and it's quite scientific to use it in this particular way. Thank you, Toni.

Appendix 1
Reprogramming of the Sonic Output of the Dolphin: Sonic Burst Count Matching

JOHN C. LILLY, ALICE M. MILLER,
AND HENRY M. TRUBY
Communication Research Institute,
3430 Main Highway, Miami, Florida 33133

The sound-producing mechanisms in the bottle-nosed dolphin (*Tursiops truncatus*) operate naturally under water with a closed blowhole. In these experiments, Tt's reprogrammability in the vocal air-borne mode and in vocal–acoustic interlock with another species is demonstrated. Human-speech (Hs) output programs were constructed from randomized vowel–consonant (VC) and

Reprinted from *Journal of the Acoustical Society of America*, Vol. 43, No. 6, 1412–24, June 1968. Copyright, 1968 by the Acoustical Society of America.

consonant–vowel (CV) lists and simple English words and phrases. The analysis of the dolphin's sonic vocal output in response to these Hs vocal programs demonstrates Tt's reprogramming: in matching number of and trains of bursts, interburst silences, and latencies; ability to differentiate between Hs stimuli and other Hs comments or corrections, and ability to program from natural delphinic sounds to "humanoid" emissions.

Introduction

Some physical analysis of the sonic and ultrasonic emissions of bottle-nosed dolphins (*Tursiops truncatus*) under water has been previously reported in the literature by us and by others.[1-12] The frequency bands covered by these underwater emissions extend as follows: from approximately 5 to 25 kHz for the fundamental frequencies and to at least 120 kHz for the harmonics of the whistles ("squeaks"), and from approximately 800 Hz to 170 kHz (fundamentals and harmonics) for click trains (pulses).

[1] J. C. Lilly and A. M. Miller, Science **133**, 1689–93 (1961).

[2] J. C. Lilly and A. M. Miller, Science **134**, 1873–76 (1961).

[3] J. C. Lilly, *Man and Dolphin* (Doubleday & Co., Inc., Garden City, N.Y., 1961), p. 312.

[4] J. C. Lilly, Proc. Am. Phil. Soc. **106**, 520–29 (1962).

[5] J. C. Lilly, Science **139**, 116–18 (1963).

[6] J. C. Lilly, *The Mind of the Dolphin* (*a nonhuman intelligence*) (Doubleday & Co., Inc., Garden City, N.Y., 1967), p. 310.

[7] W. N. Kellogg and R. Kohler, Science **116**, 250–52 (1952).

[8] W. N. Kellogg, R. Kohler, and H. N. Morris, Science **117**, 239–43 (1953).

[9] W. N. Kellogg, *Porpoises and Sonar* (University of Chicago Press, Chicago, Ill., 1961), p. 177.

[10] J. J. Dreher, J. Acoust. Soc. Am. **33**, 1–2 (1961).

[11] W. E. Evans and J. H. Prescott, Zoologica **47**, 121–28 (1962).

[12] T. G. Lang and H. A. P. Smith, Science **150**, 1839–44 (1965).

The adult *Tursiops* usually emit sounds without losing air either from the lungs or from the sound-producing mechanisms. Thus the normal predominant mode of vocal signaling behavior of the bottle-nosed dolphin is by means of sounds produced inside the body, under water. (A less frequently observed event is the loss of air from the closed blowhole slit during whistling or clicking. This air loss is observed frequently in sucklings and youngsters, and in adults under stress situations.)

Under special circumstances, the dolphin exposes the blowhole to air, opens it, and emits loud sounds in air; some of these sounds that resemble human speech sounds we call "humanoid vocalizations."[3, 4, 6, 13, 14a] The present account is a description of experiments on the programming of this vocal behavior.

I. Apparatus, Materials, and Techniques

For picking up and transmitting the air-borne voice output of the dolphin and the speech output of the human, either two Shure model 545 Unidyne II microphones were used or a model 545 plus a Lavalier model 560. The outputs of these microphones were recorded on a Wollensak 3M model 1580 tape recorder (*Tursiops* No. 11) and on a Sony model 262D tape-recorder deck with its recording amplifier SRA-2 (*Tursiops* No. 26). The useful frequency characteristics of this equipment extended from 100 Hz to 10 kHz. A satisfactory recorded amplitude range of approximately 35 dB was found.

Sonic analyses of these materials were made on a sonic spectrum recorder (12-kHz range, Kay Electric Co. Sona-Graph model 662-A). A mirror galvanometer oscillograph (Honeywell–Heiland model 906B) was used for

[13] J. C. Lilly, Arch. Gen. Psychiat. **8**, 111–16 (1963).

[14] (a) J. C. Lilly, Science **147**, 300–1 (1965). (b) J. C. Lilly and A. M. Miller, J. Comp. Physiol. Psych. **55**, 73–79 (1962).

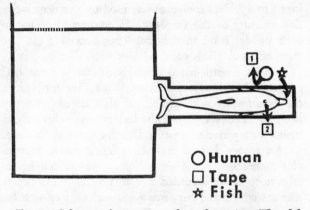

○ **Human**
□ **Tape**
★ **Fish**

FIG. 1. Schema of experimental configuration. The dolphin (Tt) is in the recording position in the side arm. The programmer (○) is standing beside the side arm reading from the program developed from Table I and displayed in Table II. The Hs voice program is recorded through Microphone No. 1 and Tape Channel No. 1. ("Tape" is indicated by □.) The Tt voice outputs are recorded through Microphone No. 2 and Tape Channel No. 2. When a food reward ("fish"★) is used, it is either manually given to Tt or dispensed by means of a mechanical feeder triggered outside the tank room. The Fiberglas tank (2.5×2.5 m) has a door (.....) opening into the other tanks. The transparent side arm is ~2.5 m long by 0.5 m wide by 0.5 m deep.

envelope and fundamental-frequency recording. The mirror galvanometers are linear to 4800 Hz. An inkwriter oscillograph (Grass polygraph model 8, 12 channels) was used for envelope recording and continuous-frequency analyses in isolated passbands with a limit of 45 Hz for rectified and integrated envelopes. A storage oscilloscope (Tektronix model 564) was used for checking analyses of waveforms, burst count, burst timing, and train latencies. A 29-channel narrow-band (135-Hz) analog spectrum analyzer (Kay Electric model 30 modified) at the input to a LINC computer was used to give a quantitative measure of the frequency of occurrence of use of each narrow band in the range 135–8000 Hz (in two steps of 29 channels each).

Two male bottle-nosed dolphins (*Tursiops truncatus*) cooperated in these experiments. With *Tursiops* No. 11, the experiments were carried out after the dolphin had been in close vocal and physical contact with investigators for a period of 4 years. This dolphin was estimated to be 2 years old at the time of his first intensive interspecies programming. *Tursiops* No. 26 was placed in the laboratory at an estimated age of 2 years; these experiments were carried out after 3 years of contact with the investigators.

In the experiments with Dolphin No. 11, a special tank with a side arm (Fig. 1) was used. The dolphin was free to go from his home tank into the side arm at any time. The tank room had sound-absorbing carpets on walls and ceiling. The investigator entered the room, stood beside the side arm with a bucket of fish, put on his own microphone, and adjusted the microphone for the dolphin. He held his list of stimulus cues in the left hand and fed the dolphin with the right hand. If not already positioned, the dolphin was induced to enter the shallow (25 cm deep) water in the side arm placing the blowhole in air near the microphone.

In the second set of experiments with Dolphin No. 26, the investigator entered a flooded room (13 m × 7 m, 45 cm water depth). The dolphin was free to swim into or out of this room from a flooded balcony (5 m × 7 m). An experimental area within the room was soundproofed (carpet on walls and ceiling). Both the *Tursiops* and the human moved freely in the room, most frequently between two microphones suspended from the ceiling.

With Dolphin No. 11, a male's human voice was used

as the stimulating source; with Dolphin No. 26, the voice of a female human was used.

II. Definition of Terms Used

A *program* is defined as a set of detailed instructions (expressed or implicit) transmitted by one biocomputer and received by another and/or used by both in interlock relationships. A program includes guidelines as to expected recordable and analyzable behavioral performances, vocal and nonvocal. A program defines values of time intervals between events, their amplitude, phases, durations, frequency ranges and modes of transmission, conduction, and reception. When possible, an attempt to measure the accuracy of the transmission and reception of a given program is made.

In a program, a *"burst"* is defined as a physical entity: a continuous series of pressure variations in a gas, liquid, or solid, the amplitude of which remains above an arbitrarily chosen threshold value for a minimum period of time, and of which the waveform frequencies and group repetition rates remain above a given value for the same period of time (Plate I). For the purposes of this discussion, the *burst source* is either a dolphin or a human. For psychophysical experiments, the chosen amplitude, repetition rates, and minimum time durations are a function of the source's previous programming, hearing curve, frequency difference limens, and time functions (man, woman, or dolphin).

The determinants of the "burst" for physical recordings and displays are a function of the instrumental modifications of the original waveforms (the over-all instrumental transforms) of the sequence of the original pressure variations. Such variables as frequency passbands, impulse responses, differential phase shifts, inter-

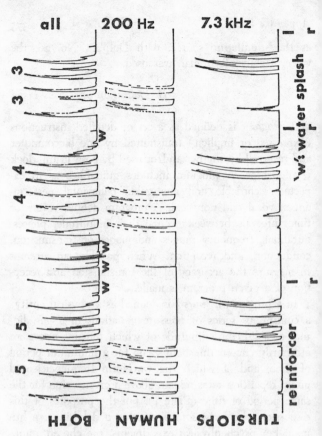

FIG. 2. Three typical Hs stimulus trains and the Tt voice output responses to each train. Analysis and graphic presentation of a portion of a magnetic-tape recording of Expt. 5 without cutting or editing (real time, continuous). The Hs voice program consists of three stimulus trains: the first has five bursts (mI ik iz te zi); the second has four bursts (lI va ol nI); and the third has three bursts (aIz i otʃ). To cover the wide amplitude range (40 dB), an automatic gain control circuit was applied to the combined signals, and the resulting signal is displayed on the uppermost trace (Hs train precedes each Tt response train). In the middle and bottom

modulation, rectification, and time transforms determine part of the definition of the burst in the program.

In the sequence of such bursts, the period of time between the instant of the end of one burst (below threshold instant) and the beginning instant of the next (above threshold instant) is defined as the "interburst silent interval" or *"interburst silence."* The duration of the interburst silent interval is the time measured from the "below-threshold instant" of burst one to the "above-threshold instant" of the next burst in sequence (Plate I).

A *train of bursts* is defined as a sequence of bursts in time in which the burst repetition rate and interburst silence maximum durations are programmatically (i.e., by the imposed program and/or given programs in the man or the dolphin) defined within a certain range of values and within a certain frequency-of-occurrence distribution (Fig. 2).

The time interval between individual separate trains is defined either in the program, or is to be determined experimentally.

In dolphin–human experiments, the human programming is specified by programs arbitrarily assigned to the operator, by those already existing below levels of awareness in the operator, and by those developed between the operator and the dolphin in the experiments. In the case of the dolphin, similar programming exists. Some human and some dolphin programs are already present, others can be created and certain behavioral parts of both recorded experimentally by objective methods. A limited set of these programs are found and described in this paper (the experiments, the results, and the analyses).

---

traces, the two voices are separated for graphic purposes by two narrow-band filters (SKL 302) and displayed separately. Food reinforcement was used at times indicated by r; w indicates water splashes.

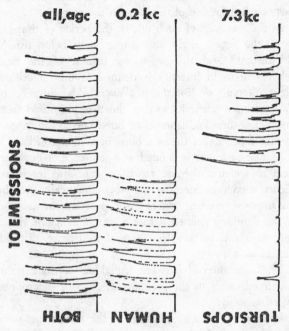

FIG. 3. A train of 10 bursts, man–dolphin. An oscillographic presentation in real time and continuous of a portion of the magnetic tape recording of Expt. 1. The stimuli
train of 10 bursts (oIn ot laI tʃu kI tʃi aIn ki oIl tI) by the
human programmer is number matched in the dolphin's
vocal output response. In the middle and bottom traces the
Hs (middle trace) and Tt (bottom trace) outputs are separately displayed for graphic purposes by two narrow-band
filters (Spencer–Kennedy). To cover the wide amplitude
range (40 dB), an automatic gain-control circuit was applied to the combined signals and the resulting signal is displayed in the uppermost trace.

III. Programming Subroutines

The two dolphins were each separately exposed to human-speech transmissions delivered under water or in air, formally and informally, several times a day. Between experiments, the feeders spoke loudly in air to the immersed dolphins during feeding, two times per day. At no time was food deprivation a part of the program. The weight of the consumed fish was measured at every feeding for each *Tursiops*. Normal daily food intake was maintained, when needed, by supplementary feedings.

Initially food (fish) was used as a behavior-starting reinforcer. As the program developed, the time of application of this reinforcer was manipulated. In some experiments, the dolphin was fed to satiation prior to the session; later, in other experiments, fish giving (by operator or by machine) was eliminated completely.

For descriptive purposes, the imposed programming techniques are divided into arbitrarily chosen subroutines. In the real situation, these subroutines were used simultaneously or in overlapping sequences.

The first subroutine was designed to increase the incidence of air-borne vocalizations and to inhibit the dolphins' natural waterborne emissions. At each feeding period, the dolphin was given a fish for each air-borne sound produced (no matter the type); spontaneous air-borne vocalizations were rewarded. Within a few sessions, each dolphin learned to use the air-borne mode as a vocal operant.[14b] All approaches and contacts by the investigators outside of the normal feeding sessions reinforced this behavior.

The second subroutine was designed to select and reinforce the production of only certain kinds of sounds and to extinguish others. Quick extinction of air-borne whistles was achieved. In this process, slow and rapid click trains that occurred were rewarded.

The third subroutine selected only the rapid (greater than approximately 100 pulses per second) click trains. The slow clicks were not reinforced and became extinguished to a rare-occurrence level.

The fourth subroutine further selected only those rapid clickings that approached the range of parameters of the human voice. During this programming, the dolphins were exposed to the human voice, speaking very loudly. It was found that gradually the dolphin emitted the desired sounds within the limits of his programs, of the low-frequency end of his hearing spectrum, and the low-frequency end of the spectrum of his sonic output.[3, 4, 5, 9, 15-17] (See also Discussion, below.)

The fifth subroutine selected only those sounds that occurred in response to the immediately preceding voice stimulus—i.e., he was rewarded for producing sounds only after a human voice utterance.

In the sixth subroutine, the sounds emitted were shaped further. The rapid click trains were found to resemble some physical aspects of human speech—e.g., vowel sounds, timing, and intonations of the preceding human utterance.

During Subroutine VII, the human used a paired-syllable list and the number of the dolphin's bursts were programmed to be two for a speech output of two human *syllables* in each train. For those human syllables that contain more than one burst ("it" for example), the program called for the dolphin to give one burst.

Subroutine VIII called for the dolphin to match a number of syllables (1 to 10) with an equal number of bursts: For the actual performances, see Results.

15 W. N. Kellogg, J. Comp. Physiol. Psych. **46,** 446–50 (1953).
16 W. E. Schevill and B. Lawrence, J. Exptl. Zool. **124,** 147–65 (1953).
17 C. Scott Johnson, NOTS TP 4178, 1–27 (1966).

IV. Choice of Vocal Program

In the experiment with Dolphin No. 11, the human-speech output program is constructed from a list of nine vowels and eleven consonants,[18-20] arranged in vowel—consonant (VC) and consonant–vowel (CV) pairs (Table I). Only the easily pronounceable combinations in General American language are used (187 out of 198 items). Two sets of this population of "nonsense syllables" are arranged.

The first list gives the CV and VC pairs in a systematic order (Table I). The second list was constructed from a randomized arrangement of the CV and of the VC syllables. This randomized set was divided up into subsets of syllables containing from 1 to 10 syllables. The order of these subsets was randomized (Table II).

The investigator read the first list to the *Tursiops* in a loud, natural voice. (Later, a tape recording of the reading voice was used.) Initially, the rate of the presentation of syllables in the human-speech output during each train was paced by a small light flashing once every 0.7 sec within the visual field of the reader.

In the first experimental series, the list of Table I was used, with Subroutines V–VII. The programming called for extinction of other sounds by withholding reward. When the production of whistles and slow pulsing trains was reduced to a small fraction of the number of the humanoid sounds produced, no further extinction was demanded.

Once the dolphin followed the "two-bursts-for-two-

18 G. A. Miller, *Language and Communication* (McGraw-Hill Book Co., New York, 1951), p. 298.

19 R. K. Potter, G. A. Kopp, and H. C. Green, *Visible Speech* (D. Van Nostrand Co., Inc., New York, 1947), p. 433.

20 H. Fletcher, *Speech and Hearing in Communication* (D. Van Nostrand Co., Inc., New York, 1953), p. 461.

syllables" rule (Subroutine VII), he was programmed with Subroutine VIII with the second list (Table II). If, in the judgment of the phonetically untrained human operator, the dolphin failed to match burst number to syllable number, Subroutine VII was reinstituted briefly before returning to Subroutine VIII. For each number-

TABLE 1

		r	l	z	v	tʃ	w	m	n	t	k	s
VOWELS OR DIPHTHONGS	i	ir / ri	il / li	iz / zi	iv / vi	itʃ / tʃi	wi	im / mi	in / ni	it / ti	ik / ki	is / si
	ɪ	ɪr / rɪ	ɪl / lɪ	ɪz / zɪ	ɪv / vɪ	ɪtʃ / tʃɪ	wɪ	ɪm / mɪ	ɪn / nɪ	ɪt / tɪ	ɪk / kɪ	ɪs / sɪ
	e	er / re	el / le	ez / ze	ev / ve	etʃ / tʃe	we	em / me	en / ne	et / te	ek / ke	es / se
	ɛ	ɛr / rɛ	ɛl / lɛ	ɛz / zɛ	ɛv / vɛ	ɛtʃ / tʃɛ	wɛ	ɛm / mɛ	ɛn / nɛ	ɛt / tɛ	ɛk / kɛ	sɛ
	a	ar / ra	al / la	za	av / va	atʃ / tʃa	wa	am / ma	an / na	at / ta	ak / ka	as / sa
	o	or / ro	ol / lo	oz / zo	ov / vo	otʃ / tʃo	wo	om / mo	on / no	ot / to	ok / ko	os / so
	u	ur / ru	ul / lu	uz / zu	uv / vu	utʃ / tʃu	wu	um / mu	un / nu	ut / tu	uk / ku	us / su
	aɪ	aɪr / raɪ	aɪl / laɪ	aɪz / zaɪ	aɪv / vaɪ	aɪtʃ / tʃaɪ	waɪ	aɪm / maɪ	aɪn / naɪ	aɪt / taɪ	aɪk / kaɪ	aɪs / saɪ
	ɔɪ	ɔɪr / rɔɪ	ɔɪl / lɔɪ	ɔɪz / zɔɪ	ɔɪv / vɔɪ	ɔɪtʃ / tʃɔɪ	wɔɪ	ɔɪm / mɔɪ	ɔɪn / nɔɪ	ɔɪt / tɔɪ	ɔɪk / kɔɪ	ɔɪs / sɔɪ

TABLE I. The human speech output program is constructed from this list of nine vowels (first vertical column) and eleven consonants (first line of the table) arranged in a vowel–consonant (VC) and consonant–vowel (CV) list. Only the easily pronounceable combinations of these VC and CV "nonsense syllables" were used (187 combinations out of the possible 198 items). This program was utilized for many experiments. From this program a randomized list was developed (see Table II) for the programs used in this paper.

matching response, the dolphin was rewarded with a fish. The number of seconds of time delay between the end of the dolphin's reply and the presentation of the fish were randomized. [This instruction avoided the use of this event as a "stop signal" by the dolphin—i.e., as a signal to terminate the dolphin's series of sonic bursts (see Discussion).]

The experiments reported here are those using the syllable subsets in randomized orders (Table II). Various control procedures to avoid the transmission of information to the dolphin other than by the vocal mode were done. Elimination of the food reward was achieved. The investigator was removed from the room; tape-recorded human speech outputs and a mechanical fish dispenser were substituted for the operator. Thus, undesired sonic, visual, and tactile sources of guides for starts, rates, durations, and stops were eliminated.[21]

The experiments with Dolphin No. 26 were carried out with simple English words and phrases. Intensive sessions were carried out over a period of 2 years. After the initial contacts and interlock were established, no food reward was used. The vocal output in air of the dolphin was shaped to a closer approximation of the human-speech output. The operator raised her pitch near the magnitude to which he had lowered his formantlike frequencies and pitch. Overlap of the pitch and of the formants of the female human-speech output and the male dolphin output were achieved (see Results).

[21] O. Pfungst, *Clever Hans (The Horse of Mr. von Osten). A Contribution to Experimental Animal and Human Psychology,* C. L. Rahn, Translator (Henry Holt and Co., New York, 1911). Also O. Pfungst, *Clever Hans,* R. Rosenthal, Ed., *The Horse of Mr. von Osten* (Holt, Rinehart and Winston, Inc., New York, 1965).

TABLE 2: EXAMPLE OF HUMAN PROGRAM AND PHONETIC OUTPUT ANALYSIS (Session 5)
The first line of each numbered group is the syllable read by the operator.
The second line is the I. P. A. symbols for the items of the first line.
The third line is the transcribed version of the recorded output of the operator.

1.	*in*	*ool*	*oom*							
	ɪn	ul	um							
	ɪn	ul	um							
2.	*at*	*ree*								
	ɑt	ri								
	æt	ri								
3.	*oyn*	*oat*	*lye*	*chew*	*kih*	*chee*	*ine*	*key*	*oil*	*tih*
	oɪn	ot	laɪ	tʃu	kɪ	tʃi	aɪn	ki	oɪl	tɪ
	oɪn	ot	laɪ	tʃu	kɪ	tʃi	aɪn	ki	oɪl	tɪ
4.	*en*	*ane*	*eat*	*ayer*	*noo*	*we*	*ate*	*chay*	*moe*	
	ɛn	en	it	er	nu	wi	et	tʃe	mo	
	ɛn	en	it	ɛr	nu	wi	et	tʃe	mo	
5.	*ta*	*rah*								
	tɑ	rɑ.								
	tɑ	rɑ								
6.	*oh*	*lee*	*vay*	*coy*	*aim*					
	o	li	ve	koɪ	em					
	o	li	ve	koɪ	em					
7.	*woe*	*moo*	*itch*	*wye*	*wih*	*moy*	*ehh*			
	wo	mu	itʃ	waɪ	wɪ	moɪ	ɛ			
	wo	mu	ɪtʃ	waɪ	wɪ.	moɪ	ɛ			
8.	*oys*	*air*	*eem*	*say*						
	oɪs	ɛr	im	se						
	oɪz	ɝ	im	se						
9.	*ett*	*ighch*	*ace*	*eel*	*ah*					
	ɛt	aɪtʃ	es	il	ɑ					
	ɛt	ɜɪtʃ	es	il	ai					

#									
10.								zoo ut ut	
11.	roy rɔɪ rɔɪ	kah ka ka	ovv ɑv ɑv	kehh kɛ kɛ	oyv ɔɪv ɔɪv	noy nɔɪ nɔɪ	rye raɪ raɪ	nigh naɪ naɪ	ootch utʃ utʃ
12.	mih mɪ mɪ	eek ik ik	ease iz iz	tay te te	zee zi zi			oo u u	
13.	lih lɪ lɪ	va vɑ vɑ	ole ol ol	nl nɪ nɪ					
14.	eyes aɪz aɪz	ee i i	atch otʃ otʃ					ose os oz	
15.	ah ɑ ɑ	ass ɑs ɑs	over ɔɪr ɔɪrʷ	oy ɔɪ ɔɪ	so so so				
16.	kay ke ke	lieu lu lu	ick ɪk ɪk	etch ɛtʃ ɛtʃ	cha tʃɑ tʃɑ				
17.	teh te te	aitch etʃ etʃ	I've aɪv aɪv	zi zɪ zɪ	cha tʃɑ tʃɑ	me mi mi	choy tʃɔɪ tʃɔɪ		
18.	oak ok ok	i i ɪ	loy lɔɪ lɔɪ	vie vaɪ vaɪ	see si si	chi tʃɪz tʃaɪz	rih rɪz rz		
19.	toy tɔɪ tɔɪ								

The human-speech output program for Expt. 5 is composed of 38 stimulus trains. The number of bursts in each train varies from 1 to 10. This randomized list was developed from the VC and CV list shown in Table I. Each stimulus train has been numbered in the order of presentation. The second line is the Hs stimulus program. These IPA symbols were transcribed (Line 1) for the Hs operator's convenience to facilitate reading from list. Line 3 is the Hs speech output program transcribed from the magnetic-tape recording of the experiment.

#				correction						
20.	aze ez ez	coo ku ku	ees is iz	ir ir ir	eve iv iv	oll al ol	I'm arm arm	meh me me	el ar ax	ray re re
21.	it rt rt									
22a.		own on on	im xm xm	wah wa wa	an an an					
22.	may me me	own on on	im xm xm	wah wa wa	an an an	toe to to	kfe kaz kaz			
23.	ees is iz	ooze uz uz	or or or							
24.	zeh ze ze	iss is iz								
25.	knee ni ni	are ar ar	ite art art	reh re re	row ro ro	ove ov ov				
26.	ma ma ma	is iz iz	too tu tu	zoo zu zu	een in in					
27.	eer ir ir	ev ev ev	oyt oit oit	veh ve ve	la la la	no no no				
28.	ice ais ais	sa sa sa	ek ek ek							

										zoe
										zo
										zo
									eli	
									el	
									el	
									em	
									ɛm	
									ɛm	
								si	*isla*	*as*
								si	aɪl	os
								saɪ	aɪl	os
						atch	*sue*	*my*	*ale*	*woy*
						atʃ	su	maɪ	el	wɔɪ
						ætʃ	su	maɪ	el	wɔɪ
					vous	*zah*	*chie*	*ike*	*voe*	*oym*	*weh*
					vu	za	tʃaɪ	aɪk	vo	ɔɪm	we
					vu	zo	tʃaɪ	aɪk	vo	ɔɪm	we
				voy	*ack*	*tie*	*ache*	*vih*	*zay*	*koe*
				vɔɪ	ak	taɪ	ek	vɪ	ze	ko
				vɔɪ	æk	taɪ	ek	vɪ	ze	ko
			zye	*choe*	*rue*	*omm*	*av*	*woo*	*ooke*	*ezz*
			zaɪ	tʃo	ru	am	av	wu	uk	ez
			zaɪ	tʃo	ru	am	av	wu	uk	ez
		each	*iv*	*leh*	*fay*	*oyz*	*tea*	*seh*	*oor*
		itʃ	ɪv	le	fe	ɔɪz	ti	sɛ	ur
		itʃ	ɪv	le	fe	ɔɪz	ti	sɛ	ur
	tre	*soy*	*oyk*	*ohm*	*lo*	*way*	*neh*	*oych*	*zoh*
	azr	sɔɪ	ɔɪk	om	lo	we	ne	ɔɪtʃ	zo
	azr	sɔɪ	ɔɪk	om	lo	we	ne	ɔɪtʃ	zo

29. *vee* / vi / vi
30. *oove* / uv / uv
31. *oon* / un / un
32. *cheh* / tʃɛ / tʃɛ
33. *nay* / ne / ne
34. *oze* / oz / oz
35. *nah* / nɑ / nɑ
36. *oos* / us / uz
37. *sigh* / saɪ / saɪ
38. *ill* / ɪl / ɪl

V. Results

The tape-recorded materials of the Hs (human) and Tt (dolphin) outputs from the two sets of experiments were analyzed by various methods for number of bursts per train, burst timing, frequency spectrum, and pulsing rates.

The first analyses were generated by an acoustic monitoring of the taped sessions. The number of bursts in the Hs train and the number of bursts in the Tt response train were counted. Several observers counted what they heard with the tapes played back at either normal speed or at slowed down speeds (2× to 32×). Independent counts were made from oscillographic recordings of the rectified and integrated envelopes of bursts, with the full passband and with bands isolated with various high-pass and low-pass filters. Counts were also made from spectral records (sonagrams). The primary recorded waveforms displayed on a storage cathode-ray oscilloscope were also used to count bursts.

Figure 2 shows a typical oscillographic recording of part of Expt. 5 of the Hs bursts and the Tt bursts. Each separate envelope is defined by its ends (below 30 dB from peak). The man emits five bursts and the dolphin emits five; the man emits four and the dolphin emits four; the man emits three and the dolphin emits three. In Fig. 3 is shown another part of the same experiment, a train of 10 bursts by the man, and a train of 10 bursts in the response of the dolphin.

Plate II shows an oscillographic record of Expt. 5, in which the dolphin matches number of bursts with few errors. Thirty-eight Hs trains and 38 Tt trains were recorded. (Table II gives the nonsense-syllable list used as stimuli). (Plate IV shows some detail of Train 22 not shown here; see Sec. VI.)

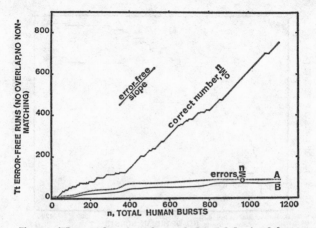

FIG. 4. The results of analysis of the dolphin's ability to match number of bursts are summated over six experiments using a vocal program developed from Table I and represented by Expt. 5 in Table II. Curves A and B are represented 10 times enlarged on the vertical scale in Fig. 5. Error-free number of burst matching increases with exposure to the program. Each successful response is plotted as a quantum jump on the Y axis and the X axis. When an error is made on the main curve, it is stepped one on the X axis and zero on the Y axis. The error curves (A and B) are stepped zero on the Y axis when there is no error, and for each response train with an error is stepped one on the Y axis and on the X axis. Σ_0^n is the summation from response train$_0$ to the response train$_n$.

Figure 4 shows the time course for six such experiments of the acquisition of the ability to match number of bursts. It is to be noticed that the error-free runs increase in duration with further exposure to the program.

Figure 5 shows the dolphin's errors on a vertical scale enlarged 10 times over that of the previous figure. Two kinds of errors are plotted. Error A is the overlapping of the human delivery time by the dolphin—i.e., putting

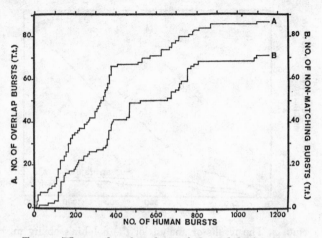

Fɪɢ. 5. The results of analysis of the dolphin's errors are
summated over six experiments using a vocal program developed from Table I and represented by Expt. 5 in Table
II. Two kinds of errors are plotted: Curve A represents Tt's
vocal output response as events when they overlap the Hs
vocal output train of stimuli either during a burst or an interburst silence; Curve B represents Tt's mismatch in response
to every burst of each Hs stimulus train. Error Curves A
and B demonstrate that initially the dolphin has a random
distribution of errors; later runs show an alternation in type
of error; there are error-free runs first of one kind, then for
the other, and finally for both. (See also Fig. 4 where these
two error curves are represented on a vertical scale one-tenth
this size.) Curve A represents a total "overlap" burst error
of 7.16% and Curve B a 6.21% "nonmatching" burst error.

bursts in the interburst intervals during the time the human is speaking. Error B is mismatch of number of Hs
bursts and Tt number of bursts. From these two figures,
it can be seen that the dolphin at the beginning has a
more-or-less random distribution of errors. Later runs
show alternation in type of error; there are error-free

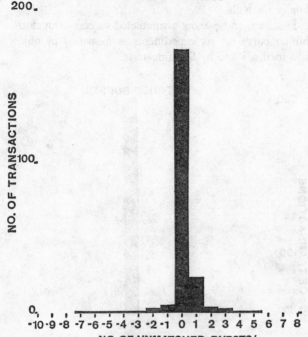

FIG. 6. Dolphin's success–error distribution curve by naïve listening tests for six experiments on one dolphin using a vocal program developed from Table I and represented in Table II. *Abscissa:* zero position is the correct number of bursts per train of stimuli; plus numbers represent numbers of bursts above those in stimulus train; minus numbers represent deficiency in number of bursts by the dolphin in response to Hs stimulus train. Analysis by naïve observers who count "nonsense syllables" rather than objective bursts. This important source of error was corrected by a phonetician, and by coordinated CRO observations (storage scope) and listening tests (Fig. 7).

runs first for one kind of error, then for the other, and finally for both.

Figures 6 and 7 show a summated success–error distribution curve for six experiments as measured by objective methods and by listening tests.

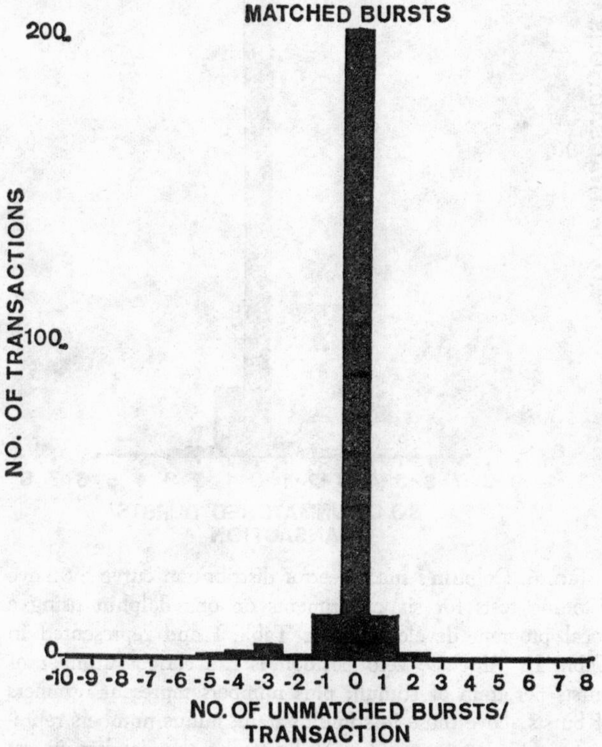

FIG. 7. Dolphin's (Tt) success–error distribution curve by objective and by listening tests for six experiments using a vocal program developed from Table I and represented in Table II. Analysis by listening tests by trained observers who count bursts rather than nonsense syllables and by objective methods. (See also Fig. 6.)

During these experiments, normal nonprogrammed Tt outputs (such as slow clickings and whistlings) were not included in the statistical data.

Further analyses of the dolphin's sounds and of the human speech include sonic spectrograms prepared on both voices covering 85-Hz to 8-kHz ranges, both narrow and wide band (45 and 300 Hz). Plate III(a) and III-(b) show a sample sonic spectrogram of the human voice and of the dolphin's reply.

These spectrograms plus sections at chosen times were then analyzed for (1) pulsing rate (45- and 300-Hz analyzing filters) and (2) peak partials of the fundamental that showed maximum amplitudes (formants and formantlike occurrences). The instants of time for the analyses were chosen during vowel production by the human and during corresponding periods of relatively steady-state activity in the dolphin's record.

These measurements are plotted as shown in Fig. 8. The source pulsing-rate values (in the human case, laryngeal pulsing, or pitch) are plotted along the X axis (log scale). Log frequency is plotted on the Y axis, showing the frequency of each of the partials above the fundamental for varying values of the fundamentals. The maximum amplitude partials (peak partials) were selected at a given instant of time and are represented by dots (human) or rectangles (dolphin) plotted at the location of each peak partial on the log-log plot.

Figure 8 shows the Tt's output to occur at higher values of pulsing rate and higher frequencies of the peak partials ("resonance") as compared with that of the Hs outputs.

Figure 9 shows a population of 120 corresponding human male and dolphin male sounds taken late in the programming sequence. The period of the experiments chosen is that in which the dolphin was giving correct numbers of bursts matching the numbers of human

bursts, and is chosen from corresponding human and
dolphin trains.

Figure 9[22, 23] thus shows the corresponding parametric regions of the human vowel sounds and the sounds
emitted by the dolphin. Notice the separation of the parametric regions of the two voices.

As a consequence of these measurements, a program
was instituted to use the female human voice in vocal
interlock with another dolphin (No. 26). The rationale
employed was that the human female voice is higher
pitched (has a higher fundamental source pulse rate)
and has somewhat higher peak partials (formant frequencies) than the male human voice. Figure 10 shows
some of the results after 2 years of programming. It was
found that the human female moved her voice up toward
the pulsing rate and peak-partial frequency regions of the
programmed dolphin.

VI. Discussion

A. CHANNEL LIMITS

Figure 11 summarizes the communication channels
used in these experiments. The human (1) and the dolphin (5) are information transmitters and receivers with
quite different characteristic ranges of hearing (4, 8)
and of sonic outputs (2, 6). The human operator transmits bands of frequencies (2) only some of which he is
aware (8, 1) and hence controlled by his own hearing
feedback (1, 2, 8). The dolphin receives some of these
bands, modified by the physical means of transmission
(3), and his own hearing ranges (4). The dolphin (5)
computes on the basis of this modified input, and trans-

[22] G. Fant, "Acoustic Analysis and Synthesis of Speech with
Applications to Swedish. Ericsson Technics No. 1., p. 108 (1959).
[23] H. M. Truby, "Acousticol-Cineradiographic Analysis Considerations" Acta Radiol. Suppl. **182,** 199, Fig. 2-64 (1959).

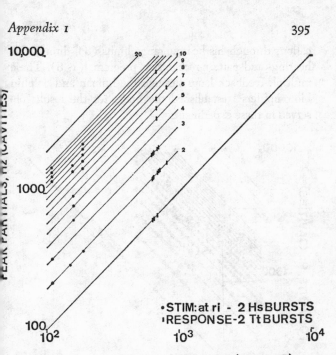

P.R.R., PULSES/SEC. (SOURCE)

FIG. 8. Parametric analysis of the source pulsing-rate values are plotted along the X axis (log scale) and the log frequency is plotted along the Y axis showing the frequency of each partial (peak partials) varying fundamental frequencies (cavity resonances). The Hs speech output program is a stimulus train consisting of two syllables (bursts) "at ri." The sonic analysis of the vowels are represented by the black dots. Tt No. 11 voice response train with its two bursts is represented by the black rectangles. The distinctly isolated regions between the Hs (male) programmer's pitch and the Tt's response is readily apparent; no overlap is evident.

mits a sonic output (6) controlled by his own hearing feedback from that output (6, 4, 5). This output (6) then passes through the physical modifiers (7). The human operator (1) hears this output (6, 7) with modifications through his hearing-range limits (8), through his hearing- and pattern-recognition programs (1, 8). These multiple-feedback loops through the human and dolphin biocomputers[24] established the limits for the results observed in these experiments.

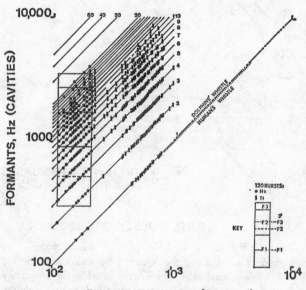

P.R.R., PULSES/SEC.(SOURCE)

FIG. 9. The Hs speech-output program for this display was selected at random from the experiments developed from Table II. The 120 bursts selected (Hs and Tt No. 11) for analysis were extracted from matching trains (stimulus and response) in the experiment. (●) represents the Hs vowel output and (■) the Tt voice responses. (See Fig. 8 for parameters.) Key in lower right shows the human speech-formant regions for the first, second, and third. (Key—see refs. 22 and 23.)

[24] J. C. Lilly, "The Human Biocomputer. Theories of Programming and Metaprogramming," CRI Scientific Rept. No. CRI-0167 (1967).

Figures 12 and 13 illustrate quantitatively some of the physical and psychophysical limits on these feedback loops. The human-speech output covers a much higher range of frequencies than the hearing detects. The dolphin's hearing detects the higher human output frequencies, but probably not the lower ones (refs. [17], [25-28], and Lilly, unpublished data).

The dolphin's sonic output covers a range as large as (if not larger than) his hearing. The very high frequencies in the dolphin's output are not detected by the human hearing. The loop-shared regions are shown in Fig. 13, as well as the regions that are only human detected, only dolphin detected, and not detected by either.

B. REPROGRAMMING MODE OF TRANSMISSION

The sound-producing mechanisms in the dolphin operate naturally under water with a closed blowhole. In these experiments, the dolphin's ability to open the blowhole and make air-borne sounds is selectively programmed and thus forces the phonatory apparatus to function in another mode in vocal–acoustic interlock with another organism. That the dolphin adapts to this mode of signaling with man is shown in these experiments. It is also shown that the dolphin can be programmed (within determinable limits) to reproduce some physical aspects of the human-speech output. In spite of the natural use of a band of frequencies approximately ten to twenty times that normally utilized in the human voice range, the dol-

[25] J. F. Corso, J. Acoust. Soc. Am. **35**, 1738–43 (1963).

[26] J. Zwislocki, J. Acoust. Soc. Am. **29**, 795–804 (1957).

[27] W. E. Montague and J. F. Strickland, J. Acoust. Soc. Am. **33**, 1376–81 (1961).

[28] J. C. R. Licklider, "Basic Correlates of the Auditory Stimulus," in *Handbook of Experimental Psychology*, S. S. Stevens, Ed. (John Wiley & Sons, Inc., New York, 1951).

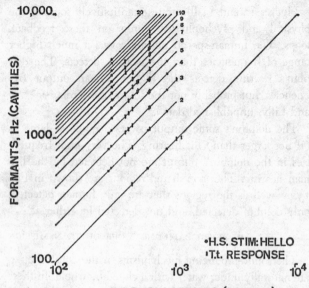

FORMANTS, Hz (CAVITIES)

P.R.R., PULSES/SEC. (SOURCE)

•H.S. STIM: HELLO
ᵗT.t. RESPONSE

Fig. 10. The Hs speech-output program stimulus train analysis was "hello" (●) and (■) is the analysis of Tt No. 26's voice output response. In this program analysis, it is demonstrated (compare with Figs. 8 and 9) that the Hs (●) output (pitch) and the Tt response overlap in the frequency ranges. In this experiment, the pitch of the Hs (female) voice output has been raised and overlaps the dolphin's. In a sense, the dolphin's high-pitch reprogrammed the Hs female voice to unusually high values (up to 800 Hz). (See Fig. 8 for parameters.)

phin can shape up the transmissions in the lower end of his output frequency spectrum. His hearing curve (and probably his frequency-differentiation threshold) extend into the upper portion of the human-speech frequency spectrum; therefore probably in a limited way he can hear human speech (Figs. 12 and 13).

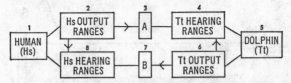

Vocal Mode: The sonic-ultrasonic feedback loop for human-dolphin exchanges. A and B are physical transmission systems including electronic apparatus and air-water environment.

Fig. 11. Vocal-mode flow diagram for (Hs) and dolphin (Tt) vocal programming. Hs and Tt are both confined on the input and output side by (3) and (7)—the physical transmission systems including electronic apparatus and the air–water environment. The Hs programmer (1) has specific vocal-output ranges (2) and vocal-input ranges (dependent upon his hearing curve) that effect the programming of Tt (5). Tt, on the other hand, is restricted by the effects of his hearing curve on the input side and his vocal-output ranges. Cognizance of this interlock system in the programming is essential in the analysis–interpretation of every experiment. (See Fig. 12 for hearing curves, and Fig. 13 for vocal-output curves.)

C. START AND STOP SIGNALS

What guides does the *Tursiops* use to initiate the vocal response at the correct time? Latencies between the end of the Hs train and the beginning of the dolphin response were measured.

The values of these latencies fall within the distribution curve of the values of the interburst silent intervals in the human presentation. On the average, the dolphin tended to start his replies with a latency approximately the same as that of the interburst intervals in the human trains (Figs. 2, 3, and Plate II). How he is able to do this is not clear. It is probable that the dolphin picks up clues from some special modifications of the human voice for the last items in a train. No effort was made to control

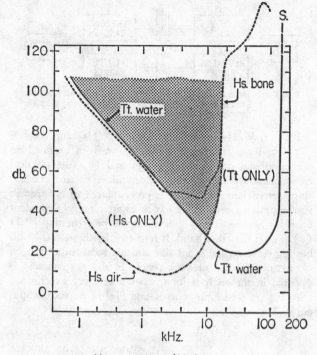

------- Homo sapiens (Hs.), air
------- Homo sapiens (Hs.), bone
——— Tursiops truncatus (Tt.), water
▓▓▓ Hs. and Tt. shared hearing area
S   Sonar peaks, 150 kHz, 140 db, 12 cm.

Fig. 12. Comparison of the human (Hs sonic) and dolphin (Tt sonic and ultrasonic) hearing curves in air and in water plotted from the data developed by Lilly, Corso, Zwislocki, Johnson, and Montague (see refs. 17, 25–28). Only a limited narrow band of frequencies is shared and consequently defines some limits of (2) through (8) in the vocal-mode flow diagram (Fig. 11) (decibels *re* 0.0002 dyn/cm² peak pressure).

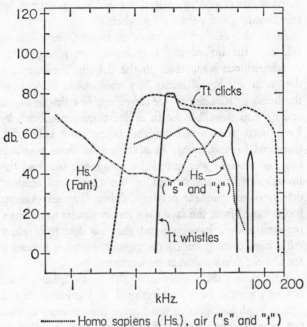

FIG. 13. Comparison of the sonic and ultrasonic vocal output curves of the human (Hs) in air and the dolphin (Tt) in water. The Hs curve (....) represents sonic–ultrasonic high-frequency energy for the consonants "s" and "t". The Hs curve (–·–·–) represents Fant's vowel and consonant 40-phon equal-loudness contour curve (ref. 22) (decibels *re* 0.0002 dyn/cm² peak pressure).

the voicing of the human reading from the list—i.e., the male investigator gave the usual list-reading-intonation to this presentation. For example, he often used a falling pitch on the last item of each train. It is probable that the dolphin developed a pattern-recognition program for this change (and possibly for others).

As in the case of the counting horse (Clever Hans, ref. 21), the investigator may have been giving visual or adventitious sonic clues to the dolphin for matching the given number of bursts in a train. As in the case of the horse, a "start signal" for the repetitive trains of bursts and a "stop signal" to finish at the correct number may have been transmitted by the investigator below his threshold for awareness. As a control on these possibilities, the material was recorded on magnetic tape and the investigator was moved out of the visual and acoustic detection environment of the dolphin. The experiment programmed from the tape gave results similar to the ones reported above. It was found that no detectable clues other than those given by the taped voice were necessary for the dolphin's accurate performance.

To estimate the influence of the presentation of the fish as a start, stop, or timing signal, and to eliminate the fish as a physiological reward, experiments were carried out immediately after the dolphin was fed to satiation. During these experiments, when presented with a fish the dolphin accepted it, allowed it to drop to the bottom of the side arm, and thus accumulated a pile of fish during the session. (At this stage, the fish giving and receiving were still part of the program.) When the dolphin wished to terminate the experiment, he lifted a fish on the end of his upper jaw and either threw it out of the side arm or moved it toward the investigator. Random reinforcement schedules were successful. Complete elimination of the giving and receiving of fish was also successful, thus the reinforcing and cueing possibilities of the fish were eliminated.

D. COUNTING OR RECENT ACOUSTIC MEMORY?

Several working hypotheses were developed during these experiments. Of all of the processes the dolphin may be using to respond with the correct number of bursts there are at least three of importance: conditioned programs, "counting," or straight readout from recent acoustic storage. The concept of conditioned programs can be analyzed further and shown to be equivalent to one or both of the others or is a name for unknown processes at present unanalyzable.

The dolphin may "count" the number of bursts heard and put out an equal number. One way that the dolphin could indicate that he knows that the experimenter expects an equal number of bursts would be for him to give back an equal number of bursts of simple sonic structure—i.e., even to the point of making each of his bursts in the train very similar. If this were the case, one might expect all of his sounds to be similar, if not identical. However, the dolphin's bursts in a number-matching train are distinguishably different in pitch contours, durations, interburst silences, and complexity of patterning. The last burst of each of his trains has a characteristic patterning. These variations favor the recent-acoustic-memory playback hypothesis over the counting one. To count bursts, a very brief acoustic memory span is needed with a quick registration of the count for the summed total; in the playback hypothesis, there is a longer memory span; there is storage of the whole train (up to 10 items) and subsequent playback of the output equivalent of the stored acoustic image of the whole train. The latter process makes possible a more complex patterned output than a repetitive reproduction of a train of, say, clicks, of the same number as in the human train. In addition, on listening tests it has been found that there are resemblances when comparing *corresponding bursts* in the human train and the dolphin's response train despite differences within the train. At times, there are resemblances (though in different frequency and pitch regions) between the patternings of the human and the dolphin. Further work needs to be done in this area to determine what parameters the dolphin is mimicking.

Additional complex behavior occurred during many of these experiments. For example, in the session with Tt No. 11, it was noted that if the human corrected his output after he made an error that the dolphin matched only the corrected version of the output. Plate IV shows an example of such an occurrence. (In Plate II, the rest of the session is shown with Line 22a of Plate IV left out.) The programmer (Hs) says (Line 22a) "me, on, am," hesitates and says "correction" and starts over, giving "me on Im wa an to kaI me aI er," i.e., a train of 10 nonsense syllables (Line 22 of Plate II). The dolphin (Tt) replies with only 10 bursts, the total number in the train of the corrected version, with no reply to the previous three bursts ("me on am") or the word *correction*. Similar events are frequent enough to lead to the hypothesis that the dolphin has learned (at the very least) to recognize that pattern that is to be matched (stimulus) and that which is to be ignored (instructions, corrections, deletions). What clues Tt uses for this selection are at present obscure.

The dolphin (No. 26) working with the female human programmer learned to reproduce only the Hs output given in an emphatic loud voice and did not match asides, instructions, laughter, etc.

One aspect of these experiments that is considered to be important is the initiation and termination of a session by the behavior of the dolphin. If, at the beginning of the experiment, the dolphin did not swim into the side arm he was left alone in isolation (visual and tactile), solitude, and confinement for a few minutes. A second attempt was then made, and if he did not come into the side arm at that point, he was isolated further for an hour or more. All the above experimental runs were made when the dolphin was ready to start.

Similarly, each experiment was terminated by the dolphin. During a given run, the dolphin may stop vocalizing and back out of the side arm into his home tank. If this happened, the investigator waited for a short period (5 min.); if the dolphin did not return in that time, the investigator (in a loud voice) said that the experiment was over and left the room. With this technique, three experiments were scheduled each day.

Signs of fatigue in the dolphin during an experiment were shown by decreased amplitudes of the Tt output. At times, by using proper shaping-up techniques, the amplitude could be restored. At other times, a rest period sufficed to restore the amplitude.

Anatomical, biophysical, and physiological studies were done on the sound-producing mechanisms in the head of the dolphin. The results of these analyses are reported elsewhere, important results for purposes of explication of parts of these experiments are given here.

In the natural state, emitting underwater sounds, the dolphin employs two mechanisms located below and on each side of the blowhole. Some of the anatomy of these systems have been described.[29] In this state, this system operates as a closed set of membranes, tubes, and sacs. During the sound production in air, these mechanisms function as a resonating system with one end open in the air, thus changing its resonance and other characteristics.

In several experiments, the air-borne vocal outputs of the dolphin were picked up with an air microphone and

[29] B. Lawrence and W. E. Schevill, Bull. of Mus. of Comp. Zool. **114**, 103–52 (1956).

simultaneously the underwater outputs were recorded through a hydrophone in separate channels on a tape recorder (Crown 800 series). When the blowhole was open in air, most of the sonic energy was recorded from the microphone; there was a radical reduction of the amount of energy recorded in the water. With the blowhole closed and most of the head under water, most of the voice energy was recorded under water through the hydrophones (ref. 4). In the natural immersed state (underwater sounds), the monitoring of his own sounds through his ears is easily accomplished. With the blowhole open in air and the ears under water, the dolphin probably has difficulties hearing the sounds he is releasing in the air itself (Fig. 11). The direct transmission in his head of the sounds produced is probably the only clue that he has as to what he is producing.

His underwater hearing of the voice of the human in air has a large reduction in amplitude owing to the air–water interface (reflection of most of the sonic energy). Thus the interspecies feedback in the sonic–ultrasonic sphere introduces a new set of conditions for which the dolphin must adaptively program. That the dolphin does so reprogram reproducibly and accurately to these artificial conditions shows a flexibility and a plasticity of vocal reprogramming of a high order.

Bastian's experiments[30] with *Tursiops truncatus* illustrate further the dolphin's reprogrammability. Using arbitrarily assigned environmental changes (visual) and operant controls (levers), two dolphins were induced to communicate with natural underwater sounds in order to solve a problem requiring cooperative efforts. The dolphins succeeded in these tasks (at a high level of con-

[30] J. Bastian, *NOTS TP* 4117, 1–42 (Jan. 1967), and also in *Les Systemes Sonars Animaux, Biologie et Bionique*, R. G. Busnel, Ed. (Laboratoire de Physiologie Acoustique, Inra Cnrz-Jouy-en-Josas, France, 1967).

fidence) by using short bursts of clicks (one to the other) at the crucial time in the program sequence to indicate which of two levers to press. These results imply an already known (or else an acquired) meaning for the click sequence—a meaning shared by at least two dolphins.

In these experiments in which a food reward (fish) or "physiological reinforcer" was eliminated, it is not obvious what the reinforcers are (what motivates the dolphin). As a working hypothesis, we assume that *Tursiops truncatus*, like *Homo sapiens*, has a sufficiently large and complex brain to have (or to develop) programs that motivate performances and hence act as "reinforcing programs" or "symbolic reinforcers" in the absence of explicitly humanly programmed rewards (such as fish giving). Presumably such hypothesized reinforcing programs include pattern-recognition and "success–failure" criteria with storage of the performance record as it develops. Such high-level programming does not seem to exist in the smaller-brained mammals (rat, cat, or monkey), nor in the "talking" birds (parrot or mynah).

Acknowledgments

The authors wish to thank the following individuals for their assistance: Dr. Franklin Cooper and W. A. Munson and for the technical assistance of S. McVay, H. McFarland, and M. Lovatt.

This work was supported at various times in part by grants from NINDB and NIMH of NIH, AFOSR, ONR, NASA, and various private foundations and contributors.

Appendix 2

Communication with Extraterrestrial Intelligence

The title that I might choose for my discussion is "The Need for an Adequate Model of the Human End of the Interspecies Communication Program," a plea for self-conscious, open-ended, general-purpose, nonspecies-specific cognition research into models of theory for communication with nonhuman minds. I believe that this is the first time the word "mind" has been mentioned in this respect.

In recent years, I have struggled with the problem of devising working models of the interspecies communication problem at a relatively highly structured cognitive level. Despite overglamorization and excessive public exposure, the embryo has remained viable and hard working.

The major portion of the total problem has been found to be my own species rather than the delphinic ones. There is apparently no currently available adequate theory of the human portion of the communication network. The lack of such a theory has made it difficult for

Reprinted from *IEEE Spectrum*, Vol. 3, No. 3, March 1966, pp. 153–63. © 1966, and reprinted by permission of the Institute of Electrical and Electronic Engineers, Inc.

most scientists to see the reality of the problems posed in the interspecies program. As long as the conscious–unconscious basic belief exists of the pre-eminence of the human brain and mind over all other earthside brains and minds, little credence can be obtained for the proposition that a problem of interspecies communication exists at all.

Despite arguments based on the complexity and size of certain nonhuman brains, little if any belief in the project has been instilled in the scientific community at large. Support has been obtained for further examination and demonstration of the large-sized, detailed excellence of structure and description of the large dolphin brain. There is no lack of interest in this area. The falling out comes in obtaining the operating interest of competent working scientists in the evaluation of the performance of these large brains. Interest and commitment of time and self are needed for progress.

The basic assumptions on which we operate are as follows. Each mammalian brain functions as a computer, with properties, programs, and metaprograms partly to be defined and partly to be determined by observation. The human computer contains at least 13 billion active elements and hence is functionally and structurally larger than any artificially built computer of the present era. This human computer has the properties of modern artificial computers of large size, plus additional ones not yet achieved in the nonbiological machines. This human computer has stored program properties, and stored metaprogram properties as well. Among other known properties are self-programming and self-metaprogramming. Programming and metaprogramming language is different for each human, depending upon the developmental, experiential, genetic, educational, accidental, and self-chosen variables, elements, and values. Basically, the verbal forms are those of the native language of the individual, modulated by nonverbal language elements acquired in the same epochs of his development.

Each such computer has scales of self-measuration and self-evaluation. Constant and continuous computations are being done, giving aim and goal distance estimates of external reality performances and internal reality achievements.

Comparison scales are set up between human computers for performance measures of each and of several in concert. Each computer models other computers of importance to itself, beginning immediately *post partum*, with greater or lesser degrees of error.

The phenomenon of computer interlock facilitates model construction and operation. One computer interlocks with one or more other computers above and below the level of awareness any time the communicational distance is sufficiently small to bring the interlock functions above threshold level.

In the complete physical absence of other external computers within the critical interlock distance, the self-directed and other-directed programs can be clearly detected, analyzed, recomputed, and reprogrammed, and new metaprograms initiated by the solitudinous computer itself. In this physical reality (which is an as completely attenuated as possible environment with solitude), maximum intensity, maximum complexity, and maximum speed of reprogramming are achievable by the self.

In the field of scientific research, such a computer can function in many different ways—from the pure, austere thought processes of theory and mathematics to the almost random data absorption of the naturalistic approach with newly found systems, or to the coordinated interlock with other human computers of an engineering effort.

At least two extreme major techniques of data-collection analysis exist for individual scientists: (1) artificially created, controlled-element, invented, devised-system methods; and (2) methods involving the participant–observer, who interacts intimately and experientially with naturally given elements, with nonhuman or human computers as parts of the system.

The former is the current basis of individual physical–chemical research; the latter is one basis for individual, explorative, first-discovery research of organisms having brains larger than those of humans.

Sets of human motivational procedural postulates for the interlock research method on nonhuman beings, with computers as large as and larger than the human computers, are sought. Some of these methods involve the establishment of long periods—perhaps months or years—of human to other organism computer interlock. It is hoped that this interlock will be of a quality and value sufficiently high to permit interspecies communication efforts on both sides on an intense, highly structured level.

In essence, then, this is the problem of communicating with any nonhuman species or being or mind or computer. We do not have, however, the full support in basic beliefs in the scientific community for these postulates. Obviously, we as a species do not believe, for example, that a whale, with a brain six times the size of ours, has a computer worth dealing with. Instead, we kill whales and use them as fertilizer. We also eat them. To be fair to the killer whale, I know of no instance in which a killer whale has eaten a human, but I know of many instances in which humans have eaten killer whales.

Therefore, on an historical basis, I do not feel that at present there is much chance that any species of greater attainments than ours will want to communicate with us. The dolphins want to communicate only with those people who are willing to live with them on the terms the dolphins set up and that certain kinds of human beings set up. Other types the dolphins drive away. Every year we lose people from the dolphin research program. Usually it is because of fear of the power of these animals and fear of damage, even though in the history of the laboratory no one has yet been injured by the dolphins. Sometimes we think that these people who are lost are projecting their own hostilities outward onto the animals in a very unrealistic fashion. The people who survive either realize that this mechanism is operating and conquer it, or else their nature is such that they do not have hostilities to project.

Appendix 3

Anatomical Contrasts: Anatomy and Physiology
of Tursiops Truncatus

The body of the bottle-nosed dolphin, like that of all of the delphinids, is founded on the general mammalian plan, built into a streamlined container for maximum propulsion efficiency in sea water. There are certain unique features of the anatomy and physiology of this group of animals which may be a help in our understanding of their differences from us. Their anatomy limits their behavior in certain regions, extends it in others, and generates some needs that are different from ours. The description below presents many known anatomical features and also tries to point out where our knowledge is sketchy or lacking. With one or two exceptions (thalamus and pituitary gland) no given portion of these animals' anatomy or physiology has had anything like a thorough scientific job done upon it. As far as possible I have checked most of the previously known gross anatomical facts by my own dissections.

Much of the anatomy and physiology of these animals can be understood in the light of their presumed evolution. They are supposed to have evolved from an early mammalian form or forms that had developed upon the land and later returned to the sea. This evolutionary working hypothesis is of help in understanding various aspects of their anatomy, such as the residual hind limb and pelvic bones, the bristles on the beak of the embryo, etc.

A. SKELETAL SYSTEM

The skeleton is vaguely like ours with fairly drastic modifications in form; hands and legs are lacking. Considered systematically, the following facts are known:

A dolphin's skull has long upper and lower jaws jutting out forward from the base of the skull to form a beak. This beak contains 88 teeth which interlock in the upper and lower jaws. The lower jaw is undershot, with a "chin" sticking out in front of the upper jaw. It is this lower jaw that takes the brunt of the shock when the animal rams a shark or a whale, for example.

The frontal bone lies behind the blowhole and behind the maxillary and premaxillary bones that overlap and thicken the forepart of the skull to about an inch and a half in the midplane behind the blowhole.

Dolphins ram sharks to kill them; during ramming, the lower jaw is locked to the upper through the interdigitating teeth; the ram shock is transmitted from "chin" to upper jaw to "forehead" to skull to spinal column. This thickening of the forepart of the skull distributes the forces over the rest of the large area of the skull. Very powerful muscles fasten onto the skull from the posterior portions of the body, thickening up the neck to the point where it can hardly be seen and filling it out into the streamlined form.

The typical mammalian forelimb is present in these animals but disguised in their flippers. A flipper contains a five-fingered "hand" (or five-toed foot) all bound together. Within the flipper are all the bones of our hand: fingers, wrist, forearm (two bones), and upper arm, with very little mobility at any of the joints. It is only the ball-like shoulder joint that has any great mobility. These

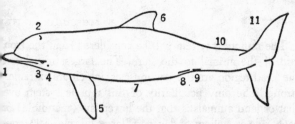

Dolphin, *Tursiops truncatus*, Schematic, Diagram of
External Anatomy (*this animal is body-spiraled
in a twist to show all points*).

(1) Rostrum (beak): upper and lower jaws (88 teeth).
(2) Blowhole: forward of this hole is the "melon," behind
are the skull and the brain. (3) Eye: overlapping visual
fields of two eyes mostly forward and downward; by appropriate movements eye can scan over head, forward, down,
or straight back along flanks. (4) Ear: small hole just posterior to eye, connecting with wax-filled tube to middle
ear. (5) Flipper ("paddle"): contains complete bones of
5-fingered "hand" and "arm"; delicate, easily injured; used
for steering and "palpation." (6) Dorsal Fin: soft tissues
only, no bone. (7) Umbilicus, as in man. (8) Genital opening (slit) for penis and urethra. (9) Anal opening (in female combined with genital slit). (10) Peduncle, connects
body to flukes (11): contains vertebrae ("tail"), muscles,
and tendons; powerful flexion dorsally and ventrally for
swimming, laterally for offensive action. (11) Flukes: mostly
soft tissues, delicate, thins out to rear, easily torn.

animals can rotate, adduct, and abduct the flipper as a
whole unit.

The only vestigial remains of the hind limb and pelvis
are two little bones near the genitalia. The peduncle
running to the flukes consists of articulated vertebrae and
muscles for propulsion. The spinal column, starting at
the skull, ends at the fluke's notch. There are 64 vertebrae: 7 cervical; 13 thoracic; 17 lumbar; no sacral; and
7 caudal.

B. MUSCULAR SYSTEM

The muscular system will be considered from the front
end of the animal to the stern. The largest muscles in
the head region are the jaw muscles, which are extremely
strong. The only peculiarity of this muscle system over
that of land animals is that the lower jaw (mandible) on
each side is hollow and a very large muscle is inserted
well inside the bone, coming out through the aftermost
part of the jaw and fastening to the skull. The temporal
muscle, one of the muscles closing the jaw, is extremely
strong and well developed.

Probably among the most important muscles in the
body are the very small, delicate, and well-differentiated
muscles connected with the respiratory tract and used
for phonation. Starting at the blowhole, there are numerous small muscles around the skin opening used for
opening it; it closes passively.[1] One particularly prominent part of the blowhole looks like a "tongue" made of
skin, which can be moved in the blowhole with great
dexterity. Many of these muscles attach mainly to skin
blubber and other tissues anterior to the blowhole. Just
below the blowhole are air sacs; below the air sacs is the
division of the airway by the nasal bony septum.

These sacs have extremely complex muscle system
running in practically every direction around them; they
are apparently used for the production of sounds under
water. The sacs are also used when the animal wishes
to produce sound in air through the blowhole. Proceeding on down the airway, below the nasal septum there
is a sphincter in the nasopharynx that grips the upper
ends of the laryngeal cartilages and thus maintains the
continuity of the airway across the oropharynx. This ar-

[1] Lawrence, Barbara, and Schevill, William E. The functional
anatomy of the delphinid nose. Bull. of Mus. of Comp. Zool.
(Harvard Col.), 114: 4, Feb. 1956.

rangement separates the air passage from the food passage, most of the time. The larynx itself has innumerable small muscles under extremely fine nervous control, apparently given over to some of the underwater phonation and control of breathing.

The flipper is controlled by the "shoulder" muscles and a small scapula as in other mammals; these muscles give delicate and fine control of the directions of the flippers in order to control the direction of swimming. The flippers seem to act mainly like vanes with which the animal can do everything from barrel rolls to all the usual "flying" maneuvers of an airplane. The flippers in this sense correspond to the control surfaces of an airplane or the diving vanes of a submarine. They are used for propulsion by rowing-like motions in slow body movements such as rising or descending directly up or down with the body horizontal. The flipper from the shoulder out is relatively stiff; in the adult there seem to be no important muscles.

The body muscles, running from the head region, in the back and along the abdomen are extremely powerful and are used to bend the body and to move the head during the peculiar vertical-S-curved kind of swimming movements of these animals. The propulsive muscles proper are in four sets, compartmented by the vertebrae and their processes; each set terminates in tendons that parallel the muscle bundles and pass the fluke joint in large sheaths. There is an upper pair and a lower pair; one set on each side is attached into the flukes top and bottom. These terminal tendons are about a half inch in diameter, are extremely strong, and transmit the pull of the very powerful muscles on the body to the flukes themselves. By alternating the pulls between those on the upper set and those on the lower set the animal makes the fluke oscillate up and down, bending the peduncle at the same time, thus propelling himself through the water with a peculiar oscillating up-and-down movement characteristic of all whales. For right or left turns he can give a differential contraction of the right and the left set, thus "banking" with the flukes. He apparently has completely independent control of each of the four sets of muscles to give any sort of a tilt to the flukes and/or bend to the peduncle. The fluke is hinged at the after-end of the peduncle and these tendons attach just at the "hinge." The last of the caudal vertebrae are in the fluke.

C. INTEGUMENTARY SYSTEM

One of the puzzles about these animals is how they are able to swim at very high speeds—up to about thirty knots—with very small horsepower—about two. Part of the answer seems to lie in the construction of the skin and the underlying structures. The skin is an envelope of extreme smoothness extending over the whole body, and it determines the fairing out of the streamlined form over the blubber base. The skin seems to have at least two main functions: one is to prevent fouling by marine organisms and the second is to cancel out incipient turbulence in the flow of the water by the skin itself.

In line with this maintenance of a streamlined form with minimum resistance to flow, the hair usually found on mammals is not present. However, in the embryo at a certain stage there are six bristles at each side of the snout that are lost before birth.

The color of the skin, like that of most predators in the sea, is dark on the top of the animal and light on the bottom. This is said to offer protection in the sea: an enemy looking at the side would not see any great contrast across the animal. The dark top is brightly lighted and the light bottom is dimly lighted, so the animal tends to blend with the sea, especially in the large amount of scattered light that is usually present. *Tursiops* is usually gray to black on the top and almost pure white and pink on the bottom.

The skin is incredibly smooth and has absolutely no marine growth on it whatsoever; no barnacles, no algae, none of the organisms one finds on man-made devices in the sea. I found one mechanism by which the smoothness is maintained. I enclosed an animal in a white sheet and left him in a tank for a period of two days. When removed, the sheet was full of thin layers of the black skin from the back of the animal and the white skin from the belly. Apparently these animals in their natural state form tremendous quantities of skin, which is gradually shed into the sea, carrying any contaminating organisms with it.

To the touch, the skin is not only smooth but has a rubbery quality. Apparently this rubberiness is given to the skin by the underlying reticulum of collagenous fibers surrounded by oil. It is said that this flexible skin overlying the oil can cause damping of incipient turbulence in the water immediately adjacent to the skin, thus helping in the destruction of turbulent flow and maintaining a low resistance during swimming.[2]

An additional factor in the maintenance of laminar flow over the skin seems to be the muscle layer inside the blubber. These muscles run in every direction and are apparently well supplied with nerve fibers. It may be that there are local reflex pathways between pressure or vibration sensors (end organs) in the skin itself which allow these muscles to deform the shape of the blubber and overlying skin so as to maintain laminar flow. These muscles and circuits add an active process to the passive

[2] Kramer, M. O. *Missiles and Rockets*, Feb. 1, 1960. Essapian, Frank S. Speed-induced skin folds in the bottle-nosed porpoise, *Tursiops truncatus*. Breviora, Mus. of Comp. Zool., **43**, Apr. 7, 1955.

one of the damping action of the oil and flexible overlying skin.

When we were puncturing the skin with needles from a small size up to large ones, say, 3 or 4 millimeters in diameter, we found that the integument has an additional property—it is self-sealing. The blubber below the skin wells up into the hole and seals the opening, stopping the bleeding. This can be seen when an animal has been injured. The immediate response is bleeding and then a white substance comes up and trails out of the opening. I have seen little fish eating away the strings of blubber from around the hole, which is thus left with a short small plug. The skin then grows back, constricting the plug and finally closing off the opening. The skin covers the propulsion and control surfaces, maintaining the smoothness of those also; at the trailing edge of both the flippers and the flukes, the skin is extremely thin. The skin here maintains the perfectly streamlined shape of these objects and is supported only by a collagenous reticulum underneath the skin. Both the flukes and the flippers have a peculiar rubbery consistency and will restore themselves to their usual flatness when distorted by hand. However, they are very easily injured when they come up against any solid object and are easily torn by the lines in a net.

The dorsal fin, the flippers, and the flukes all act as heat exchangers.[3] The dorsal fin itself also acts as a keel about which the animal does his turns. It is one of his sources of lateral resistance during the turn.

D. RESPIRATORY SYSTEM

Like all mammals, these animals breathe air. The primary exit and entrance for the respiratory system is the

[3] Scholander, P. F., and Schevill, William E. Counter-current vascular heat exchange in the fins of whales. J. Applied Physiology, 8: 3, Nov. 1955.

blowhole at the top of the head. We have not seen an animal breathe through his mouth; however, we have accumulated some evidence that they can vent air through the mouth from the lungs and can even make noises through the open mouth in air.

From the blowhole to the lungs is a rather complex airway. The blowhole is just anterior to the forehead of the animal. Anterior to the blowhole is the large so-called "melon," resting on the upper jaw, which contains a reticulum of collagenous fibers filled with oily and fatty substances. Thus the true forehead of the animal is buried behind the blowhole and well aft of the apparent external "forehead." (F. G. Wood has suggested that this melon could act as an acoustic lens.)

The blowhole is the equivalent of our nose moved up anterior to the forehead, and turned upward, with its opening upward. It has a "nasal tongue" within the entrance and its own anterior external lip, over which the animal has a control comparable to that of our oral tongue and lips. Inside the blowhole, below the first two air sacs, are two inner lips above two lower air sacs to control the opening—for instance, to open it extremely wide during expiration and inspiration. The function of the air sacs and lips seems to be (1) to collect the water that enters the open blowhole at the end of an inspiration, (2) to discharge this water when the sphincters below are closed, and (3) to store air and blow it back and forth between them in order to make sounds, either under water or in air.

When the animal wishes to produce sounds in air he can blow air back through the blowhole between the tongue and the outer lip, forming some sounds in the ambient air. He can also open the outer tongue and lip and use the inner lips to produce loud siren-like and Bronx cheerlike noises; apparently he can also form these cavities (sacs) and lips to make whistles.

During inspiration and expiration all of this system is wide open, above the divided airway through the bony septum. The nasopharyngeal sphincter seems to hold on to the larynx during inspiration, though this is not as yet certain. The larynx itself is open with the arytenoid cartilages separated so that there is direct air access through the larynx into the trachea. The arytenoid cartilages of the larynx can be closed across the airway, thus sealing off the trachea from the upper nasal airway. The larynx can also be disengaged from the nasopharynx entirely by the throat muscles connected to the hyoid bone and dropped down in order to discharge water into the mouth from the upper bronchial tree and trachea. Normally, however, the larynx is connected into the nasopharynx for breathing and possibly phonation.

The food passageway goes on each side of the larynx. It is not yet known what happens to the larynx during swallowing; presumably it stays engaged in the nasopharyngeal sphincter.

The arytenoid cartilages are very large and have long contiguous edges that meet in the center of the airway. It may be these edges that produce the little shock waves —the "creaking-door" sound of their sonar as well as the "humanoid" sounds. However, this point is yet to be cleared up.

The trachea is wide and short. A 1⅛-inch-diameter tube is found to fit through the disengaged larynx and into the trachea, sealing it off for artificial respiration with a respirator. On dissection we found the trachea to be only about 2 inches long and immediately it trifurcates (or even quadrifurcates) into the larger bronchi. The bronchi then immediately break up rapidly into the smaller passageways, maintaining the cartilaginous bands all the way from the trachea down through the bronchials. If one cuts across the lung with a knife one finds resistance to cutting because of the large amounts of cartilage contained in the bronchioles. It is found that the alveoli are very large compared to the human ones and are from 1 to 3 millimeters in diameter, quite visible to the naked eye. This whole system seems to be designed for extremely rapid outflow and inflow during the 0.3 seconds of the active part of the breathing cycle: 5 to 10 liters of air flow out and then in during that short interval.

The flow pattern through the respiratory system during the active phase seems extremely turbulent, allowing complete mixing of gases, possibly even in the depths of the alveoli. However, there is plenty of time between active respiratory movements for diffusion exchange of CO_2 and O_2 to take place within the large alveoli. This period of time is approximately 20 seconds under most conditions.

E. ALIMENTARY SYSTEM

These animals are primarily fish eaters as far as can be determined. Their long beaks fitted with sharp teeth are used to catch fish, hold them, and cut rather than chew or grind them. The teeth are conical in shape and eventually become flattened at the ends in a truncated fashion (hence the species name, *truncatus*). Apparently there are no primarily grinding teeth such as our molars.

Watching the catching and swallowing actions of these animals, one can see that they catch a fish crosswise with these teeth and then with the tongue gradually work it around so that the long axis of the fish is parallel to the long axis of the trunk. They then clamp their jaws together, apparently crushing the fish into a cylindrical shape that can then travel by the larynx into the esophagus. During this action the salt water on the fish is squeezed off by the throat sphincter so that the animal does not necessarily swallow the salt water of the sea. One of the mysteries of their alimentation is how they handle the salt water if they do swallow it and where they get their fresh water if they do not use salt water. They may possibly obtain it from fish lymph and the metabolic processes of digestion of the tissues of the fish.

Along the gut track from the esophagus downward they have four compartments reminiscent of the ruminants. The muscular coats of the first enlargement or "stomach" and the esophagus are longitudinal on the outside and presumably run in a spiral or circular fashion on the inside. The apparent function of the first two compartments is to hold the fish and to digest them almost completely, not to form cuds of grass to be regurgitated and chewed as in the ruminants. We saw no whole parts of fish left in the feces but did find regurgitated fish vertebrae and bones in the tank every day. The scales, gills, and all other parts are completely digested.

The natural food is whole fish. Apparently they need an oily fish to prevent avitaminosis. Suitable fish are butterfish, mackerel, blue runner, and thread herring. This is based on the experience of the Marine Studios in feeding their animals over a period of fifteen years. Whether in their natural state they eat plants is not known.

The mouth has a very powerful sphincter before the conjunction with the larynx. It is this sphincter that allows the animal to squeeze the salt water off the fish it is swallowing. The fish, passing the larynx, enters the esophagus and from there passes into stomach Number 1, which is a holding stomach. It is a very large bag with a white and smooth lining.

In the transition from stomach Number 1 to stomach Number 2 there is a constriction in the alimentary tract, which, however, is distensible. It apparently does not have a true sphincter. It appears that regurgitation could be carried out as far down as Number 2 stomach. Stomach Number 2 is rather remarkable in that from the outside it is almost a spherical object that feels as though it is filled with soft rubbery tissues, or even a rubber ball. Upon opening the side wall, it is found that this stomach has red walls that consist mainly of cords and lacunae crisscrossing in every direction around the lumen.

The muscular wall of stomach Number 2 is outside of all the cording and the lacunae. Between stomachs Number 2 and Number 3 there is a small narrow passage 65 millimeters long and about 1 centimeter in diameter with a very well-developed circular muscle coat that apparently can exert a true sphincter action. This little tube seems analogous to the pylorus of the human.

Stomach Number 3 has a fairly smooth wall with pits in it and little gray spots with a general whitish background.

From Number 3 into Number 4 there is a very constricted opening only about 6 millimeters in diameter with a very powerful fibrous tissue coating and muscles in the wall.

Number 4 is filled with yellow bile and possesses a typical fecal odor of the upper intestine and corresponds to our duodenum. Radiating from this small entrance hole and surrounding it is a purplish circle with four radiating purplish lines that go down inside of the wall of this enlargement. It constricts down into the typical small intestine but there is no true sphincter at the exit. The pancreatic and bile ducts enter into Number 4.

The rest of the intestine below enlargement Number 4 to the anus is a small distensible tube with typical mammalian muscle coats. Toward the lower end the tube seems to enlarge slightly. However, there is no cecum and no appendix. There are no pocketings or pouchings of the peritoneum. This whole intestine hangs by a single root from the region of the spinal column in the belly wall. The upper four enlargements ("stomachs") hang mainly from the lower portion of the diaphragm, which is about two feet long.

The intestine is terminated in a very small rectum with weak and thin muscular coats, and by a very small anus, opening into the cloaca in the female and into the anal slit in the male.

The feces come out into the water either in a liquid form or in long threads slightly mixed by the swimming movements. Sometimes the feces float and sometimes they sink. It is not certain what factors go into the various sizes, shapes, colors, and consistency of the feces of these animals.

The whole intestinal tract reflects the freedom of this animal from the necessity of maintaining an upright position under a gravitational field. In other words, this animal is floating in water and all of the growth and evolution of the intestinal tract need only satisfy the functions of collecting, holding and passing, and digesting food rather than maintaining itself against gravity. The necessity of violent movement of the stomachs every so often during the quick expiration-inspiration is shown by the binding of the upper three enlargements to the diaphragm by thickened tissues contained within the parietal and visceral peritoneum.

The blood supply to these four compartments is particularly rich, with rather large arteries running especially to Number 2. The details of the blood supply and the nerve supply to these regions should be further determined by future research; some of the older descriptions in the literature are not too clear.

Apparently most of the breaking up of the ingested food takes place in stomachs 1 and 2. The softening process probably takes place in Number 1, and Number 2 breaks it up into small particles, as well as adding some digestive juices.

F. GENITOURINARY SYSTEM

The kidneys are extremely large and well lobulated

with many independent lobes. There are no notable features of the urinary system, except that this kidney may have the properties of excreting vast quantities of salt taken in by these animals from the sea. However, this is not yet certain and the physiology of this system is yet to be determined. Obviously they urinate directly into the sea and the urine is quickly mixed with the sea water, leaving only a faint trace after the passage of the animal.

In the female the cloacal opening is taken up mainly with the genitalia. The anus takes up only a very small portion, as does the urethra. The clitoris is approximately 2 centimeters long in the opening of the vagina. The vagina is approximately 5 centimeters deep and there is a single cervix. Inside the cervix the uterus divides into a right and a left horn.

The female has a bicornate uterus but bears only one young per gestation in captivity. No twins are yet known. The slit-like vagina lies within the slit of the streamlined lower portion of the external opening which matches the flattened fore-and-aft penis of triangular shape of the male. The baby is born (usually tail first) into the water through this opening.

The male has "voluntary control" of the penis in an almost "switch-blade" fashion, and can be trained to push the penis quickly outward.

The genitalia of the two animals seem to be designed for a very rapid conjunction while swimming under water. Intercourse has been described by Tavolga and Essapian as a very rapid process. During the relatively long mating season in captivity the males are extremely amorous and persistent, especially in warm (84° F.) water.

Gestation takes a year. The young are born under water and pushed to the surface by the mother for their first breath. The baby swims beside the mother for eighteen months. Lactation is a reflex, rapidly squirting process in which the baby nudges or pinches the mammae on each side of the genital opening. The milk is squirted into the baby's mouth in the water. The baby begins to take solid food, including very small fish, before the full weaning process is completed. We do not yet know where he gets his first fish, whether he catches it himself, whether his mother catches it and gives it to him whole, or whether she regurgitates some prepared "soup" from her rumen (stomach Number 1).

G. NERVOUS SYSTEM

The brain of *Tursiops truncatus* in the mature eight-foot adult weighs around 1700 grams—that is, approximately 350 grams more than that of the adult human six-foot male. For many years it was thought that large size did not necessarily mean high quality.[4] Research on specimens had indicated that the nerve cells of the brain seemed to be more sparsely distributed than in the human brain. In 1955, eight of us from five laboratories collected new specimens in first-class shape. We were able to perfuse several animals before the heart stopped beating and thus obtained preserved brain cells in excellent condition. Careful study of the thalami and cortex of these animals showed the cell counts to be quite as dense as in the case of the human.[5]

As a result of these investigations, it is known that the brain of *Tursiops* is a first-class brain, of the same order of complexity as that of the human. There are more folds, fissures, sulci, and gyri in the cortex than in the human

[4] On the basis of specimens collected by Othello Langworthy. Langworthy, O. R. A description of the central nervous system of the porpoise (*Tursiops truncatus*). J. Comp. Neurol., **54**, 437–88, 1932. Tower, Donald B. Structural and functional organization of mammalian cerebral cortex: the correlation of neurone density with brain size. J. Comp. Neuro., **101**, Aug. 1, 1954.

[5] Kruger, L., *loc. cit.*

cortex. There are more total numbers of cells in the cortex. The cortex is thoroughly differentiated as in the case of the human, with all six layers. The thalamus has, as well as the extrinsic nuclei, the same number of intrinsic nuclei, plus one or two extra ones. In other words, all of the so-called association nuclei of the thalamus are present; hence, presumably the dolphin has the same association areas in the cortex as we do. This point is yet to be clarified experimentally. Langworthy traced out the origins of the pyramidal tract. He suggested that the

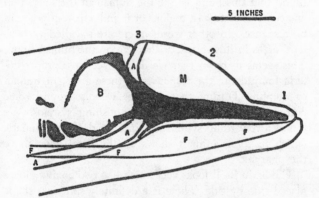

A Diagram of the Head of a Bottle-nosed Dolphin
(*Tursiops truncatus*)

The drawing is to scale from a tracing of the midplane of an anatomical specimen. The labeled areas are as follows: 1. rostrum; 2. external surface of melon (M); 3. blowhole. The skull and bone of upper jaw are cross-hatched. The blowhole is shown closed and the airway (A) as open. The airway passes through the bony nares anterior to the brain (B) in the skull. The food-way (F) starts in the mouth and passes on each side of the airway (A) at the larynx. Two of the flat cervical vertebrae can be seen posterior to the atlas-axis joint of the skull. The spinal canal can be seen in this region. The brain of the animal weighed 1600 grams.

motor cortex should be where the supraorbital cortex is in the human; in other words, in these animals the motor area should be very far forward and up underneath, instead of on top of the brain as in the case of the human.

In 1957 we found this suggestion to be correct. I stimulated (in an unanesthetized animal with implanted electrodes) portions of the motor strip. We found a very highly differentiated "eye-movement" area, as well as a very highly differentiated flipper-control area.

During the studies with implanted electrodes we also found that this brain is like the human in the sense that one can stimulate vast regions of it and apparently obtain no responses. In other words, there are so-called vast "silent" areas in this cortex, as there are in the human brain. This seems to mean that we do not yet have proper criteria for judging the responses of these areas, in human or dolphin. During these studies we also found some portions of the rewarding and punishing systems. We found a rewarding system near the head of the caudate, which in these animals shows on the basal floor above the pharynx.

The brain itself looks very much like two boxing gloves placed side by side. There is a definitely spherical shape to it—far more than in that of the human. It has large temporal lobes. The occipital lobes are extremely large. If one wishes to call everything from the temporal lobe to the motor strip "parietal" lobe, the parietal lobe is as large as our parietal plus our frontal lobes. The cerebellum is very large and has been described in great detail by Langworthy; Jansen has studied it in detail in other cetacean species.

Further explorations of the brains in unanesthetized animals are needed for complete understanding of these large and magnificent structures.

One remarkable feature of the odontocetes (as opposed to the human and the mysticetes) is the lack of an olfactory bulb. When one removes the brain from *Tursiops truncatus* no large olfactory tract or bulb is visible. This does not mean that there are not olfactory fibers: some may have been missed because of their small size. This matter should be explored in greater detail, and possible olfactory endings searched for in the rather complex airway.

Apparently these animals have a very well-developed sense of taste. Some of their behavior (with respect to the fish that they eat and the water in which they swim) seems to be "tasting maneuvers" rather than anything else. The sense of taste may be the one that leads them to fish and allows them to follow their own species by detecting fecal and urinary traces in the water. However, detailed anatomy has not yet been done upon the taste end-organs. Presumably they may be in the rather rigid lips and lining the forepart of the mouth and tongue. Every so often the animals seem to open their mouths slightly to allow the water to flow through the mouth. The thin fore and lateral edges of the tongue are richly supplied with papillae presumably carrying taste sense organs.

The papillae on the forward edge of the tongue are very prominent and are 2 to 3 millimeters long and 2 to 3 millimeters across. Apparently the tongue can be pushed up close to the teeth with the mouth barely open to allow salt water to flow by it, so the animal can taste it as it passes through, and thus trail one another or special fish. The posterior portion of the tongue has prominent crypts in it and a few circumvallate papillae are visible. In general, the tongue has very powerful musculature in the posterior two-thirds. The forward third is very thin and flexible. Posterior to the tongue is the mouth sphincter, which apparently clears the salt water off the fish as it is being swallowed. Looking into the open mouth of a live animal, this sphincter is seen closed down behind the tongue. Crypts are visible on the mucosa over the sphincter.

The vision of these animals is truly remarkable. They can see quite as well in air as they can in water. In the Marineland training program they can catch a small football as they back off from the trainer with both their eyes out of water and jump up into the air to catch the ball. From the water they can sight and line up on a target sixteen feet out of the water to which they will jump; they take off from the water in precisely the correct place in order to catch this object. At Seaquarium they ride on their flukes with the rest of the body out of water, backward, backing away fifty to sixty feet at six or more knots to catch fish in air.

It is still a mystery as to how their vision can be so remarkable, both in water and in air. There seem to be at least two novel possible mechanisms. The extreme degree of accommodation may be achieved by means of a peculiarly shaped cornea: it may be shaped differently in the center than it is at the edges. The iris definitely has a curtain which in bright light causes the eye to show a U-shaped slit. The cornea over this U-shaped slit is apparently a different shape than it is in the center. It would be this U-shape that they would use in air. In the center, the curtain of the iris in water would be raised as the light intensity is reduced. The center of the cornea would focus in water on the same fovea.

The eyeball is a nearly spherical container made of "cartilage" mainly. The orbit is bony only in the top of the eye. The back of the eye socket is the upper ramus of the lower jaw. The lower portion of the orbit is formed by a cord going from anterior to posterior attached to the skull. The eye itself has closable lids, a brownish iris and white sclera, and one can see the yellow-green reflex, like that of a cat, when shining a light into the eye at night. The iris has a little brown curtain which in bright lighting conditions is lowered, bearing only a U-shaped slit for the entrance-pupil. The cornea may be a very complex water-containing bag. The eyeball is large, about two inches in diameter.

The hard cartilagenoid structure over the back of the eyeball allows the animal to turn the eye outward in order to look upward, or forward, or downward. The position of rest is looking somewhat laterally and downward.

The lens is a sphere, 1 centimeter in diameter, and lies immediately behind the iris. The eyeball is almost spherical and has a shell of "cartilage" except at the iris-corneal region. By muscular control the cornea could be made to bulge by squeezing the free edge of the cartilage shell, and to flatten by relaxing this edge; in air they may squeeze the edge and in water relax it in order to focus the eye in the second media.

The ear under water is extremely good. Hearing ranges from about 400 cycles per second to 200 kilocycles per second.[6] The external auditory opening is very small, in the outer skin, posterior to the eye, and is visible as a little dimple and minute hole in the skin. There is a tube going from here down to the tympanum. However, it is only a small-diameter tube, usually plugged up, and may have no function except water-pressure equalization. Sound is transmitted extremely well to the tympanum through the flesh of the body from the water. The tympanum is rather large and there is a eustachian tube for pressure equalization with the respiratory system.

The cochlea is remarkable in that there is one large

[6] Schevill, William E., and Lawrence, Barbara, *loc. cit.*

nerve fiber for each end-organ,[7] as opposed to several
end-organs per nerve fiber in humans. The cochlea is
about the same size as the human. However, the acoustic
nerve is much larger, about a quarter inch in diameter,
packed with large fibers, presumably of high conduction velocity. The cochlea is in a separate bone called
the bulla, which is separate from the skull. The bulla has
a flat hinge and several muscles so that it can be rotated
relative to the skull. The dolphin may rock it back and
forth in order to scan stereophonically the echoes coming back from clicks he emits when using his sonar.
Investigations of this sonar show it to be extremely exact
and every time the animal is forced to use it in muddy
or dark water there is a concomitant creaking-door
sound as he swims through the water.[8]

The end-organs of the skin have yet to be studied.
Presumably there are very sensitive pressure and vibration receptors in the skin for the detection of the waver-
ing of streamlines in the flow stage before the development of turbulence. Such end-organs would be the
sensors for the feedback mechanisms to the blubber
muscles to maintain skin form so as to abolish the
incipient turbulent flow.

There are probably also other special senses to be
found in these animals, as they have not yet been thoroughly explored histologically.

[7] Grant Rasmussen, personal communication.
[8] Schevill, W., Kellogg, W., Norris, K., *loc. cit.*

Appendix 4

Intellect, Intelligence, Language and the Brain

CLASSES OF INTELLIGENCE AND OF INTELLECTUAL CAPACITY

First I shall set up a scale, very rough, very provisional, with large jumps in it—a spectrum for a gross categorization of intelligence and intellectual capacity. This spectrum uses known animals for comparison and gives us a scale against which we can provisionally compare any alien species we may encounter. In terms of known variables, we may be able to place an alien between two known animals or families of known animals, in case we cannot place the alien on more accurately quantitative scales.

Let us make a distinction between intellectual capacity and intelligence. For purposes of discussion I am defining intellectual capacity as *the potential or realized ability to develop or use a language in the complex human sense of that term.* I am not defining language in terms of the ants or the bees of Von Friesch or the *signaling* of other kinds of animals, such as the birds and the fish of Tinbergen and of Lorenz. I am using language in the usual extremely complicated sense of a *human* language.

I agree with Jacques Barzun's book *The House of*

Intellect, in which he makes extremely exact differentiations between the words *intelligence* and *intellect.* Intellect is a distinctively human characteristic in so far as we know it to date in the scientific and humanistic sphere. The word *intelligence* can be applied to lower animals at levels lower than that of human intelligence. Intellect is a phenomena appearing steplike only at an intelligence brain level comparable to that of the normal human being possessing a full language. In this sense a small human child does not have intellect as yet, according to Barzun; he does not yet possess the language and the traditions that this language will carry with it into the brain of the small child during the educational process. Intellect in this sense means an intelligent individual who has acquired or is acquiring a large share of the complex knowledge of the previous generations of his particular species through the medium of a language.

Alien intellectual capacity is only *detectable* in those cases in which at least one human individual can detect and learn the alien language or languages and/or at least one individual of the alien species can detect and learn a human language at or above the most primitive level of use and understanding. In other words, as yet *we have no measure of intellectual capacity of another nonhuman species. We shall not have such a measure until we can communicate with individuals of that species through the medium of some sort of complex language,* either a vocal language, a written language, or a language in some other form of which we may not yet be aware. In this sense, then, intellectual capacity cannot be measured until there can be an exchange of ideas and all of the other things which we conceive as so characteristically human at the present time. In our present state of ignorance only a human being is said to have intellectual capacity. This does not mean that at some future date humans may not give some other species the human distinction of having intellectual capacity. It merely means that to date no such measurement has been available for any other species than the human.

We can arbitrarily divide all of the known animals in a rough categorical fashion in the form of a spectrum starting near zero intelligence, moving up through the intelligence spectrum and suddenly coming upon an intellect "first level," as it were, and moving into the more complicated possibilities.

Let us start with the lowest possible level of intelligence, in terms of our present knowledge, that of a single cell. Let us call this the first level of intelligence. If there can be such a thing, this would be the level of intelligence of viruses, bacteria, and protozoons such as the amoeba and the paramecium.[1] We probably should also include at or near this particular level the sponges, which are loose social organizations of protozoons, the Metazoa.

At the next level, which I arbitrarily call level 2, we should place the simpler of the invertebrates and practically all of the insects. I arbitrarily carry this level all the way up through the sharks. It is possible that there should be many, many more levels between our lowest level and the shark—that is, from virus to shark. For example, we know the octopus is an extremely intelligent animal compared to most of the other creatures of the sea that surround him. In so far as science has anything to say about it today, the octopus is probably the genius of level 2.[2]

Level 3 is the intelligence level of the birds and the reptiles and possibly some of the fishes. Admittedly this

[1] Of course there may be many hundreds of levels between the intelligence of a virus and that of a paramecium. See H. S. Jennings, *Genetics of the Protozoa.*

[2] See the work of J. Z. Young, Prof. of Anatomy, University College, London, England.

is a large wastebasket covering our ignorance of the
distinctions between animals at a given size of nervous
system. It may be that after a more thorough investigation
of the shark, the octopus, various of the birds, reptiles,
and fishes, we shall be able to make distinctions between
them which will make these categories more numerous
and more exact. It is only in recent years that some of
these factors have begun to be thoroughly investigated.[3]

Level 4 is the low mammal level. This is a bare beginning of the warm-blooded (and hence closer to us)
animal intelligences. Probably this level also must be sub-
divided into hundreds of smaller divisions: from the
smallest known mammal, the shrew, all the way through
the largest monkeys, not including the anthropoid apes.
In thinking about this level, it can be seen that already
we consider the monkey much closer to us in terms of
"alienness" than, for example, a giant squid of the sea.
It is at about this level that we begin to have troubles:
we usually stop "zoomorphizing" and shift to "anthropomorphizing." The little monkeys begin to resemble
little human beings in external appearance and the presence of the hand makes us begin to empathize more with
them than with the other animals.

On level 5 we begin to identify even more strongly
with the animals in question. Level 5 is that of anthro-
poid-ape intelligence. They are, as it were, a special class
of "super-animal." Here we have the orangutan, the
chimpanzee, and the gorilla. Many of these animals
"ape" human beings so closely that many people feel they
are almost human. This is why they are called *anthropoid*
apes and why we have the term "aping." However, this
level is far below that of the human being in terms of

[3] Tinbergen, N. *The Study of Instinct* (Oxford University
Press, London, 1951). Lanyon, W. E., and Tavolga, W. N.,
Animal Sounds and Communication, 1960. Am. Inst. of Biol. Sci.,
Washington, D.C. (Pub. No. 7).

intelligence, and there is no intellect. The apes are below the threshold for the first level of intellect, as far as can be made out.

Kathy and Keith Hayes tested the hypothesis that these animals could be taught English, by taking a chimpanzee, Vicki, into their home and raising her as if she were a human child for a period of two years. Vicki has been presented in a book called *The Ape in Our House* by the Hayeses. In an all too brief summary we can say that on the receiving side Vicki had a very large vocabulary in English but on the transmitting side she was limited to "Mama," "Papa," "cup," and "up," delivered in an explosive fashion.

This degree of performance we do not call intellectual. It shows a high order of animal intelligence but not of intellect. Between this level and a fully developed normal adult human being with a complex language, there is a vast gap unfilled by any known animal. It is as if once the early human beings learned language they killed off all members of the next lower level, at least those that were on land.

The next level I number 6 on the intelligence scale and 1 on the intellect capacity scale. In searching for a name for this level, I chose "proto-humanoid" as meaning "barely human," or extremely primitive humanlike. This is the beginning of the detection threshold for intellectual capacity.

Among individuals born to human beings there are probably some members of this class, such as low-grade morons, whose intellectual capacity is just detectable because they can learn only a small vocabulary on both the transmitting and receiving sides of a human language. They have enough language so they do not have to be institutionalized and controlled like the imbeciles and the idiots, who are below the threshold for intellectual capacity.

Proto-humanoid individuals may have existed and paralleled their development with that of man or may be direct progenitors of the early races of man. The Australopithecines and Pithecanthropus may have belonged to this level. Paranthropus and Sinanthropus may have belonged to the next level (7). It is at this level 6, the proto-humanoid one, that it is hypothesized that the brain has become just large enough so that a language is possible and so that the fine control of the necessary musculature for vocal and written expression can be developed within the nervous system; the fluid patterns of movement necessary for creation of speech and writing appear.

Intelligence level 7 I call humanoid. This is intellectual level number 2. This category is placed between the bare beginnings of a humanlike language and a fully developed human language. This level is a necessary one because we know that there are human tribes who are not quite as complex in their language ability as the fully developed civilized man. This may be an extra step which ultimately can be eliminated; these individuals are definitely above the threshold of detection of intellectual capacity.

The humanoid peoples, the primitive human tribe level, have extremely complex traditions and the beginnings of written languages. They pass on their knowledge from one generation to another by long legendary monologues memorized by one individual who passes them on from previous older individuals. They do not depend upon books or written materials for their records. Practically all of their culture is learned by one individual from previous ones and enforced by taboos and similar rules passed on from one generation to the next. There are artifacts which carry over from one generation to the next but no libraries or other such forms of externally recorded data. Legends, myths, and facts are tied only to external realities and to hypothesized spirits, gods, etc. The level of explanation is that of sorcery, magic, and similar devices which civilized man attempts to eradicate and forget.[4] These are strictly pragmatic and superstitious humans who have yet to reach the level of civilized man. Associating with such peoples, one feels them, for example, to be far more alien than a civilized man from another culture which possesses libraries and other human cultural artifacts like ours.

The next level I call 8 on the intelligence scale and 3 on the intellectual level. I call it "iso-human." This is the level of civilized man with all its complexities of social institutions, sciences, national relations, international relations, etc. This is the level at which this book is being written. We all know that within this level there are thousands more distinguishable levels; this is the level on which we operate daily, the intellectual level at which we set our status and all of the matters taken up so avidly by social scientists, politicians, educators, and the other specialists and nonspecialists within the civilized cultures. Here is where the large brain of the human reaches its maximum flowering, producing works of art, thermonuclear bombs, medical control of disease, etc. This is the level of human compassion well expressed, as well as human destructiveness thoroughly organized.

Above level 8 we should place at least one more level, level 9 in terms of intelligence and level 4 in terms of intellectual capacity. The obvious term for this level should be "supra-human," unspecified. Who are we who are so human to say who or what occurs on the next level or even what its characteristics and properties should be? Here we are in the position of the chimpanzee trying

[4] See Frazer, Sir James George, *The Golden Bough*, for example.

to specify what a human being is like. We can ask questions here and cannot obtain answers, as yet.

Many human beings before us have attempted to answer what is on this level; some of the most influential books in the world are devoted to giving us a picture of what men have thought should be and is on this level above ours. However, to date, the science of this level is entirely lacking. Such a lack may be a result of the non-existence of such beings or of a convenient definition that they cannot exist and a refusal to look at the proper kinds of evidence.

Are there terrestrial members of the fourth intellectual level? It was once thought that we could answer this with a secure "no" in spite of human wishes to the contrary. Science in its infancy was quite dogmatic in stating that there were no such individuals on the earth. There was an intellectual revolt against accepting ideas of God, or gods, after the intense preoccupation of all of pre-civilized and civilized man with such ideas for many centuries. Science, in order to survive as science, had to deny and categorize as fantasy all of the religious literature. At the present date about all we can do is say we do not know. We do not have direct experience with those of level 4 such as we have with other human beings and with animals below the level of the human being. We have no experience with any supra-human being.

It may be possible that there are types of experience with supra-human beings which are being denied access in scientific circles. Such experiences may be so alien to the present methods of science that at the present time there is no way of studying such communications by our known scientific methods.

Much science fiction has been written about contacts at this level. See, for example, *The Black Cloud* by Fred Hoyle. Hoyle, as an astronomer, takes an extremely alien supra-human intelligence and intellect and creates credible fiction based upon modern astronomy and modern physics. His huge "intelligent cloud" is completely outside terrestrial biology. So far as we know, all living matter on the earth depends for most of its operation upon being within a liquid medium. Hoyle's being exists in a dust cloud in physical fields in outer space instead of in water.

Thus we can develop grossly at least nine levels of intelligence and four levels of intellect, ranging in each case from the most primitive to the most complex in a rather arbitrary fashion, and we link intellect to certain kinds of intelligence. This may or may not be proper to do once the experimental evidence is in. This whole spectrum and all of these categories should not be taken too seriously. They are convenient boxes in which to place information rather than functioning living categories based on secured experiments.

The categories I have devised are convenient for filing information. They crudely organize knowledge for purposes of discussion. In the face of our present-day ignorance about matters of intellect and intelligence on a scientific basis, it is well to accept any such categorizing with a grain of salt. It may be proper to neglect the words "intellect" and "intelligence" completely and organize the same knowledge on another set of co-ordinates, such as the presence or absence of provable two-way language on a highly empirical basis.

EXPERIMENTAL DEFINITIONS FOR INTELLECTUAL CAPACITY

We can set up certain formal prerequisites for determining whether known biological organisms have an intelligence level high enough to include intellectual capacity. Then we can define intellectual capacity in pragmatic and experimental fashion.

So far as is known at the present day, detectable intellectual capacity has the following prerequisites connected with the known biology:

(1) A brain (or its equivalent) above the threshold of size and complexity of structure for the development of language: a big brain.

(2) Access channels to and from the environment suitable for humans to detect and use.

(3) Sufficient time for learning and storage of the contents of category 4 below.

(4) Effective exposure to a language and language-provoking experiences.

(5) Proper living conditions for the well-being of the individual.

Let us discuss each of these items in detail in the above order.

(1) What do we mean by a big brain? One above the language threshold. So far as we can determine in humans, a brain must be of approximately 1000 grams or more in order to have the capacity to learn a human language. Furthermore, this brain must be complex. It must contain between 5 and 10 billion neurons and their 100 billion satellite glial cells or their equivalent. These neurons must be interconnected with a high degree of connectivity and able to form new connections rapidly within the brain's substance. (Let me hasten to add that this is a viewpoint with which all of my scientific colleagues do not necessarily agree.) Here I am presenting the view that those who speak are those who are capable of learning language. Those who do not speak and cannot learn to speak are those without language. We know that certain portions of our brain ultimately turn out to be essential for language. These essential portions are not very large. However, we still must have a fantastically large storage capacity, which means an extremely large number of neurons (and glial cells) as far as can

be determined. Modern human language contains an enormous complexity of structure and of total numbers of memorized forms within it. Scientific linguistic analyses of modern languages are just being completed and show what a vastly complex and fantastically great achievement a human language is.

(2) The access channels to and from the brain, between the environment and the brain, suitable for humans to detect and use, must be of sufficient numbers and effective kinds of controllable inputs and outputs. When we examine closely our ears, for example, designed for hearing in air, we find an extremely complex set of end-organs, very large in number, which can analyze very well the sounds impinging upon the ear. When we look at the opposite end of the communication system in our bodies, the instruments of phonation, we find that they are also extremely complex. The acquisition of the ability to control the muscles of phonation is an achievement probably far beyond that of, say, building the Empire State Building, in terms of man's rise from the level of the lower animals.

(3) Our third requirement, sufficient time for learning and storing of experiences, is obvious. It takes a human child many years to acquire the necessary experience to become a human being. We start out at a very low "animal" level, quickly come up through the proto-humanoid level at a rather young age, and then spend many years acquiring the necessary language facility and data to use that language to communicate with human beings of equal (and lesser and greater) attainments.

(4) If a human being is isolated from his kind he lacks the effective exposure to language and language-provoking experiences and never does learn to speak. To learn to speak, one must be exposed to effective language experiences in an environment presenting simultaneously several things: (a) language packets in the proper media,

(b) personal rewards and personal punishments contingent on the proper use of these packets, (c) examples of other similar individuals exchanging rewards and punishments with proper accompanying packets. A child must be rewarded for making attempts to speak so that he will repeat the experiments of speaking. In a way, he must be "punished" for not speaking: for instance, by not receiving the rewards he could demand if he spoke. This reward-and-punishment view of the acquisition of any habit is now demonstrable in scientific laboratories. (Of course, there are additional factors, some of which I am purposely neglecting to keep the discussion under control and some of which are not yet in scientific laboratories, although we meet them in everyday life.)

(5) Obviously a young human being or other young animal with the previous prerequisites for intellect needs proper living conditions for well-being. As can be shown even with civilized man, if he is put in conditions on the very edge of survival he is so busy with survival necessities that there is relatively little chance of acquiring additional language (except on a very primitive level). All of the complexities in intellectual attainments in our civilization presume the conditions for well-being and for education. Education can be intellectual in the proper sense of the term only when excess energy, well above survival conditions, is available.

It is my purpose to explore in the next section how we can use the above kind of organization of our knowledge to recognize, deal with, and test other alien (terrestrial or nonterrestrial) individuals for intelligence and intellectual capacity.

DETECTION OF ALIEN INTELLECTUAL CAPACITY

In approaching any alien species, we should first ask ourselves whether the individual we are investigating or propose to investigate has (1) a large enough brain of sufficient complexity to be above what we consider to be the language-threshold level and (2) sufficient numbers and control of access channels to and from this brain operating in media that we can manipulate in a communicating fashion. If it does have each of these proper biological basic prerequisites, we can then ask the following questions:

(A) Does this species have a language of its own, a native language?

(B) Can any individuals of this species learn our language?

(C) Can they teach it to their young?

In exploring the first question, we can propose many kinds of experiments. Crucial experiments are yet to be designed, but probably the best results will be obtained by continuous contact between qualified humans and several individuals of the alien species. In my experience the best bet seems to be as follows: first we record samples of the exchange between two isolated individuals, each in solitude. We record the exchanges of pairs of captive individuals on tape and have a way of identifying which individual emitted what. We also record their movement simultaneously on film. We do both over periods of many weeks. At the same time we force one to help the other remotely, allowing each to use only "verbal" directions, bilaterally.

On these records we do statistical studies somewhat like those that are done to break a code or an unknown human language. We do statistical distributions in rank order for various kinds of message packets; we analyze and try to find the basic units; we do precedence studies of who did and said what first, and what the results were in terms of subsequent action and subsequent productions of packets. We do auto- and cross-correlations and various other kinds of analyses of the sounds, if it is sounds that they are emitting.

In the course of such studies one of the individuals is submitted to stressful conditions and the exchanges and actions that take place between them in consequence of the stress are recorded. We can then do a psychophysiological analysis to develop criteria to separate the emotionally expressive built-in packet from those that are more intellectual and intelligent. We find those signals that correspond to fear, anger, sexual needs, hunger, the need for release from isolation, and so on. By analysis of their violent, quick behavior, we obtain an idea of the "command" language as opposed to the "emotionally expressive" one. We can also begin to have a toehold on other primitive levels within the possible language.

By proper feedback techniques under proper conditions, we can send portions of the recordings back to the individuals and see how this modifies their behavior. I say "proper conditions" because if one sends them back under improper conditions an intelligent animal quickly realizes that he is being fooled—that the recording is not being emitted by a living being in a real situation. If we merely put a loudspeaker in the situation, for example, and play back a tape-recording, an intelligent animal can be fooled briefly and only once. If the loudspeaker emits the distress call for a given species, the other animals come to the rescue of the loudspeaker once and after that, when the distress call issues from the speaker, they do not respond. (Aesop's wolf story immortalized this view.) It is as if they said, "Well, that's just that box on the wall, forget it." The proper conditions seem to be those in which the emission in the appropriate fashion has a consequence to the animals. In other words, if they emit a hunger call and a hunger call comes out of the box on the wall and they again emit the hunger call and then we give them food, the box on the wall acquires some sort of meaning to them in a fundamental sense. Proper feedback systems and sequences are currently being worked out for the case of the dolphins. We are also beginning to analyze "delphinese" as a possible language in this way.

Experiments and possibilities in trying to answer question (B) are the most exciting. Can the alien species learn our language and teach it to their young? If they can learn even a very primitive version of one of our languages, the attainment will be far beyond that of any known animal other than man. This will immediately raise them to the proto-humanoid, if not the humanoid, level—that is, it will prove they *have* an intellectual capacity. This is the most crucial and difficult test for intellect and for high order of intelligence that we can devise at the present time. We should not underestimate the greatness of the achievement of the human race in devising languages.

If another species learns our language it will be an equally great achievement for them. Somehow we do not seem to feel that it would be as great an achievement for us to learn the alien's language as for them to learn ours. However, it would be a great achievement for us to learn a completely nonhuman language. If, for example, we take the sounds produced by dolphins as a possible prototype alien language, it may be extremely difficult for us to learn it: it is a series of short complex whistles. It may not even have words as we know them within its structure, but our latest records make this seem improbable.

There can be no more convincing evidence of the level of attainment of a given animal than to have him learn a human language and speak it with human beings. If we find an animal which has the first two prerequisites, what additional conditions are necessary if he is to learn our language, assuming his *brain capacity* is equal to that of modern man—that is, that he is above the language threshold in brain size and complexity and has the proper *access channels* to and from his brain with the environment? I said in the previous section, the individual must have *sufficient time* for learning and storage of the language elements. He must also have *effective exposures* to language and language-provoking experiences. He must have the *proper living conditions* for his own well-being, whatever his particular biology may require. We will not have a problem in regard to those aliens which need conditions similar to ours; we will have a problem with those which have dissimilar requirements for survival. Before we can create conditions for the well-being of those individuals we must find the best conditions for their health and relative contentment.

We define language as a very large (10,000 to 100,000) set of primitive message packets which are exchangeable between many individuals of a group of the same species, race, or tribe. This set of packets is taught to the young of that group and contains important meanings connected with description and prediction of social and personal necessities (at the very lowest level of complexity).

We must answer lots of additional questions about the alien's capacities, actual or potential. On a very primitive level, is he capable of mimicking our speech, for example, or our writing? If so, this gives us at least a toehold on the possibility of teaching the particular individual our language. (The ability of very young humans to mimic vocally seems to be one of their basic characteristics.) Once he has mimicked, is he capable of using some of the words he has mimicked as demands for necessities: for food, a change of temperature, etc.? We would then go on to investigate his ability to use and make long-lasting connections between given vocalizations and other events, between other processes and between his feelings, whether vocal or not vocal. We would attempt to investigate his ability to abstract and generalize uses of certain words such as connectives and other vocal "cements." And we would investigate his ability to play games, do various kinds of arithmetical operations, algebra, geometry, etc.

There are some further matters that we should investigate in our attempts to discover whether another species has or has not a language.

(1) We should find out what the physical medium of exchange is. For example, is it sound in water, electromagnetic waves, or something else? We know that whales and dolphins emit complex patterns of sound in water; is water being used as a physical medium of exchange?

(2) Once we have determined that there is a sufficiently complex series of patterns going on, what is the formal structure in the physical sense of this exchange? Is the animal using amplitude modulation, frequency modulation, pulse-time code modulation, some other form of packet, counting, etc.?

(3) What are the basic linguistic units and meaning modulations? In our language we have such things as "words," "grammar," "declensions," and "analogues." The alien's language may have other things than words as we know them. Instead of breaking up the communication in the short "word burst" the way we do, they may slide up and down a frequency scale, for example.

(4) What is the logical structure—are they using a two-valued logic or multivalued logic?

(5) What is the semantic reference structure? What kinds of things, events, processes, feelings, etc., are exchangeable within the language?

Surprisingly enough, it may turn out that it is scientifically easier to collect data on all of these levels than it is to proceed in a slavishly systematic fashion from the simplest possible level—that is, from the physical medium of exchange to the most complex level, the semantic reference structure. The above descriptions and divisions are only a crude map to the kinds of analysis, showing the different levels and complexities on which the questions are asked and answers sought.

We must remember that it is not necessary for an alien to have developed a language of his own in order to learn ours. There may be an unused potential capacity to learn a language. This seems extremely unlikely but is a possibility that must not be neglected, especially with young aliens.

We could pursue two kinds of investigation simultaneously: probing for the existence of a native, already-developed language, and trying to teach the alien one of our languages. One pursuit does not rule out the other. He may have a native language but be totally incapable of learning ours.

In our work on the dolphins, we are pursuing both lines of research. We are trying to interest linguists in analyzing the sound productions of the dolphins for the possible existence of "delphinese"; meanwhile, we are pursuing our own attempts to teach the dolphins a primitive version of English.

BRAIN SIZE AND LANGUAGE FUNCTION

I stated above that our working hypothesis is that until a brain reaches a certain size, language as it is known by normal human beings is not possible. Conversely, if a brain is above a certain size, then it has the capability to learn a language. Previously we discussed concomitant requirements such as exposure to language-provoking situations and a sufficient period of time for learning to take place. This section will be devoted exclusively to the question of brain size and the appearance of language at a critical minimum brain size. Table I shows the brain weights of the nonspeaking animals, mouse through chimpanzee; Table II shows the brain weights of the young human at various ages related to anthropoids and presumed human forebears with unknown speech-capabilities.

Our best and most secure evidence comes from a study of human children. Table III gives the quantitative data relating brain size to age of the average normal child. Correlated with this are those ages and hence brain sizes at which language develops in its full-blown human fashion (see also Table VI below).

Understandable speech begins with a brain mass of about 1000 grams at an age of about eighteen months. This is a brain mass very much larger than any of the anthropoid apes have ever achieved (Table II). It is also a brain mass at the upper level achieved by Peking man and very much larger than that of Pithecanthropus and the Australopithecines (Table II). Neanderthal man and Cro-Magnon man were the first to achieve this critical size so far as we know (Table III).

Mimicry of the vocalizations of adults is well under way at a brain size of approximately 400 to 900 grams —that is, from a few weeks of age to several months (Table II). The beginnings of speech appear at 1000 grams of brain at eighteen months of age (Table III). It has been found recently that it is possible at 1100

Table I: Absolute Weight of Brain: Small Animals

Grams of Brain	Adult Animal
0.4	mouse
1.6	rat
4.8	guinea pig
9.3	rabbit
31.0	cat
65.0	dog
88.5	monkey (M.r.)
350.0	chimpanzee & beef

(after Tower's figures)

Table II: Absolute Weight of Brain: Animals, Human and Prehuman

Grams of Brain	Human, Age in Months	Animal	Prehumans
350		chimpanzee	Australo-pithecines
450	1	gorilla	
550	3		
650	4		Pithecanthropus
750	6		
900	12		Pekiniensis (fire)
950	14		

Table III: Absolute Weight of Brain: Early Man, Modern Man, and Speech

Grams of Brain	Human Age	Early Men	Speech
950	14 mo.	Neanderthal	?
1000	18 mo.		(understandable)
1200	36 mo.	Cro-Magnon	(typing, Moore)
1250	4 yrs.		(mastery intern. voices, Erikson)
1400	10 yrs.		
1450	17 yrs.		(average max. weight)
1800	?		(max. found for modern man)

Table IV: Absolute Weight of Brain: Man and Dolphin (*Tursiops truncatus*)

Grams of Brain	Age of Man	Age of Dolphin	Length of Tursiops Truncatus
1200	41 mo.	23 mo.	6 ft. 6 in.
1350	78 mo.	28 mo.	7 ft. 1 in.
1450	17 yrs.	8 yrs.	7 ft. 8 in.
1600		10 yrs.	7 ft. 10 in.
1700		?	8 ft. 6 in.

grams of brain (at approximately thirty months of age) to teach the child typing with an electric typewriter by a special method.[5]

As the brain grows in size and as the child ages, immersed in many daily language-requiring situations, both the brain and the language increase in complexity (Table VI). The usual human reaches 1400 grams at around ten to seventeen years of age (Table III). The levels of complexities of thinking at that time have increased tremendously over that of the beginnings of speech. The numbers of connections established are so large that they are uncountable. At the present time we do not know whether this increase of mass of brain is due merely to new connections growing throughout its mass and connecting the already existing cells, or whether new cells (glial and/or neuronal) are actually formed, or both. At one time it was said that the number of cells of the brain at birth were fixed and never increased; the increased mass is then said to be that of fiber growth. At the present time there is no secure way of choosing between these alternatives.

Empirically we can correlate brain mass with language in man in a gross way. We can do this not only in the case of the normally developing human but in those humans who fail to reach the critical level of 1000 grams. In them language either remains extremely primitive or does not appear at all.[6] Imbeciles, idiots, and very low-grade morons belong in this group. Apparently this is true even in those cases in which there are complete nervous mechanisms for motor control and for hearing but there is a deficiency in the total mass of cerebral

---

[5] Moore, O. K., *loc. cit.*

[6] For specific examples of exchanges at the level of 350 grams with thirty years' experience, see Ireland, W. W., *Mental Affections of Children* (J. & A. Churchill, London, 1900).

Table V: The Largest Known Adult Brains (best* weights)

Refs.	W, Weight in Grams	L, Body Length	Species	W/L	Common Name	Weight Ratio
Vierordt, H.[1] 1890	1450 (av.) (1250)	5'9"	Homo sapiens	256 (220)	man	1.00 (1.00)
Lilly, etc.[2] 1958	1700°	8'6"	Tursiops truncatus	200	bottle-nosed dolphin	1.17 (1.42)
Tower[3] 1954	6075	(?)	Proboscidae (species unspec.)	(?)	elephant	4.19 (4.86)
Jansen[4] 1952	7200°	54'	Balaenoptera physalus	133	fin whale	4.97 (5.76)
Kojima[5] 1951	9200°	49'	Physeter catadon	188	sperm whale	6.34 (7.36)

* Freshly removed in each case so marked: such selected individual weights are in line with weights of other individuals. Selected individuals in any one species could be even larger: Cuvier said to have 1800 gram brain, for example.

[1] Vierordt, H. Das Massenwachsthum der Korperorgane des Menschen. *Arch. f. Anat. u. Physiol. Anat.* s62 (1890).

[2] Lilly, J. C. *Am. J. Psychiatry*, Dec. 1958.

cortex: in the storage capacity and in relational abilities within the mental sphere.

As I stated in Chapter 1, very few earth animals other than man achieve this critical brain size of 1000 grams. The Cetacea in general all seem to achieve this, as do the elephants. The elephant's adult brain varies from 4000 grams to 6000 grams (Table V). Apparently the Proboscidea are yet to be studied from the viewpoint presented in this book. Some scientific study of their intelligence has been made.[7]

The only cetacean that has been studied extensively from the standpoint of brain size and intelligent performance is the bottle-nosed dolphin, *Tursiops truncatus* (Table IV). Their brain size at birth is comparable to that of ours at birth and during their lifetime develops well into the upper level of the maximum size for modern man—about 1700 grams. Their brain size increases very rapidly during youth and seems to slow down at nine years but less than ours does at a human age of about seventeen years. Their brain continues to increase slowly after that time. The largest brains in the world are those of other Cetacea; some are larger than even those of the elephants (Table V).

[7] Rensch, B. The intelligence of elephants. Scientific American, Feb. 1957, pp. 44–49.

[3] Tower, *loc. cit.*, 1954.

[4] Jansen, Jan. On the whale brain with special reference to the weight of the brain of the fin whale (*Balaenoptera physalus*). Norwegian Whaling Gazette, No. 1: pp. 480–86, 1952.

[5] Kojima, T. On the brain of the sperm whale (*Physeter catadon, L.*). Sci. Rep. Whales Research Inst., No. 6, pp. 49–73. Tokyo, 1951.

SMALL BRAINS VS. LARGE; REWARDS AND
PUNISHMENTS

In this section we discuss the rewarding and punishing
effects of various kinds of stimulation in relation to the
size of the brain of the animal which is being rewarded

Table VI: Threshold Quantities for Human
Acquisition of Speech: Age and Brain Weight

Age Months	Brain Weight[1] Grams	Speech Stages[2] (First Appearances)
2	480	Responds to human voice, cooing, and vocalizes pleasure
4	580	Vocal play Eagerness and displeasure expressed vocally
6	660	Imitates sounds
9	770	First word
11	850	Imitates syllables and words Second word
13	930	Vocabulary expands rapidly
17	1030	Names objects and pictures
21	1060	Combines words in speech
23	1070	Uses pronouns, understands prepositions, uses phrases and sentences

[1] From Boston Children's Hospital data, 1198 records, by Coppoletta, J. M., and Wolbach, S. B. Am. J. Pathology 9: 55–70, 1933.

[2] From summary by McCarthy, D., in *Manual of Child Psychology*, L. Carmichael, ed. (Wiley, New York, 1946).

or punished. The problem of biological (as opposed to symbolic) rewards and punishments is discussed from the viewpoint of a psychophysiologist. As far as possible, this discussion is tied to experimental materials from my laboratory and from laboratories of neurophysiologists and comparative psychologists. A whole vast literature of educational psychology is neglected here. I feel that I can keep the discussion more succinct and meaningful by restricting it pretty much to the regions of my own experiences.

Within the brain there are many kinds of systems subserving many kinds of functions. Most of these are yet to be delineated by experimental work. The sources of our most dramatic results are direct stimulations of brain systems by implanted electrodes placed within them in unanesthetized animals and humans. Such procedures give the purest instances of the actions of these systems when they are intensely excited.

The advantage of such experimentation over that using normal inputs is that control of stimulation time and intensity of the central states are completely available to the operator. Many of these systems stimulated in this way do not show the fatigability or the satiability they may exhibit when stimulated through normal inputs. Let us attempt to derive more accurate and definitive descriptions of these systems. The ones of special interest are those that have effect on motivations.

When the special motivational systems are directly stimulated electrically, they act as powerful "forces" and "causes" for learning novel and new things. When stimulated, the motivational systems cause deep and lasting traces of the just previous and concurrent events to become fixed in the brain; memory is enhanced; certain events and actions are given very high values; an impetus to learning is excited, and learning itself is accelerated.

In general, these motivational systems can be split into

two kinds, based on the effects of their stimulation. The system of the first kind drives the animal to seek more of the conditions just preceding and occurring with the stimulation of the system and thus to enchance and/or to *start* or to *increase* such stimulation again and again. This type is called a "rewarding" system (in a shorthand way).

The second kind of system is the obverse of the first kind. Stimulations of the system of the second kind drive the animal to seek *less* of the conditions just preceding and occurring with such stimulation and thus *to stop* or at least *to lessen* such stimulation if it starts again. This type is called a "punishing" system (in a shorthand way).

Each of these systems can excite an animal to action, sometimes violent action. In the case of the small-brained animal (rat, cat, and monkey) the urgency of the action is very apparent in the resulting high velocity of body movements within the allowed restraints and confinements. In the cases of the large-brained dolphin and of humans, the action can be limited to the vocal and autonomic spheres with less violent body movement, if any.

A few "inner" reports from direct brain stimulation in the case of human beings give hints as follows: (1) the first kind of system causes intensely pleasurable, positive feelings, and (2) the second kind causes intensely antipleasure, negative feelings. The antipleasure negative feelings are fear (escape), anger (attack), or pain referred to some specific body part.

The above definitions and findings lead us to reinvestigate several basic instances of learning a language, for example in the case of a human child. Early in life a human child acts the way the smaller-brained animals do. Its vocalizations are pretty much limited to two major categories: those expressing pleasurable feelings and those expressing negative antipleasure feelings. At birth these vocalizations are characteristic of just the species—

for example, a Japanese baby and an American baby sound very much alike. Quickly, however, these vocalizations become modified and within a few weeks correspond to a typical baby of a particular culture. Eventually words begin to appear among the other sounds emitted. One of the characteristics of the human child at this period is his fascinating ability to mimic exactly sounds and actions of other people. Mimicry is associated in general with good feeling, with positive rewarding experiences, but it can be associated with the negative antipleasure ones in a more limited (but more demanding), simpler fashion.

A lot has been written of the vocal play of human children and its importance to speech learning. Early in life this play is associated with good feeling (high activity in the rewarding systems within the child's brain). At this time the negative-system activities are pretty much responded to by rather violent vocalization, such as crying, screaming, etc.

A well-rested child tends to babble, do vocal play, and apparently attempt to mimic the noises of the persons satisfying his needs who may be around him. There seem to be a good deal less of the rather violent muscular movements that are associated with the very young of the rat, cat, and monkey. Obviously there are some movements, but they are not as active as those of the smaller-brained animals. A good deal more vocalization is noted in these larger-brained animals than in the smaller-brained ones.

In fact, to teach an adult rat, cat, or monkey to vocalize in order to obtain a reward by stimulating his brain is extremely difficult if not impossible. But when the brain of a dolphin is stimulated in the rewarding systems, the vocalizations pour out in a quite uninhibited fashion and concurrent attempts to mimic the sounds in the environment are detected.

It seems that one of the properties of the large brain is to convert internal feelings into vocal expressions and to reproduce sounds from the environment, especially those emitted by the persons in control—that is, the rewarding and the punishing "animals" surrounding the young. Apparently quite empirically parents in general learn how to stimulate rather specifically rewarding and punishing systems through their normal inputs and outputs in the brains of the young. Parents do not have the pure means of stimulation of these systems that the neurophysiologist does. However, I believe that most children would agree that a violent spanking excites negative feelings even though these may be mixed with some violent positive ones, at times. Many would also agree that when they are hungry, and someone gives them some food, this is a rewarding experience. These are all, as it were, on the agreed biological level of rewards and punishments. After the first few experiences a hungry child seeks food and food-producing situations and may attempt to avoid spanking-producing situations. The constant presentation of appropriate words during these experiences etches them into the memory of a child on the receiving side and causes him to mimic them on the transmitting side. While transmitting, he can make changes and comparisons of his copies with the originals and thus improve his copies.

Each rewarding experience and each punishing experience now acquires labels in the mind of the human "animal." He quickly begins to find that giving vocal signals of the state of his needs can (sometimes) influence the persons in his surroundings to satisfy those needs. During this phase of the development of his language, words and sentences themselves begin to acquire rewarding and punishing significances. *Words have such an intense reality for children at this stage that the proper words can evoke an extremely heightened rewarding or punishing state within their brains.* This stage is the beginning of the later complete formation of symbols and "symbolic" states as opposed to the "real" state of reward

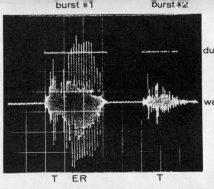

burst #1   burst #2

duration, 50ms/cm

waveform

T ER   T

DISPLAY OF TWO SONIC BURSTS

PLATE I. The term *burst* is a sonic physical term. An oscilloscope display from a Tektronic model 564 storage cathode-ray oscilloscope of two bursts as defined in this program. The upper trace shows the duration of each burst (50 msec/cm), and the lower trace is the waveform of each burst using a wide-band filter (SKL 302). The word *tert* contains two bursts with a silence of 100 msec between "er" and the final "t".

PLATE II. An oscillographic record of a train of 38 human (Hs) vocal output stimuli trains and 38 dolphin (Tt) vocal-train responses from the magnetic-tape recording of Expt. 5

EXCHANGES	Number of Bursts Per Exchange human, dolphin		EXCHANGES	Number of Bursts Per Exchange human, dolphin
1	3,3		20	7,7
2	2,2		21	1,1
3	10,10		22	10,10
4	9,9		23	3,3
5	2,2		24	2,2
6	5,5		25	6,6
7	7,7		26	5,5
8	4,4		27	6,6
9	5,5		28	3,3
10	1,1		29	7,7
11	9,9		30	8,8
12	5,5		31	7,7
13	4,4		32	2,2
14	3,3		33	10,10
15	4,4		34	9,9
16	5,5		35	1,1
17	8,8		36	6,6
18	8,8		37	4,4
19	1,1		38	6,6

developed in real time. The Hs and Tt outputs have been separated for graphic purposes by narrow-passband filters and their rectified signal (General Radio model GR1142A) output displayed. The Hs output was filtered using an Allison model 2DR set between 300 Hz L.P. 30 dB/oct and 780 Hz H.P. at 30 dB/oct. The Tt output signal was filtered using an SKL 302 set at 5 kHz H.P. at 18 dB/oct and 5 kHz L.P. at 18 dB/oct. The Hs output generally appears in the downward galvanometer deflection at the beginning of each trace (presentation of each train of stimuli which varies in numbers of bursts from 1-10) and the Tt output in the upward deflection of each trace sequential to the Hs train (except in those instances of Tt overlap and in those instances when the energy distribution of peak partials and frequencies in an Hs or Tt burst are such that they also appear in the other channel). The specific vocal program utilized in this experiment is displayed in Table II. (See also PLATE IV.) The numbers after each trace refer to the burst count by a phonetician: for the human (first number) and for the dolphin (second number). In Presentations 7, 19, 36, and 38, an untrained observer counting nonsense syllables instead of bursts gave a score of one less than the correct value for the human, thus generating "dolphin errors" artificially. In certain instances in the above graphic recording, some of the dolphin's responses that are audibly detectable above the noise level of the tape do not give large enough responses to be seen on the photographically reproducible record—e.g., in Presentation 3, a listener counts 10 bursts in the dolphin's vocal output. An additional source of error in the graphical presentation is that extraneous noises such as water splashes caused deflects that must be eliminated in the burst counts.

PLATE III. Sample of technique for sound spectrographic and sectioner display of two syllables "at ri" here defined as two bursts of the Hs stimulus train [the Tt response is portrayed in PLATE III (b)]. The sonic analysis was prepared from the magnetic-tape record of Expt. 5 in real time using the narrow-band (45-Hz) analyzing filters covering the ranges from 85 Hz to 8 kHz. The sectioner (amplitude) display [upper portion of PLATE III (a)] covers the same

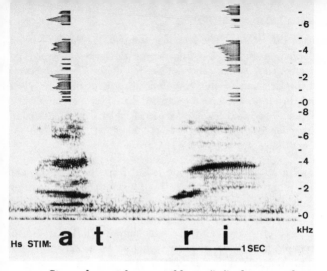

Hs STIM: a   t   r   i
1 SEC

ranges. Six peak partials are visible in "at"; there are three in "ri." For the analysis plotted in Fig. 8, additional sections were made and the peaks counted (not shown). (b). Sound-spectrographic and sectioner display of two Tt bursts, the dolphin's voice output response to the Hs stimulus train "at ri" [see PLATE III (a)]. The sonic analysis was prepared from the magnetic-tape record of Expt. 5 at a speed $2\times$ slowed (using the narrow-band 45-Hz analyzing filter) covering the ranges from 85 Hz to 12 kHz (170 Hz to 24 kHz

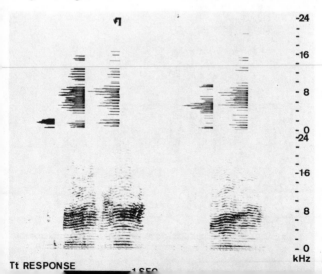

Tt RESPONSE
1 SEC

from the record). The sectioner (amplitude) display [upper portion of PLATE III (b)] covers the same ranges. The symbol close to the center at the top of the figure indicates a displacement of this amplitude display to the left when relating it to the spectrogram in the lower portion of the figure. The numbers of peak partials shown for each section from left to right are 2, 19, 10, 7 and 10. Other sections (not shown) were used for Fig. 8.

PLATE IV. An oscillographic record from the magnetic-tape recording of Expt. 5. There has been no editing or cutting from the onset of 22A to the end of 22 except for display purposes. In PLATE II, the graphic display of stimulus-train 22 (10 Hs bursts) and Tt's voice output (10 Tt bursts) responses have been included, whereas trace 22A was not. This example illustrates the dolphin's acoustic-storage and pattern-recognition ability that enabled him to respond only to the correct Hs stimulus train with the correct number of matching bursts. (See PLATE II for parameters used to develop graphic display.)

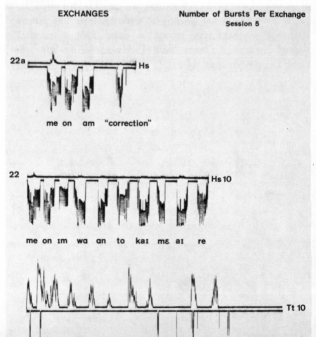

and punishment. It takes a fairly large brain—that of an adult human—with a lot of experience to move away from these primary word experiences that evoke primary states in the biological sphere (Table III). Part of what we mean by sublimation is gaining control in the vocal and verbal sphere over the symbols of the biological states: such control that they do not necessarily evoke the primary state itself with any degree of intensity. All of the questions of belief in one's own words and those of other persons are tested against this background. If a child is told that he is now to be punished and will be spanked, he may act as if he were being spanked, whereas at a little later stage he will laugh and run away.

In order to mimic, a child must live out and become the words and transmissions of the persons controlling him. He can do this only because he has a brain sufficiently large to store all of the materials coming from another very complicated entity, another human being. A chimpanzee may "ape" a human being but a child personifies and lives out another human being. The distinctions are obvious to those who have studied apes and young children.[8]

The intellectual attainments of civilized man are finally reached by a child as the educational processes culminate and, as it were, he is able to remove his own rewarding and punishing further and further from the original words which could evoke their stimulation. Simultaneously the differentiation of the rewarding and punishing situations within the environment increases rapidly. There is less tendency to generalize the situations: causes and effects become more restricted. Rewards and punishments now become, in addition to the original biological causes, attached to the civilized conception and uses of such things as money, clothing, ideas, etc.

[8] Köhler, Wolfgang. *The Mentality of Apes* (Humanities Press, New York, 1956).

At any time an adult human being can be reduced to the childish level by changing his situation. Such a state can be induced by lack of sleep, by starvation, by torture, by isolation, by profound confinement, by drugs, by direct electrical brain stimulation. The original biological prototypes of learning can be reintroduced and even an adult can be forced to learn once again by means almost thoroughly beyond his control. I am speaking here of powerful means used ruthlessly with very few scruples.

Biological means of controlling learning and motivation are ever present and are of the highest priority when they are used in this fashion. I emphasize these points because this is the way we are treating our dolphins and teaching them. This is also the way we teach our young children and the way that certain propagandists teach cultural prisoners and prisoners of war. When used in the educational process, in the United States at least, rewards and punishments are rather attenuated compared to these "police-state" methods. Even in the United States, however, external controls can be attenuated only after and if the children involved have already been put through the necessary processes for internal control to develop.

Here I wish to emphasize that the symbolic rewards and punishments which operate every day in civilized life operate just as continuously as do the biological ones. We cannot separate ourselves completely and become totally sublimated, nor can we become totally unsublimated once we are civilized. The built-in verbal control in our huge cerebral cortex continues to operate unless the conditions are made so extreme that they are rarely encountered except in conditions of war or servitude.

Presumably such considerations may apply to other large-brained creatures on this earth, in its seas, or even not of this earth. Our first tests of nonhumans of this sort will be on *Tursiops*.

Appendix 5

Origins of Dolphins and of Men

The modern whales, including modern dolphins, first appear in the Miocene period 25 million years ago. Previous to this appearance there were ancient whales (Archeoceti) whose remains are found in the early Eocene and late Eocene periods about 60 million years ago. Between these two groups no transitional forms have yet been found, according to Remington Kellogg.[1]

The Archeocetes are said to be descended from very early general mammals of insectivore-creodont forms in the late Cretacious and early Paleocene periods 100 million years ago. These ancient whales had separate nares ("nostrils") near the end of the upper beak (rostrum) rather than a blowhole on the "forehead" farther back as in the case of modern dolphins. The teeth of these early forms were of the cutting form in the cheeks and conical at the rostral end of the jaw; modern dolphins in general have conical teeth. Other differences are demonstrable in the bones of the skull, trunk, limbs, etc.

In the opinion of R. Kellogg, the primitive insectivore-creodont stock gave rise to a generalized prototype which

[1] Kellogg, Remington. *A Review of the Archeoceti* (Carnegie Institution, Washington, D.C., 1936).

developed separately into each of three lines: the Arche-oceti, the Odontoceti (including dolphins), and the Mysticeti (balleen whales).

In relation to brain size the earlier whales had smaller brains (800 cc cranial capacity per 60 feet for toothed Prozeuglodon of middle Eocene) than the modern ones (9000 cc per 60 feet for toothed sperm whale).

The origins of *Homo sapiens* have been traced through similar epochs.[2] The primitive mammals of the early Eocene period (70 million years ago) also included the earliest Primates. The first apes (Parapithecus) are found in the Oligocene period, 40 million years ago. In the Miocene (25 million years ago) the ape type is Proconsul of the big jaw and small brain: these are said to have given rise to the modern apes. Man's predecessors presumably were among the many types of apes of the Miocene and Pliocene (15 million years ago) periods but the evidence is still fragmentary and unsatisfactory. (As stated above, the first good evidence of progenitors of modern whales is found in the Miocene.) In the early Pleistocene period (1 million years ago) the Australo-pithecines appeared with a brain of about 600 cc (a little less than half our brain). (This value is to be compared with Prozeuglodon which lived 50 or so million years earlier with 800 cc.) The Australopithecines are "exceed-ingly primitive representatives of the family which in-cludes modern and extinct types of Man." There is no evidence of speech or tool-making; there is suggestive evidence that they crushed the skulls of baboons with weapons of unknown sort: this fact places them above modern apes in intelligence.

Later, Pithecanthropus appears (Middle Pleistocene period, 500,000 years ago) with a brain of about 900 cc

[2] Clark, W. E. LeGros, *History of the Primates* (University of Chicago Press, Chicago, 1957).

(but larger ones are found). He made primitive tools, used fire, hunted other animals such as deer, and practiced cannibalism, eating the brains of his own species. Evidence is fairly strong that he was a progenitor of modern man.

Strictly modern man arose from traceable progenitors living during the Pleistocene period: Old Stone Age Man (Paleolithic Man) was of many varieties and places in Europe and Asia. His brain was almost up to ours (1300 cc). This group includes Neanderthal man of Europe, Rhodesian man of Africa, and Solo man of Java.

In the late Paleolithic period about 50,000 years ago modern men, "the Aurignacians," suddenly replaced Neanderthal man. This group includes the Cro-Magnon man. They are hardly distinguishable from present-day *Homo sapiens.* Their cave paintings, sculpture, personal ivory jewelry, and fine javelin blades show their high level of achievement.

By 10,000 years ago the cultural artifacts have an extremely high level. The first written records seem to begin at least 7000 years ago in Sumeria.[3]

The parallel kinds of development of the whales are not known: since whales do not, as far as we know, create tools, jewelry, drawings, or other artifacts, and since they usually die in the sea or at its edge, most of them are eaten by predators ranging in size from large sharks to small bacteria. The best remains are in silt deposits on present land which was formerly ancient seas. Only a few skeletons have been found. As the science of oceanography progresses, we may find the whales' complete skeletal record in the oceans' bottoms. Until then the guesses are further apart than those for man's evolutionary record.

[3] Kramer, Samuel Noah. *History Begins at Sumer* (Doubleday Anchor Book, New York, 1959).

One systematic schema for the evolutionary inter-relationships of the Delphinidae is given by Herluf Winge.[4]

The first recorded contacts between man and dolphins may be those given by Aristotle (fourth century B.C.). His account of the dolphins' anatomy and behavior is fairly exact: he distinguishes the dolphin (of the Mediterranean) from the porpoise (from the Black Sea). The contacts are quoted[5] as follows:

"Among the sea-fishes many stories are told about the dolphin, indicative of his gentle and kindly nature, and of manifestations of passionate attachment to boys, in and about Tarentum, Caria, and other places. The story goes that, after a dolphin had been caught and wounded off the coast of Caria, a shoal of dolphins came into the harbour and stopped there until the fisherman let his captive go free; whereupon the shoal departed. A shoal of young dolphins is always, by way of protection, followed by a large one. On one occasion a shoal of dolphins, large and small, was seen, and two dolphins at a little distance appeared swimming in underneath a little dead dolphin when it was sinking, and supporting it on their backs, trying out of compassion to prevent its being devoured by some predaceous fish. Incredible stories are told regarding the rapidity of movement of this creature. It appears to be the fleetest of all animals, marine and terrestrial, and it can leap over the masts of large vessels. This speed is chiefly manifested when they are pursuing a fish for food; then, if the fish endeavours to escape, they pursue him in their ravenous hunger down to deep wa-

[4] Winge, Herluf. *A Review of the Inter-relationships of the Cetacea* (Smithsonian Institution, Washington, D.C., 1921).

[5] *The Works of Aristotle*, translated into English under the editorship of W. D. Ross, and reprinted by arrangement with Oxford University Press for The Great Books, Vol. 9, p. 156, Encyclopaedia Britannica, Inc., Chicago, 1952.

ters; but, when the necessary return swim is getting too long, they hold in their breath, as though calculating the length of it, and then draw themselves together for an effort and shoot up like arrows, trying to make the long ascent rapidly in order to breathe, and in the effort they spring right over a ship's masts if a ship be in the vicinity. This same phenomenon is observed in divers, when they have plunged into deep water; that is, they pull themselves together and rise with a speed proportional to their strength. Dolphins live together in pairs, male and female. It is not known for what reason they run themselves aground on dry land; at all events, it is said that they do so at times, and for no obvious reason."

Later contacts with "wild" dolphins include those of "Opo" (a *Tursiops*?) in New Zealand, whose story and photographs have been published.[6]

[6] Alpers, Antony. *A Book of Dolphins* (John Murray, London, 1960).

Bibliography
Man and Dolphin

Alpers, Antony. *A Book of Dolphins* (John Murray, London, 1960).

Andrews, Roy Chapman. *Whale Hunting with Gun and Camera* (D. Appleton and Co., New York, 1916).

Aristotle, The Works of, translated into English under the editorship of W. D. Ross, and reprinted by arrangement with Oxford University Press for The Great Books, Vol. 9, p. 156, Encyclopaedia Britannica, Inc., Chicago, 1952.

Clark, W. E. LeGros. *History of the Primates* (University of Chicago Press, Chicago, 1957).

Coppoletta, J. M., and Wolbach, S. B. Boston Children's Hospital data, 1198 records. Am. J. Pathology 9: 55–70, 1933.

Essapian, Frank S. Speed-induced skin folds in the bottle-nosed porpoise, *Tursiops truncatus.* Brevoria, Mus. of Comp. Zool., 43, April 7, 1955.

Frazer, Sir James George, *The Golden Bough.*

Hezeen, Bruce C. "Whales Entangled in Deep Sea Cables." *Deep-Sea Research,* Vol. 4, pp. 105–15 (Pergamon Press, London, 1957).

Ireland, W. W. *Mental Affections of Children* (J. & A. Churchill, London, 1900).

Irving, L. P., Scholander, P. F., and Grinnell, S. W. The

Respiration of *Tursiops truncatus.* J. Cell. and Comp. Physiol., 17: 145, 1941.

Jacobs, Jake. *Marineland Diver* (Dodd, Mead, New York, 1960).

Jansen, Jan. On the whale brain with special reference to the weight of the brain of the fin whale (*Balaenoptera physalus*). Norwegian Whaling Gazette, No. 1, pp. 480–86, 1952.

Jennings, H. S. *Genetics of the Protozoa* (Nijhoff, The Hague, Netherlands, 1929).

Kellogg, Remington. *A Review of the Archeoceti* (Carnegie Institution, Washington, D.C., 1936).

Kellogg, W. N. Auditory perception of submerged objects by porpoises. J. Acoust. Soc. of Am., 31 (1), pp. 1–6, January 1959.

Köhler, Wolfgang. *The Mentality of Apes* (Humanities Press, New York, 1956).

Kojima, Tokuzo. On the brain of the sperm whale (*Physeter catadon, L.*) Sci. Rep. Whales Research Inst., No. 6, pp. 49–73, Tokyo, 1951.

Kramer, M. O. *Missiles and Rockets*, February 1, 1960.

Kramer, Samuel Noah. *History Begins at Sumer* (Doubleday Anchor Book, New York, 1959).

Kruger, Lawrence. The thalamus of the dolphin (*Tursiops truncatus*) and comparison with other mammals. J. Comp. Neurol., 111, No. 1, pp. 133–94, 1959.

Langworthy, O. R. A description of the central nervous system of the porpoise (*Tursiops truncatus*). J. Comp. Neurol., 54, 437–88, 1932.

Lanyon, W. E., and Tavolga, W. N. *Animal Sounds and Communication,* 1960. Am. Inst. of Biol. Sci., Washington, D.C. (Pub. No. 7).

Lawrence, Barbara, and Schevill, William E. The functional anatomy of the delphinid nose. Bull. of Mus. of Comp. Zool. (Harvard Col.), 114:4, February 1956.

Lewis, M. M. *Infant Speech* (Kegan Paul, Trench, Trubner and Co., London, 1936).

Lilly, J. C. Learning motivated by subcortical stimulation: The "start" and the "stop" patterns of behavior, pp. 705–

21. Chapter in: *Reticular Formation of the Brain,* Jasper, H. H., *et al.*, eds. (Little, Brown and Co., Boston, 1958).
—— Electrode and cannulae implantation in the brain by a simple percutaneous method. Science, 127: 1181–82, 1958.
—— Some considerations regarding basic mechanisms of positive and negative types of motivations. Am. J. of Psychiatry, 115: 498–504, December 1958.
—— and Miller, A. M. Vocal exchanges between individual dolphins. Manuscript, December 1960.
—— Sounds Emitted by the Bottle-nose Dolphin. The audible emissions of captive dolphins under water or in air are remarkably complex and varied. *Science,* May 26, 1961, Vol. 133. No. 3465, pages 1689–93.

McBride, Arthur F., and Hebb, D. O. Behavior of the captive bottle-nose dolphin *Tursiops truncatus.* J. Comp. and Phys. Psych. 41: 2, pp. 111–23, April 1948.

McCarthy, D. Summary in *Manual of Child Psychology,* L. Carmichael, ed. (Wiley, New York, 1946).

Moore, Omar K. The motivation and training of students for intellectual pursuits: a new approach. Tenth Thomas Alva Edison Foundation Inst., 1959.

Norman, J. R., and Fraser, F. C. *Field Book of Giant Fishes, Whales, and Dolphins* (Putnam, London, 1937).

Norris, Kenneth S., Prescott, John H., Asa-Dorian, Paul V., and Perkins, Paul. An Experimental Demonstration of Echo-Location Behavior in the Porpoise, *Tursiops truncatus* (Montagu). The Biological Bulletin, Lancaster Press, April 1961, p. 163.

Rensch, B. The intelligence of elephants. Scientific American, February 1957, pp. 44–49.

Schevill, William E., and Lawrence, Barbara. Auditory response of a bottle-nosed porpoise, *Tursiops truncatus,* to frequencies above 100 Kc. J. Exp. Zool., 124: No. 1, pp. 147–65, October 1953.
—— Food-finding by a captive porpoise (*Tursiops truncatus*). Breviora, Bull. of Mus. of Comp. Zool., No. 53, Cambridge, Mass., April 6, 1956.

Schiller's translation of *Instinctive Behavior* (International Universities Press, New York, 1957).

Scholander, P. F. Experimental Investigations of the Respiratory Function in Diving Mammals and Birds. Hvalraadets Skrifter, Acad. of Sciences, Oslo, Norway, 1940.

—— and Schevill, William E. Counter-current vascular heat exchange in the fins of whales. J. Applied Physiology, 8: 3, November 1955.

Scott, R. F. *Scott's Last Expedition* (Beacon Press, Boston, 1957).

Siebenaler, J. B., and Caldwell, David K. Cooperation among adult dolphins. J. of Mamm., Vol. 37, No. 1: 126–28, February 1956.

Spitz, René. *Hospitalism*. "The Psychoanalytic Study of the Child," Vol. 1, p. 53 (International Universities Press, New York, 1945).

—— *No and Yes* (International Universities Press, New York, 1957).

Tavolga, Margaret C., and Essapian, Frank S. The behavior of the bottle-nosed dolphin (*Tursiops truncatus*): Mating, pregnancy, parturition and mother-infant behavior. Zoologica, 42, Part 1, May 20, 1957.

Tinbergen, N. *The Study of Instinct* (Oxford University Press, London, 1951).

Tower, Donald B. Structural and functional organization of mammalian cerebral cortex; the correlation of neurone density with brain size. J. Comp. Neurol., 101, August 1, 1954.

Vierordt, H. Das Massenwachsthum der Korperorgane des Menschen. *Arch. f. Anat. u. Physiol. Anat.* s62 (1890).

Winge, Herluf. *A Review of the Inter-relationships of the Cetacea* (Smithsonian Institution, Washington, D.C., 1921).

Wood, F. G., Jr. Underwater sound production and concurrent behavior of captive porpoises, *Tursiops truncatus* and *Stenella plagiodon*. Bull. Mar. Sci. Gulf and Caribbean, 3 (2): 120–33, 1954.

General Bibliography
The Mind of the Dolphin

Aristotle, Works of, translated into English under the editorship of W. D. Ross, and reprinted by arrangement with Oxford University Press for The Great Books, Vol. 9 (Chicago: Encyclopaedia Britannica, 1952).

Ash, Christopher. Whaler's Eye (New York: The Macmillan Company, 1962).

Boulle, Pierre. Planet of the Apes (New York: New American Library of World Literature, 1963).

Carpenter, C. R. Naturalistic Behavior of Nonhuman Primates (University Park, Pa.: Pennsylvania State University Press, 1964).

Dakin, William John. Whalemen Adventures: The story of whaling in Australian waters and other southern seas related thereto, from the days of sail to modern times (Sydney, Australia: Angus & Robertson, 1934).

Doppler, Christian J. Uber Das Farbige Licht Der Doppelsterne (Prague, 1842).

Eiseley, Loren. "The long loneliness. Man and the porpoise: two solitary destinies." Am. Scholar 30: 57–64 (1961).

Erikson, Erik H. Insight and Responsibility (New York: W. W. Norton & Company, 1964).

Freud, Anna. The Ego and Mechanisms of Defence translated from the German by Cecil Baines (New York: New York International University Press, 1946).

Freud, Sigmund. *Collected Papers* (New York: Basic Books, 1959).

Gilbert, Bil. *How Animals Communicate* (New York: Pantheon Books, 1966).

James, William. *Varieties of Religious Experience; a study in human nature.* Gifford Lectures delivered at Edinburgh University, 1901–2 (New York, London, Bombay, and Calcutta: Longmans, Green & Co., 1902, 1929).

Jung, C. G. *Memories, Dreams and Reflections* (New York: Pantheon Books, 1963).

Kinsey, Alfred C., Pomeroy, Wardell B., and Martin, Clyde E. *Sexual Behavior in the Human Male* (Philadelphia and London: W. B. Saunders Co., 1948).

——, Pomeroy, Wardell B., Martin, Clyde E., and Gebhard, Paul H. *Sexual Behavior in the Human Female* (Philadelphia and London: W. B. Saunders Co., 1953).

Lilly, John C. "Mental effects of reduction of ordinary levels of physical stimuli on intact, healthy persons." *Psychiat. Res. Reports* 5: 1–28 (Washington, D.C.: American Psychiatric Association, 1956).

—— *Man and Dolphin* (Garden City, New York: Doubleday & Company, 1961).

—— "Some considerations regarding basic mechanisms of positive and negative types of motivations." *Am. J. of Psychiat.* 115: 498–504 (1958).

—— "Vocal behavior of the bottlenose dolphin." *Proc. Am. Philos. Soc.* 106: 520–29 (1962).

—— "Critical brain size and language." *Perspectives in Biol. & Med.* 6: 246–55 (1963).

—— "Distress call of the bottlenose dolphin: stimuli and evoked behavioral responses." *Science* 139: 116–18 (1963).

—— "Vocal mimicry in *Tursiops*: ability to match numbers and durations of human vocal bursts." *Science* 147: 300–1 (1965).

—— *The Human Biocomputer: Programming and Metaprogramming (Theory and Experiments with LSD-25)* (Miami: Communication Research Institute, 1967; Scientific Report Number CRI0167).

—— "The need for an adequate model of the human end of the interspecies—specific communication program in communication with Extraterrestrial Intelligence." *IEEE Spectrum* 3: 159–60 (1966).

—— and Howe, Margaret C. Progress Report, St. Thomas (1965).

—— and Miller, Alice M. "Vocal exchanges between dolphins." *Science* 134: 1873–76 (1961).

—— and Shurley, Jay T. "Experiments in solitude, in maximum achievable physical isolation with water suspension of intact healthy persons." *Psychophysiological Aspects of Space Flight:* 238–47 (New York: Columbia University Press, 1961).

Melville, Herman. *Moby Dick* (New York: Dodd, Mead & Co., 1942).

Montaigne, Michel de. Essays II, 12, 1533–92. The Great Books, Vol. 25 (Chicago: University of Chicago, 1952).

Morgane, P. J. "Lamination characteristics and areal differentiation in the cerebral cortex of the bottlenose dolphin (*Tursiops truncatus*)." *Anat. Rec.* 151 (3): 390–91 (1965).

——, Yakovlev, Paul I., Jacobs, Myron S., McFarland, W. L., and Piliero, Sam J. *An Atlas of the Brain of the Dolphin,* Tursiops truncatus (New York: Pergamon Press, in press).

Nagel, E., Morgane, P. J., and McFarland, W. L. "Anesthesia for the bottlenose dolphin, *Tursiops truncatus.*" *Science* 146: 1591–93 (1964).

Plato. "Statesman," *Dialogues of Plato,* 428–348 B.C.; The Great Books, Vol. 7 (Chicago: University of Chicago, 1952).

Plinius Secundus C. *Natural History,* six volumes (Bostock and Riley, London: Bell, 1855–90).

Skinner, B. F. *Verbal Behavior* (New York: Appleton-Century-Crofts, 1957).

Szilard, Leo. *The Voice of the Dolphins and Other Stories* (New York: Simon and Schuster, 1961).

Truby, H. M. In *Newborn Infant Cry.* A collection of articles edited by John Lind. Acta Paediatrica Scandinavica

Supplementary 163 (Uppsala: Almqvist & Wiksells Bok-
tryckeri AB, 1965).

Van Neumann, John. *The Computer and the Brain* (New
Haven, Conn.: Yale University Press, 1958).

Zuckerman, Sir Solly. *The Social Life of Monkeys and
Apes* (Trench, Trubner & Co., London: Kegan Paul,
1932).

Selected Bibliography

1961 "The biological versus psychoanalytic dichotomy." *Bull. of Phila. Assoc. for Psychoanal.* 11: 116–19.

1961 *Man and Dolphin* (New York: Doubleday & Company; London: Victor Gollancz).

1961 "Problems of physiological research on the dolphin, *Tursiops.*" (abstract) *Fed. Proc.* 20.

1961 (With A. M. Miller) "Sounds emitted by the bottlenose dolphin." *Science* 133: 1689–93.

1961 (With A. M. Miller) "Vocal exchanges between dolphins." *Science* 134: 1873–76.

1962 "Cerebral dominance," pp. 112–14 in Vernon Montcastle, M.D., ed., *Interhemispheric Relations and Cerebral Dominance* (Baltimore: Johns Hopkins Press).

1962 "Consideration of the relation of brain size to capability for language activity as illustrated by *Homo sapiens* and *Tursiops truncatus* (bottlenose dolphin)." *Electroenceph. Clin. Neurophysiol.* 14: 424.

1962 "The Sensory World Within, and Man and Dolphin" (Lecture to the Laity, New York Academy of Medicine, 11 April 1962) (Miami: Communication Research Institute, Report Number CRI0162).

1962 "Interspecies communication," pp. 279–81 in *Yearbook of Science and Technology* (New York: McGraw-Hill).

1962 *Man and Dolphin* (The Worlds of Science Series: Zoology) (New York: Pyramid Publications).

1962 *Manniskan och Delfinen* (Stockholm: Wahlstrom & Widstrand).

1962 *L'Homme et le Dauphin* (Paris: Stock).

1963 *Mennesket og Delfinen* (Oslo: Nasjonalforlaget).

1963 *Mens en Dolfijn* (Amsterdam: Contact).

1962 "A new laboratory for research on delphinids." *Assoc. of Southeastern Biologists Bull.* 9: 3–4.

1962 (With A. M. Miller) "Operant conditioning of the bottlenose dolphin with electrical stimulation of the brain." *J. Comp. & Physiol. Psychol.* 55: 73–79.

1962 "The 'talking' dolphins," in *Book of Knowledge Annual* (New York: Grolier).

1962 "Vocal behavior of the bottlenose dolphin." *Proc. Am. Philos. Soc.* 106: 520–29.

1963 "Critical brain size and language." *Perspectives in Biol. & Med.* 6: 246–55.

1963 "Distress call of the bottlenose dolphin: stimuli and evoked behavioral responses." *Science* 139: 116–18.

1963 "Modern whales, dolphins and porpoises, as challenges to our intelligence," pp. 31–54 in Ashley Montagu and John C. Lilly, *The Dolphin in History*, a symposium given at the Clark Memorial Library, 1962 (Clark Memorial Library, University of California, Los Angeles).

1963 "Productive and creative research with man and dolphin." *Arch. Gen. Psychiatry* 8: 111–16. (Fifth Annual Lasker Lecture, Michael Reese Hospital and Medical Center, Chicago, 1962.)

1964 "Airborne sonic emissions of *Tursiops truncatus* (M)." (abstract) *J. Acoustical Soc. of Amer.* 36:5, p. 1007.

1964 (With M. S. Jacobs, P. J. Morgane, and B. Campbell) "Analysis of cranial nerves in the dolphin." *Anatomical Record* 148: 379.

1964 "Animals in aquatic environment: adaptation of the mammals to the ocean," pp. 741–57 in *Handbook of Physiology: environment I* (Washington, D.C.: Am. Physiol. Soc.).

1965 "Report on experiments with bottlenose dolphins." (abstract) *Proc. Int'l Symp. on Comparative Med.* (New York, 1962).

1965 "Sonic-ultrasonic emissions of the bottlenose dolphin" in *Whales, Dolphins & Porpoises* from *Proc., First Int'l*

Symp. on Cetacean Research (Washington, D.C., 1963).

1965 "Vocal mimicry in *Tursiops*: ability to match numbers and durations of human vocal bursts." *Science* 147 (3655): 300–1.

1966 "Communication with extraterrestrial intelligence." *IEEE Spectrum* 3 (3): 159–60. 1965 IEEE Military Electronics Conf. (Washington, D.C.: September 1965).

1966 "Sexual behavior of the bottlenose dolphin" in *Brain and Behavior,* Vol. III: *The Brain and Gonadal Function* (R. A. Gorski and R. E. Whalen, eds.) *UCLA Forum Med. Sci.* No. 3 (University of California Press, Los Angeles).

1966 (With H. M. Truby) "Measures of human-Tursiops Sonic Interactions." *JASA* 40:1241 (A)

1967 "Dolphin-Human Relation and LSD-25" in *The Use of LSD in Psychotherapy and Alcoholism* (H. A. Abramson, editor) *Proc. 2nd Int'l. Conf. on the Use of LSD in Psychotherapy* 1965 (New York: Bobbs-Merrill, 1967).

1967 "Dolphin Vocalization" in *Brain Mechanisms Underlying Speech and Language* (New York: Grune and Stratton, 1967).

1967 "Dolphin's vocal mimicry as a unique ability and a step towards understanding" in *Mechanisms of Vocal Production in Man* (New York: New York Academy of Sciences, 1967).

1967 (With Alice M. Miller and Henry M. Truby) "Reprogramming of the Sonic Output of the Dolphin: Sonic Burst-Count Matching" (Miami: Communication Research Institute; Scientific Report Number CRI0267).

1972 *Center of the Cyclone* (New York: Julian Press; New York: Bantam Books, 1974).

1974 *Programming and Metaprogramming in the Human Biocomputer* (New York: Julian Press).

1975 *Simulations of God: the Science of Belief* (New York: Simon & Schuster).

1975 (With Antonietta Lilly) *The Dyadic Cyclone* (New York: Simon & Schuster).

Acknowledgments to
Man and Dolphin

During the period covered by this book we received help from many persons whose contributions cannot be described in detail. However, I do wish to acknowledge my personal debt of gratitude to several by name at least: Dr. Orr E. Reynolds, who has been extremely helpful as a scientist and friend who understands what we are trying to accomplish; David M. Lilly, whose astute observations on human institutions and how they run best has done so much for the Institute; Dr. Mottram R. Torre, whose understanding, enthusiasm, and devotion have frequently inspired our most practical administrative moves; Mr. James M. Mitchell, whose practical, efficient, and wise counsel has helped immeasurably; and Mr. Nathaniel O. Wells, whose invaluable help in plans and realization of them in construction is given in the text. Others are mentioned in the text along with their special contributions.

Those from other periods and other projects and pursuits are not named: my gratitude to them is not less because it is not expressed here.

Personally I wish to express my gratitude to the following organizations: the Coyle Foundation; the National Institutes of Health (National Institute of Neurological Diseases and Blindness and National Institute of Mental Health); the Office of Science, Department of Defense; the Office of Naval Research of the Department of the Navy; the National Science Foundation; the Office of Scientific Research of the Air Force. Over the years one or more of these organizations have given support in one form or another.

Acknowledgments to
The Mind of the Dolphin

The National Institute of Mental Health, National Institutes of Health, Bethesda, Maryland, gave a Career Award to the author for five years (1962–67). This award provided some of the essential freedom to plan, to organize, to integrate, and to think out this program. For these five years of help I am appreciative.

The National Institute of Neurological Diseases and Blindness, National Institutes of Health, Bethesda, has been most helpful in providing research grants in basic support of the research program for several years. Our collaborative studies with Drs. P. J. Morgane, W. L. McFarland, P. I. Yakovlev, M. Jacobs, A. Pilero, E. L. Nagel, R. Galliano, and H. M. Truby have been made possible with this support.

The National Science Foundation, Washington, D.C. has been very helpful with grants for facilities and equipment necessary for the scientific research. I appreciate these aids and also many valuable discussions with personnel of the Foundation.

The Air Force Office of Scientific Research has been helpful at many critical points in the development of parts of the work. Development of new techniques and new orientations toward high-speed communication are coming from this support. I am grateful for this aid.

At a critical time in the development of the program the Unger Vetleson Foundation provided a grant. The Michael Tors Foundation has contributed much-needed private funds in support of the general fund of the Institute.

In addition, many friends have given support (monetary and otherwise) as expressions of their confidence in the ongoing research. To each and every one of these I wish to express my thanks and appreciation.

I wish to thank my colleagues (past and present) in the Institute for many helpful discussions, the work accomplished, and their continuing dedication to the scientific progress. I owe a debt of especial gratitude to Peter J. Morgane and Henry M. Truby for the clarification of many scientific points, and their critical, patient education of me in parts of the neuroanatomical, phonetic, and linguistic sciences. W. A. Munson has helped in the acoustic and speech areas, and in the realization of a voice frequency spectrum translator for man and dolphin.

Index